Recreational Use of Wild Lands

The American Forestry Series

Henry J. Vaux, *Consulting Editor*

Allen · An Introduction to American Forestry
Baker · Principles of Silviculture
Boyce · Forest Pathology
Brockman · Recreational Use of Wild Lands
Brown, Panshin, and Forsaith · Textbook of Wood Technology
Volume I—Structure, Identification, Defects, and Uses of the Commercial Woods of the United States
Volume II—The Physical, Mechanical, and Chemical Properties of the Commercial Woods of the United States
Bruce and Schumacher · Forest Mensuration
Chapman and Meyer · Forest Mensuration
Forest Valuation
Clawson · The Western Range Livestock Industry
Dana · Forest and Range Policy
Davis · American Forest Management
Forest Fire: Control and Use
Graham · Forest Entomology
Greeley · Forest Policy
Guise · The Management of Farm Woodlands
Harlow and Harrar · Textbook of Dendrology
Hunt and Garratt · Wood Preservation
Matthews · Management of American Forests
Panshin, Harrar, Baker, and Proctor · Forest Products
Preston · Farm Wood Crops
Shirley · Forestry and Its Career Opportunities
Stoddart and Smith · Range Management
Trippensee · Wildlife Management
Volume I—Upland Game and General Principles
Volume II—Fur Bearers, Waterfowl, and Fish
Wackerman · Harvesting Timber Crops

Walter Mulford was Consulting Editor of this series from its inception in 1931 until January 1, 1952.

Basaltic columns resembling a huge stone organ are a significant feature of Devils Postpile National Monument, Calif. (*National Park Service Photo by Ralph H. Anderson*)

RECREATIONAL USE OF WILD LANDS

C. Frank Brockman

PROFESSOR OF FORESTRY
COLLEGE OF FORESTRY
UNIVERSITY OF WASHINGTON

McGRAW-HILL BOOK COMPANY, INC.
New York Toronto London
1959

RECREATIONAL USE OF WILD LANDS

 Library of Congress Catalog Card Number 58-13857

THE MAPLE PRESS COMPANY, YORK, PA.

Preface

This book has been written for two primary reasons. *First,* a textbook presenting a broad, basic outline of the background, importance, values, and fundamental requirements of the recreational management of wild lands is badly needed. *Second,* a general reference on the problems and interrelationships of various types of recreational lands should be useful to those who derive a large part of their recreation from the outdoors or to those who work in various aspects of the recreational field.

The importance of recreation as a factor in public health and welfare has been recognized only recently. Many things that affect our lives have brought this about. We see evidence of our exploding population in the rapid expansion of urban centers, which have spawned a multitude of knotty problems; solution of such problems is invariably costly, replete with annoying compromise, and restrictive of personal interest and activity. We see evidence of, or read about, many conflicts which develop over differences of opinion concerning various forms of land use which, in addition to being reflections of metropolitan growing pains, also affect lands far removed from our cities. Many areas that formerly provided us with pleasant outdoor recreation are no longer available, or if the welcome mat is still out, they are generally crowded, worn, and necessarily managed with increasing indications of irksome regimentation. In short, in a land which was until recently considered as having limitless space, we are suddenly faced with the fact that the well might run dry. We who have benefited so greatly from nature's bounty and who naturally want our children and our children's children to enjoy similar advantages are becoming increasingly aware of the need for proper wild-land use and the relation of such land to our spare-time interests and activities. Thus, the recreational use of wild lands is being examined now more critically than in the past.

Yet in spite of the growing recognition of both the social and economic importance of outdoor recreation and the controversial relationship which often exists between recreation and other forms of wild-land use, no general text or reference book on the subject has, to date, been made available. True, recreation is briefly related to other aspects of wild-land management in a number of textbooks on forestry, wildlife, and related subjects. Further, specific details of recreation are treated in a variety of magazine articles, specialized publications, and periodicals. But recreational use of wild land, as such, has not previously been treated specifically in one volume, nor have differences in various points of view expressed in specialized publications been coordinated. It is not meant to imply that this book is a complete answer to that need. Each of its various chapters represents but a skeletonized treatment of a particular phase of this subject; treatment of details is the province of specialized publications. Further, considerable additional information is also needed; it is hoped that this will be provided in the future by other writers.

It should also be pointed out that since the recreational use of wild lands is a rapidly expanding field, many of the statistical data bearing upon this subject quickly become obsolete. Consequently, the tabular summaries and closely related information included in this volume are not necessarily important in their own right. Because of constant changes they merely reflect particular situations at a given time; they are however, important as indications of trends.

The author has tried to avoid overstressing any particular point of view. It is felt that the value of such a book as this lies in a presentation, as unbiased as possible, of the many aspects of good recreational-land management rather than in a militant campaign for any particular aspect. It is hoped that this book, by digesting information found in widely scattered literature and by drawing liberally upon the experience of workers in the recreational field, will develop a better understanding of the recreational values of different types of wild lands. If it achieves that goal, it may help in resolving some of the numerous problems that develop as a result of public interest in the preservation, management, and use of varied areas possessed of recreational qualities.

In particular it is important that students training for professions which deal with recreational-land-management problems have the best and broadest possible understanding of principles involved. Forestry students especially should have the benefit of such training, for forest lands loom large in outdoor recreational matters. It is also important that the general public be adequately informed on various basic philosophies underlying the establishment and management of different types of recreational areas. Such understanding fosters good outdoor manners and, therefore, the preservation of recreational interests for the future. Also, since recreational opportunities are largely provided for on public lands, it is to each citizen's interest that outdoor recreational areas be properly and economically managed.

In effect, then, this volume attempts to provide an introduction to the varied concepts of recreational wild-land use to which specific details of management may be related by individual instructors, or readers, in the light of their own experience or observation. Used in this manner, it is hoped that this book will aid in the development of the broad perspective necessary to greater appreciation of the many recreational values of wild land, so that the objectives of their use may be most economically realized and properly coordinated with other requirements of modern life.

To list all those who have had a part in the preparation of this book would be impossible. Many people, directly and indirectly, have made vital contributions.

The author benefited greatly from opinions expressed in many articles found in publications dealing with specific phases of wild-land management. In addition, during nearly twenty years as an employee of the U.S. National Park Service numerous discussions about recreational-land-management problems with associates, as well as with interested national park visitors, contributed to the crystallization of many ideas reflected in these pages. More recently, as a forestry instructor in this field, the author has had the opportunity of exchanging views with others interested in or engaged in all forms of wild-land management. Of particular value were discussions with those who held quite different views from those of the author, for by this means it was possible to better relate outdoor recreation to varied public needs.

In addition, the aid of certain individuals and organizations must be specifically mentioned. The U.S. Forest Service provided photographs and important data. U.S. Forest Service personnel to whom particular thanks are given are Mr. John Sieker, Chief, Division of Recreation and Land Uses; Mr. Frank B. Folsom, Assistant Regional Forester, Region 6, and Mr. Richard Bowe, also of the Region 6 office; Mr. L. O. Barrett, Supervisor of the Snoqualmie National Forest; and Mr. Stanley B. Olson and Mr. William Meyer of his staff. Similarly, the National Park Service provided photographs and information about areas under its control. National Park Service personnel whose assistance is gratefully acknowledged are Mr. Hillory Tolson, Assistant Director; Mr. Herbert Evison, who was, until his recent retirement, Chief of Information of the National Park Service; Mr. Ralph Anderson; Mr. Harry Parker; Mr. Robert McIntyre; and Mr. Preston Macy, Superintendent of Mount Rainier National Park, and his staff. All state park organizations were equally helpful. Their policies and the nature and extent of their operations were indicated both in personal correspondence and printed material which they generously provided. In particular, the aid of Mr. Charles DeTurk, Park Planner, Mrs. Ruth E. Pike, Supervisor of Public Information, and Mr. Albert Culverwell, Historian, Washington State Parks and Recreation Commission, is gratefully acknowledged. The author's thanks also go to Mr. Kramer Adams and Mr. Frederick Billings of the Weyerhaeuser Timber Company, who assisted in supplying information on the recreational use of industrial timberlands. In addition, the chapter on national parks and related areas in other parts of the world was developed largely through the very helpful assistance of the principal administrative officers of such areas.

The author also wishes to express appreciation for the interest of his associates on the faculty of the College of Forestry, University of Washington. In this connection specific reference must be made to the encouragement given by Dean Gordon D. Marckworth, Dr. Walter H. Schaeffer, and Dr. D. R. M. Scott. For assistance in certain translations, the help of Mrs. D. R. M. Scott, as well as that of Mrs. Cecil H. Smith, current librarian of the College of Forestry, is gratefully acknowledged. Mrs. Smith, and her predecessor, Mrs. John Russo, also aided in bibliographical preparations and in obtaining necessary reference material. At various times different members of the secretarial staff of the College of Forestry did much of the preliminary typing of the manuscript; in this connection, particular thanks is given Mrs. Linton Erbland, Mrs. James Paul, Mrs. Sam Pearlman, and Mrs. Theodore Sears. An expression of sincere appreciation is also accorded my wife, Evelyn G. Brockman. In particular, her patience and cooperative support contributed in no small measure to the completion of this project.

Finally, the author also wishes to acknowledge gratefully the wise counsel of Mr. Robert Hitchman, particularly during the early stages in the preparation of the manuscript.

C. Frank Brockman

Contents

CHAPTER 1 *The Importance of Recreation*

Recreation can best be defined as "the pleasurable and constructive use of leisure time" [17]. This definition is stated at the outset, since the boundary of any problem can be outlined most clearly by defining its goal. A good definition is similar in purpose to the blueprint which serves as a guide in the construction of a building. In this instance the objective is to formulate a program of recreational activities that is best suited to public needs and that which can be adapted most logically and economically to specific land areas.

CONCEPTS OF RECREATION

The term "recreation" is subject to a great variety of interpretations. This fact in itself highlights many of the problems pertaining to the acquisition, planning, development, and administration of recreational areas, for people of various recreational interests visualize different possibilities on identical areas. For example, hunters or fishermen, as contrasted to those who wish only to observe and study wildlife, are rarely in agreement on paramount recreational values of an area; the desires of skiers and nonskiers are often incompatible; and those who desire ready access to remote regions—and comfortable, or at least convenient, accommodations when they get there—have distinctly different points of view from wilderness enthusiasts. Such differences of opinion, resulting from lack of uniformity in general objectives, as well as from an incomplete understanding of the over-all problems involved, are further complicated by the fact that the recreational possibilities of many lands are in direct competition with such necessary activities as logging, mining, grazing, production of hydroelectric power or water supply, and the development of residential or industrial sites.

Many people would state that recreation is merely fun or some activity which varies from the routine of their daily lives. Most dictionaries would define the term in a similar manner, the "act of recreating, or state of being recreated; refreshment of the strength and spirits after toil; diversion; play."[1] No one can quarrel with these basic concepts. Yet it requires only a superficial examination to recognize that such a definition could be so interpreted as to justify activities that are undesirable in publicly sponsored recreational programs.

In defining the objective of any recreational program, several factors must be recognized. First, recreation is many things. It involves any activity which is participated in, any time and anywhere, merely for the enjoyment it affords. Recreation may be purely physical; it may provide intellectual, esthetic, or emotional outlets; or it may include varied combinations of these. In its broadest sense it encompasses much more than mere physical activity. Second, the way spare time is used is very definitely individual and personal in nature. An activity which serves as recreation for one person may be work—or a bore—for another. Further, recreational needs vary at different times with specific individuals. They not only change during periods of one's life, in accordance with physical ability and intellectual capacity, but often with different periods in one day, depending upon personal moods. The rewards of recreational activities, whatever their nature, depend upon the degree to which they provide outlets for personal interests—physical development, mental improvement, cultural growth, or social adjustment—which are not attainable in one's daily routine. Third, while proper use of spare time may be beneficial, improper spare-time activities can be detrimental; in either case the effects may be temporary or capable of affecting a lifetime. Fourth, constructive recreation can be a powerful directive force which broadens and develops individual personality and achievement.

In our definition of recreation, the word "pleasurable" recognizes that recreation is fun. Maximum release from routine will accrue to the individual only if he voluntarily selects some spare-time recreational activity because of the pleasure it affords. But recreation should do more than merely enable an individual to occupy idle time—to loaf. Constructive spare-time activities can enrich, broaden, and develop individual capabilities and gratify man's natural desire for new and more satisfying ways of life. Indeed, more than a few individuals can credit their interest in a particular vocation to the germ of an idea planted during their early years by inspired direction in some sort of recreational program. Recreation can thus operate as a potent teaching force. It may be creative as well as recreative.

[1] Webster's New International Dictionary, 2d ed., unabridged, G. & C. Merriam Company, Springfield, Mass., 1947.

NEEDS, RESPONSIBILITIES, AND OBJECTIVES OF RECREATION

That each individual needs some form of recreation requires little elaboration; it is axiomatic. If maximum efficiency in the business of living is to be achieved, the stresses and strains of modern life must be relieved by periods of physical and mental relaxation properly coordinated with routine tasks. The greatly increased amount of leisure time now available as a result of technological progress will be used in some way, beneficially or otherwise. The way in which that time will be used will depend upon the opportunities available, the manner in which these opportunities are presented, and the physical and intellectual capabilities of the individual. In addition to greater leisure time, many other factors contribute to the expanding need for adequate recreational facilities and services. Our population has increased greatly; it is now primarily urban rather than rural in character, and with this has come a basic change in the general nature of occupations—from largely active to primarily sedentary. There is also a growing tendency toward a higher percentage of older people on one hand and young people on the other; both these groups, largely unproductive, require outlets for their energies and interests. Further, our standard of living is higher and the amount of available leisure time has greatly increased. We also have faster, more diversified, and more dependable means of transportation, making it possible for us to reach places far beyond the dreams of our fathers, and to do so easily, in comparative comfort, and within a shorter span of time.

These trends, which began slowly developing almost from the time the first colonists established themselves on the Atlantic seaboard, have been considerably accelerated in recent years and will undoubtedly become more acute in the future [1]. By way of prediction, consider the statement of David Sarnoff, Chairman of the Radio Corporation of America, in the January, 1955, issue of *Fortune* [13]:

> Leisure, of course, will be greatly extended. A much shorter work week will no doubt prevail in 1980, and another ten or fifteen years will have been added to the average life span. . . .
>
> Not labor but leisure will be the great problem in the decades ahead. That prospect should be accepted as a God-given opportunity to add dimensions of enjoyment and grace to life.

Society has properly assumed a large share of the responsibility in the provision of opportunities for constructive leisure-time activities. Numerous types of public recreational lands are available (national, state, county, and municipal parks as well as especially designated recreational areas in national and state forests). Schools, churches, and municipalities sponsor a wide variety of programs for different age groups.

Museums, art galleries, and similar specialized institutions are important adjuncts of recreation. Finally, there are zoological gardens, arboretums, and organizations catering to spare-time activities of almost every conceivable type.

These opportunities, however, are not well integrated. They did not result from a carefully conceived plan. They came into being largely because of obvious local need, specific group pressure, a happy coincidence of conditions at the time of the establishment of a specific recreational area, or in many instances, by reason of the energy, enthusiasm, and perseverance of perceptive individuals. A few examples will illustrate this point. Most city parks came into being as a result of readily recognizable local requirements. Many wilderness areas in the national forests were designated because of the interest of outdoor clubs and related groups who spearheaded public sentiment over their establishment. Finally, it is doubtful if some of our national parks, national monuments, or state parks would exist today had they not been set aside at a time when they were relatively more remote and consequently less important as a ready source of raw materials for industry than they are today, or had they not been championed by farsighted, public-spirited citizens.

Growth of recreational facilities has necessarily been irregular and erratic. As a result, throughout the country there is little coordination in the distribution of various types of public recreational lands or the nature of activities to which they are best adapted. Recreational areas in some sections of the nation are extensive and diverse; other regions are not only lacking in basic types of recreational opportunity but, in addition, possess too little space specifically set aside for such purposes. For instance, most of the larger and better known public recreational areas, like national parks and national forests, are in the West; of even greater significance is the fact that only a fraction of our seacoast remains in public ownership, developed—or capable of being developed—for public recreation. Specifically, a recreational survey of the Atlantic and Gulf Coasts, completed by the National Park Service in 1956, indicated that only 240 of the 3,700 miles of general coastline from Calais, Maine, to Brownsville, Texas, were in Federal or state ownership and used for public recreational purposes; the remaining major opportunities for preservation of Eastern seashore resources, largely confined to fifty-four undeveloped areas comprising 640 miles of beach front, were being depleted rapidly under pressures of a booming market for beach-front holdings [18]. Similar surveys of the Pacific Coast and Great Lakes, undertaken by the National Park Service in 1957, are expected to be completed in about two years.[2]

In short, development of public recreational areas has been charac-

[2] *Planning and Civic Comment*, vol. 22, no. 4, pp. 14ff., December, 1956.

terized by expediency. Little thought was originally given to the interrelationship of specific public recreational lands or the types of recreational activities best suited to them. As a result many superb areas have suffered severely because of the inclusion of inappropriate facilities which might have been avoided had opportunities for such development been provided on more suitable lands elsewhere in the same region.

Only in recent years has the enormity of this problem been generally recognized and have steps been taken to alleviate it [20]. In the meantime much land primarily valuable for recreation has been preempted by

FIG. 1-1. Only a small portion of our ocean shoreline is available for public recreation; Cape Hatteras National Seashore Recreational Area, North Carolina. (*Photo by Rex Schmidt, National Park Service*)

other forms of use, and the task of restoring its recreational potential is herculean in scope, made extremely difficult by tremendous cost, the nature of existing land-ownership patterns, and technical difficulties.

The most positive recent step in recreational land-use planning was the establishment of the National Outdoor Recreation Resources Review Commission in 1958 [16]. This Commission was established under provisions of the Outdoor Recreation Resources Review Act (Public Law 85-470), approved June 28, 1958. The Commission is charged with a broad and comprehensive responsibility. It will study outdoor recreational needs and resources throughout the nation and, in the light of that study, develop an inventory of recreational resources that will be required in the years 1976 and 2000. The Commission is also expected to recommend the adoption of policies and the initiation of programs which, carried out at all levels of government as well as by private organizations, will be necessary to satisfy such future recreational needs. The complete report of the Commission, developed so that it may be kept current in the future, is expected to be ready for presentation to the President and to Congress not later than September 1, 1961; within a year after that date the Commission will be disbanded. A maximum appropriation of $2,500,000 was authorized to carry out the purposes of this act.

The Commission consists of fifteen members. It includes four members of the Senate Committee on Interior and Insular Affairs, appointed by the President of the Senate; four members of the House Committee on Interior and Insular Affairs, appointed by the Speaker of the House; and seven citizens

> known to be informed about and concerned with the preservation and development of outdoor recreation resources and opportunities and experienced in resource conservation planning for multiple resources uses, who shall be appointed by the President, and one of whom shall be designated as chairman by the President [16].

The Outdoor Recreation Resources Review Act also made provision for an executive secretary and related necessary personnel, as well as an Advisory Council which works closely with the Commission in carrying out the purposes of the act. The Advisory Council consists of liaison officers appointed by various Federal and independent agencies with a direct interest and responsibility in various phases of outdoor recreation, together with twenty-five additional members representing major geographical areas and group interests, appointed by the Commission.

The Outdoor Recreation Resources Review Act specifically excludes customary urban recreational facilities and programs from consideration; it defines outdoor recreation resources as

> land and water areas and associated resources of such areas in the United States, its territories, and possessions which provide or may in the future provide opportunities for outdoor recreation, irrespective of ownership [16].

NEED FOR TRAINED LEADERSHIP IN RECREATION

It is obvious that trained, enlightened, perceptive, enthusiastic leadership is the key to proper coordination of the many largely unrelated parts of the recreational picture in the United States. If maximum recreational value is to be provided at minimum cost, varied public recreational services of diverse areas must be made to fit like pieces of a jigsaw puzzle. In that manner recreational activities inappropriate to certain lands and unnecessary duplication of services on contiguous recreational sites within specific regions can be advantageously eliminated. Properly trained recreational leadership is the best guarantee of transforming the existing pattern of recreational lands and activities from a poorly related hash to an orderly mosaic and of maintaining that standard in the necessary future expansion of recreational facilities.

These pages hold no brief for central, unified control of the nation's recreational resources. Even if that were possible, our recreational opportunities are too varied, too widely scattered, in some cases too interrelated with other natural resources, and too responsive to strictly local needs to make such a central authority practical. But there should be some means of ensuring close agreement on broad recreational objectives between top administrative levels of all agencies concerned; in that way cooperation between those agencies in fulfilling details of all recreational objectives will be enhanced. Recreation is too important to the national welfare and too costly to permit any other procedure.

Further, the sizeable investment in lands used solely and specifically for recreation today is, in itself, sufficient reason for qualified leadership in recreational land management; otherwise the recreational values inherent in those lands will not be properly maintained, and the investment will be largely nullified. In addition, since the character of public use of recreational areas, as well as cost of maintenance, is largely determined by the nature and plan of necessary physical facilities (e.g., roads, trails, campgrounds), such features must be carefully considered by personnel who not only are trained in design and construction but also have an understanding of the relationship of such facilities to proper recreational use. Also, since many areas of recreational interest have other values of equal or even greater importance, the management of multipurpose lands necessitates an understanding of all factors involved so that varied land uses on any single multipurpose area may be properly coordinated. Finally, future expansion of recreational needs necessitates careful advance planning, guided by an understanding of the reasons for those needs, so that public recreational requirements may be anticipated and provision made for them. Before rising costs make it impossible, there is great need, for instance, for the acquisition of areas suitable for recreation which are still unused for other purposes.

Nor should those recreational workers who deal directly with the public be overlooked. Such employees must not only be well grounded in fundamentals of their specific fields, but also be able to "sell" interest to others through their knowledge of the subject, their enthusiasm, and their understanding of people. Since recreation makes its appeal primarily on the basis of fun, since varied activities are entered into voluntarily, and since human beings are creatures of habit, this freedom may sometimes operate disadvantageously unless accompanied by inspired recreational leadership, for individual outlook and interests are circumscribed by background and environment. Many people will use only those recreational facilities which are most readily available and which are least demanding of personal effort; they may not only ignore opportunity to broaden their perspective through recreational channels but may even resist such opportunities vigorously. Only the most experienced, subtle, and perceptive direction can jog such people from a self-imposed rut which, in some cases, may be anything but a desirable one.

Only in relatively recent years has recreational land management been recognized in the public mind as worthy of professional status. Such recognition developed from a greatly expanded public demand for recreational opportunities, and this demand has stimulated numerous controversies between recreationalists and proponents of other forms of land use over the choice of specific areas. The problems inherent in adequately planning and providing for diverse recreational needs of the people, as well as the problems of coordinating these needs with other land values, have focused attention on the fact that recreational land management calls for far broader understanding and greater abilities than those required by simple maintenance. In a sense, the pickup man with his burlap sack and nail on a stick has been augmented by professionally trained specialists capable of relating varied public recreational interests to suitable available lands. This awakening has come about slowly and not without considerable apathy and resistance. It was spearheaded by such pioneer enterprises as the American Institute of Park Executives, founded in 1898;[3] the American Planning and Civic Association, organized in 1904;[4] the National Recreation Association, initiated in 1906;[5] *Parks and Recreation Magazine*, first publication in this field, begun in 1917;[6] the National Parks Association, established in 1919;[7] the National Con-

[3] The American Institute of Park Executives, established in 1898, was originally known as the New England Association of Park Superintendents. The name was changed to American Association of Park Superintendents in 1904, and the current title was adopted in 1921 (personal correspondence, January 10, 1958, from American Institute of Park Executives, Inc., Oglebay Park, Wheeling, West Virginia).

[4] The American Planning and Civic Association is an outgrowth of the Park and Outdoor Art Association, organized in 1897, and the National League for Civic Improvement Association, founded in 1900. These two groups amalgamated in 1904 and adopted the name of American Civic Association. In 1935 the National Conference on City Planning merged with the American Civic Association to form the American Planning and Civic Association (personal correspondence, January 7, 1958, from American Planning and Civic Association, Washington, D.C.).

[5] "Agencies of the Federal Government Concerned with Recreation: Trends, Inadequacies, Needs," National Recreation Association, New York, January, 1954.

[6] "Ulrich's Periodicals Directory," 7th ed., R. R. Bowker Company, New York, 1953.

[7] Richard Lieber, "America's Natural Wealth," Harper & Brothers, New York, 1942.

ference on State Parks, created in 1921;[8] the Wilderness Society, founded in 1935;[9] and the Division of Recreation formed in 1946 within the Society of American Foresters.[10] Schools offering professional training in the recreational use of land, although still largely concerned with the needs of municipal and county recreation departments, and thus handled primarily by departments of physical education, are gradually expanding their programs to embrace all aspects of this important field. Today, for instance, most forestry schools offer introductory courses in recreational land management; several offer specialized training in this phase of wildland management.

But in spite of recent progress, there is great need for additional understanding and development. The profession of recreational land management is still in its infancy; it stands upon the threshold of a greatly expanded future.

NEED FOR RESEARCH IN RECREATIONAL LAND MANAGEMENT

Through experience, by reason of the phenomenal increase in recreational use of land in recent years, we have learned a great deal about how to cope with many problems of recreational land management. Yet our knowledge of many of its aspects is still incomplete; it has not kept pace with public interest in and use of recreational lands, and there is growing recognition that an organized program of research in this field is needed. If recreational administrators are to plan and develop our recreational resources properly and economically and preserve our recreational heritage for future generations, they must have a satisfactory backlog of essential factual information upon which to base their conclusions.

Research in the recreational use of land demands the coordination of a great many interests and abilities. Since it is a new field, it offers fertile and interesting prospects for a great variety of qualified investigators, especially those who enjoy a pioneer venture.

Recreational research problems might be grouped into such broad categories as economics, protection, public psychology, planning and coordination, and facilities and equipment.

Economics. As emphasized in Chapter 7, there is need for the development of accepted techniques and methods of measuring the dollar value of recreational lands and facilities. These studies should apply not only

[8] "25th Anniversary Yearbook: Park and Recreation Progress," National Conference on State Parks, Washington, 1946.

[9] *The Living Wilderness*, vol. 16, no. 38, p. 21, Autumn, 1951.

[10] John D. Coffmann, "Council Approves Division of Forest Recreation," *Journal of Forestry*, vol. 44, no. 2, p. 150, February, 1946.

to secondary economic benefits (e.g., direct expenditures induced as a result of recreational activities) but, if possible, to the primary yet more intangible benefits as well (e.g., increases in individual productivity through relaxation, broadening of cultural horizons of our citizens, and reduction in costs of law enforcement).

Also needed is more generally disseminated information as to various methods of providing for the financial support of various types of current recreational areas and programs, and studies relative to improvement of these methods in the future. Further, increased recreational use of land has prompted a corresponding growth in public requests for various types of services heretofore not required. Since this trend is likely to expand as we withdraw farther from our pioneer period, meeting such demands may levy a severe financial burden on certain types of recreational administrations unless some means is developed for adequately meeting their cost. It seems desirable that ways and means of charging for certain types of services be thoroughly explored so that those actually using recreational areas would pay a slightly higher share of costs of operation than others who, although they share in the basic support of such operations through payment of taxes and similar means, do not use or enjoy them.

Protection. Although many aspects relative to the protection of natural resources have been carefully investigated, such work has not been conducted with specific relation to recreational land use. From the point of view of recreational land management, the results of many such investigations may be only partly conclusive and in need of greater refinement or modified approach.

We need to know more about the relation between recreational use and man-caused forest fires, damage to trees and other vegetation by destructive insects and fungus diseases induced by recreational use, the effects of both direct and biological control of destructive insects and fungus diseases on recreational interests, and the reduction in recreational values as a result of fire, insects, or fungus diseases—particularly of noncommercial forests.

There is need for a study of the habits and characteristics of various species of trees and other plants useful in rehabilitating areas damaged by excessive or ill-advised recreational activities. We should know more about the relationship between recreational use of land and the introduction and spread of undesirable plants and animals. Avalanche studies, pioneered in this country by the U.S. Forest Service, should be supported by a greater amount of basic factual information relative to the characteristics and mechanics of snow and ice accumulation leading to the development of dangerous slide conditions.

In addition, studies relative to the impact of concentrations of people on recreational lands are also vitally important. Such studies are most important for campgrounds and other areas which customarily receive heaviest public pressure. In short, as stated by S. T. Dana [5], we need to know more about the human "carrying capacity" of various types of lands and facilities, the relationship between crowds of people and the resultant impact upon such basic recreational land values as plant and animal life, soils, water resources, and geological, archeological, and historical interests.

Also in this category fall studies concerning public health and welfare—the incidence and causes of various types of accidents, as well as considerations necessary for the safe handling of foods, the provision of safe, adequate, water supplies, and the disposal of sewage and waste materials.

Public Psychology. Since recreational administrators deal with people, studies of human behavior are of great importance. An understanding of public recreational interests, what people do in recreational areas, and what motivates their interests and acts not only promotes better planning of recreational facilities and services but also aids administrators in formulating adequate rules and regulations for the safeguarding of human life and property. Studies of public recreational interests and human behavior are of particular importance in planning and conducting various types of programs relative to the interpretation of significant recreational interests, as well as to the development of adequate public relations programs.

Planning and Coordination. In relation to future recreational needs we should carefully analyze various types of statistical data concerning changes in our pattern of population. Also required are studies in trends in recreational interests so that recreational planning may anticipate and, if possible, provide for such needs.

Studies bearing upon logging, grazing, mining, development of dams for irrigation and hydroelectric power, expansion of metropolitan centers and related requirements of our modern way of life, and their effect on recreational values are also greatly needed. Equally important are ways and means of relating various recreational interests and activities with one another, as well as methods by which recreational uses may be most advantageously coordinated with other land values. Also, changes in methods of transportation, particularly as they concern aircraft, demand studies relative to their effects on recreational interests and values.

Facilities, Equipment, and Services. Although greater progress has been made in this facet of recreational management than in any other, continued research is needed in relation to the planning, design, location, construction, and maintenance of recreational facilities and services to ensure maximum use and greater economy of operation. Roads, trails, signs, camp and picnic grounds, drinking fountains, sanitary facilities, stoves and fireplaces, tables, museums and related interpretive needs, hotels, sports developments, and the like need to be evaluated constantly in relation to existing and future use, cost of operation and maintenance, and effect on varied recreational interests.

The foregoing items are suggestive of only a few avenues for recreational research. A complete study of the recreational field will spotlight many other problems which are in need of greater clarification through basic research and careful investigation. Of particular interest in this connection are Dana's conclusions on recreational research as applied specifically to the national forests [5].

MAJOR INFLUENCES OF PUBLIC RECREATIONAL REQUIREMENTS

Factors which have contributed to our growing recreational needs in the past, and which will continue to exert even greater influence in the future, include the nature, density, and distribution of our population, as well as the relative relationship between different groups and age classes; the amount of leisure time available to the individual; and the amount of a person's income, the nature of his occupation, and his means of transportation.

Population Changes and Their Effects upon Recreational Patterns. As noted in Table 1-1, our expanding population has brought about a phenomenal increase in the number of potential users of recreational lands and facilities. Within a relatively few years after the American Revolution the population of the United States was nearly four million, largely confined to the Atlantic seaboard. Since that time, with the western boundary of our country extended to the Pacific, our population has increased manyfold. In 1950 the United States had more than 150 million inhabitants. The numerical increase in population was greater between the years 1941 and 1950 than in any similar period in our history. During that decade the sharp upturn in percentage of increase, which had been declining steadily since 1860, may be attributed to an upward trend in the birth rate. This trend is expected to continue. It has been predicted that by 1975 the population of the United States will be 212 million [14,15].

Although the population of the United States has increased tremendously over the years, it is not uniformly distributed. From Table 1-2 it will be noted that nearly half our people live in the New England, Middle Atlantic, and East North Central divisions of our country, a region which embraces less than 14 per cent of our land. By contrast the Mountain division has over 28 per cent of the land area of the United States but less than 4 per cent of our population.

Table 1-1. Increase in Population and Area of Continental United States, Exclusive of Alaska

Census date	Population								Gross area, inc. land and inland water area	People per square mile
	Total	% of increase over preceding period	Urban	% of increase over preceding period	Rural	% of increase over preceding period	% of total			
							Urban	Rural		
1790	3,929,214	....	201,655	....	3,727,559	....	5.1	94.9	888,811	4.5
1800	5,308,483	35.1	322,371	59.0	4,986,112	33.8	6.1	93.9	888,811	6.1
1810	7,239,881	36.4	525,459	63.0	6,714,422	34.7	7.3	92.7	1,716,003	4.3
1820	9,638,453	33.1	693,255	31.9	8,945,198	33.2	7.2	92.8	1,788,006	5.6
1830	12,866,020	33.5	1,127,247	62.6	11,738,773	31.2	8.8	91.2	1,788,006	7.4
1840	17,069,453	32.7	1,845,055	63.7	15,224,398	29.7	10.8	89.2	1,788,006	9.8
1850	23,191,876	35.9	3,543,716	92.1	19,648,160	29.1	15.3	84.7	2,992,747	7.9
1860	31,443,321	35.6	6,216,518	75.4	25,226,803	28.4	19.8	80.2	3,022,387	10.6
1870	38,558,371	22.6	9,902,361	59.3	28,656,010	13.6	25.7	74.3	3,022,387	13.4
1880	50,155,783	30.1	14,129,735	42.7	36,026,048	25.7	28.2	71.8	3,022,387	16.9
1890	62,947,714	25.5	22,106,265	56.5	40,841,449	13.4	35.1	64.9	3,022,387	21.2
1900	75,994,575	20.7	30,159,921	36.4	45,834,654	12.2	39.7	60.3	3,022,387	25.6
1910	91,972,266	21.0	41,998,932	39.3	49,973,334	9.0	45.7	54.3	3,022,387	31.0
1920	105,710,620	14.9	54,157,973	29.0	51,552,647	3.2	51.2	48.8	3,022,387	35.6
1930	122,775,046	16.1	68,954,823	27.3	53,820,223	4.4	56.2	43.8	3,022,387	41.2
1940	131,669,275	7.2	74,423,702	7.9	57,245,573	6.4	56.5	43.5	3,022,387	44.2
1950	150,697,361	14.5	88,927,464	19.5	61,769,897	7.9	59.0	41.0	3,022,387	50.7

SOURCE: "Census of Population: 1950," report P-A1, chap. 1, table 4, U.S. Bureau of the Census, 1950; and "Statistical Abstract of the United States: 1954," table 2, U.S. Bureau of the Census, 1954.

Population density within the various states varies from a low of 1.5 people per square mile in Nevada to a high of 748.5 people per square mile in Rhode Island.[11] Other examples of extreme variations in population are high densities in New Jersey, 642.8; Massachusetts, 596.2; Connecticut, 409.7; and New York, 309.3; and low densities in Wyoming, 3.0; Montana, 4.1; New Mexico, 5.6; Arizona, 6.6; Idaho, 7.1; Utah, 8.4; South Dakota, 8.5; and North Dakota, 8.8. Of the Eastern states, Maine has the lowest population density, 29.4, while the greatest concentration of people per square mile in the West is found in California, 67.5.

Table 1-2. Distribution of Population and Area of Continental United States, Exclusive of Alaska, 1950

Geographic division	Population		Gross area, land and water		Population per sq. mi.
	Number	%, computed	Sq. mi.	%, computed	
New England	9,314,453	6.2	66,608	2.2	147.5
Middle Atlantic	30,163,533	20.0	102,745	3.4	300.1
East North Central	30,399,368	20.2	248,283	8.2	124.1
West North Central	14,061,394	9.3	517,247	17.1	27.5
South Atlantic	21,182,335	14.1	278,902	9.2	79.0
East South Central	11,477,181	7.6	181,964	6.0	63.8
West South Central	14,537,572	9.6	438,885	14.6	33.8
Mountain	5,074,998	3.4	863,887	28.6	5.9
Pacific	14,486,527	9.6	323,866	10.7	45.3
Total	150,697,361	100.0	3,022,387	100.0	50.7

SOURCE: "Census of Population: 1950," report P-A1, chap. 1, table 8, U.S. Bureau of the Census, 1950; and "Statistical Abstract of the United States: 1954," tables 4, 5, and 11, U.S. Bureau of the Census, 1954.

The change in the population pattern in the United States from essentially rural to primarily urban in character, first accomplished about the time of World War I (see Table 1-1), has profoundly affected the living habits and occupational pursuits of our people. Today most Americans are crowded onto relatively limited areas of land where natural conditions are largely nonexistent; employment is primarily in industrial, commercial, clerical, or professional activities which are essentially sedentary. Thus, many Americans are removed from regular contact with open spaces and to a considerable degree have lost the ability of their fore-

[11] "Statistical Abstract of the United States, 1954," table 5, U.S. Bureau of the Census, Washington, 1954.

fathers to conduct themselves properly and safely in a truly natural environment.

The rapid growth and irregular dissemination of our population, together with resultant effects upon the habits and occupations of the people, have greatly influenced our need for diverse recreational opportunities. It is obvious that we require a greater number of properly distributed recreational areas of widely varying types suited to different spare-time interests and activities. Overcrowded conditions typical of most recreational lands—particularly those in and near major centers of population—emphasize this need. The growth of metropolitan, county, and state park systems in many sections of the country is a direct result of this demand. Changes in population patterns and living habits also indicate why there is a constantly increasing pressure for the reservation of large unspoiled tracts, such as wilderness areas in national forests, where people can completely escape the confines of the city and obtain the benefits of recreation in truly natural surroundings. Nor can we afford to overlook the physical damage done to recreational lands of unique quality, such as national parks, when, through pressure of unenlightened public demand, inappropriate facilities or activities are added to the areas.

Effects of Variations in Age Classes. Since people of different ages have varying interests and physical abilities, the relationship between various age classes comprising our population is another factor which bears upon the needs and, consequently, the nature of recreational facilities required. Of particular importance is the relative number of youths and senior citizens. These two groups, largely unproductive economically and at opposite extremes of physical ability and mental maturity, obviously have widely divergent recreational interests.

Young people demand, and need, facilities for active recreation; the emphasis here is on sports, team play, and active group programs. Declining vigor of more mature years prompts increasingly greater emphasis upon physical moderation and more passive mental relaxation.

Table 1-3 shows the increasing percentage of older people in our population. This important change, a result of the advances in medical science which have materially prolonged our life expectancy, implies that careful consideration must be given to the provision of recreational opportunities suited to this segment of our population. It also explains the increased interest in areas of our country typified by less vigorous climates. Also indicated in Table 1-3 is the initial effect of the recent spurt in our birth rate, which had been steadily declining since about the time of the Civil War. Continuation of this upward trend will necessitate greater attention to the recreational needs of youth.

In a somewhat similar but less positive manner the sex ratio of our population, as well as the relationship between various racial units and groups of varying national origins, has its effects on recreational requirements.

Table 1-3. Percentage Distribution of Population by Cumulative Age Groups for the United States, 1890–1950

Age group	1950	1940	1930	1920	1910	1900	1890
Under							
5	10.8	8.0	9.3	11.0	11.6	12.1	12.2
10	19.6	16.1	19.6	21.8	22.2	23.8	24.3
15	27.1	25.0	29.4	31.8	32.1	34.5	35.6
20	34.1	34.4	38.8	40.8	42.0	44.4	46.1
25	41.8	43.2	47.7	49.6	51.9	54.1	56.0
30	49.9	51.6	55.7	58.2	60.8	62.7	64.4
35	57.5	59.4	63.1	65.8	68.4	70.1	71.7
40	64.9	66.7	70.6	73.2	75.3	76.6	77.9
45	71.6	73.3	77.1	79.2	81.1	82.2	83.0
Over							
45	28.4	26.7	22.9	20.8	18.9	17.8	17.0
50	22.4	20.4	17.1	15.3	14.1	13.2	12.6
55	16.9	14.9	12.3	10.9	9.8	9.3	8.9
60	12.2	10.4	8.5	7.5	6.8	6.4	6.2
65	8.2	6.8	5.4	4.7	4.3	4.1	3.9
70	4.8	4.0	3.1	2.7	2.5	2.3	2.3
75	2.6	2.0	1.6	1.4	1.3	1.2	1.1
80	1.1	0.9	0.7	0.6	0.5	0.5	0.5
85	0.4	0.3	0.2	0.2	0.2	0.2	0.2

SOURCE: "Census of Population: 1950," bulletin P-C1, table 100, U.S. Bureau of the Census, 1950.

Improvement of Living Standards and Increase in Leisure Time. Activities of the modern individual are highly specialized. In our work today most of us contribute to the welfare of society largely through detailed tasks which are but parts of a broad, over-all project. Creative elements are largely lacking in our daily routine; many individual workers often have little or no idea of the relationship of their efforts to the finished product. In short, modern man's existence is considerably regimented by an industrialized civilization in which personal satisfaction is sacrificed for greater productive capacity.

Such a system, however, has many compensations. Together with various technical innovations, modern techniques have materially improved our living standards so that we are better able to afford the costs of spare-time activities of our own choosing. As indicated in Table 1-4, there has been a noticeable rise in the national wealth since 1929; disposable income payments (e.g., that portion of the national product left to individuals, after taxes, for spending or saving) for the entire population rose from 136 billion dollars in 1929 to 224 billion dollars in 1952, with the prospect of a continued increase by 1975 to over 360 billion. These

Table 1-4. Disposable Income Payments in the United States, Billions of 1952 Dollars: Actual 1929–1952, Estimated 1929–2000

Year	Actual	Estimated	Year	Actual	Estimated
1929	136	135	1944	202	216
1930	126	126	1945	198	211
1931	118	118	1946	202	194
1932	101	106	1947	198	194
1933	102	105	1948	203	199
1934	111	113	1949	201	200
1935	120	120	1950	219	214
1936	138	132	1951	222	227
1937	139	136	1952	224	232
1938	130	131	....	...	...
			1960	...	268
1939	141	140	1965	...	298
1940	149	150	1970	...	333
1941	167	168	1975	...	367
1942	183	184	2000	...	526
1943	188	203			

SOURCE: "America's Demand for Wood, 1929–1975," a report by the Stanford Research Institute to the Weyerhaeuser Timber Company, Stanford, Calif., June, 1954, p. 31.

figures, when related to population changes during the same period, also indicate a sharp increase in the average annual per capita disposable income, from approximately $1,025 in 1930 to $1,450 in 1950. By 1975 indications are that the average annual per capita disposable income will have increased to over $1,700.

Modern technology also makes it possible for us to produce more goods with far less effort and in much less time than formerly. As a result the amount of leisure time available to the individual has been greatly increased. Properly used, this increased leisure time may readily satisfy man's creative needs.

During the early days of America, when the population was almost totally rural in character, people had to labor long hours each day in order to provide the necessities of life for themselves and their families. One hundred years ago the average work week was seventy-four hours

[17]; of the remaining ninety-four hours in each week, eighty-four were required for personal care (eating, sleeping, etc.). Opportunities for those activities now termed "recreation" were severely limited in a schedule which permitted only about ten hours of free time weekly. Further, the philosophy of the times regarded such interests as wasteful of time and effort—in effect, not respectable. During the formative years of our country, particularly in New England, recreation simply for personal enjoyment was severely frowned upon.

As an indication of the early American attitude toward recreation, witness the policy of Cokesbury College, as noted in the "Methodist Discipline" in 1792.[12] "The students shall be indulged with nothing which the world calls play. [illegible]t this rule be observed with the strictest nicety; for those who play when they are young, will play when they are old."

It should be stated, however, that the long hours of work characteristic of early Am[illegible] were not without their compensations. A new home, a new commu[illegible]w nation was literally being carved from the wilderness. To a la[illegible] such work represented personal achievement, and the long hour[illegible]ave the debilitating effect upon the worker that many routine tasks [illegible]oday.

Neverth[illegible]eless, al[illegible]gh time for personal care has remained fairly constant over the years, slowly developing technological progress has brought a gradual reduction in the effort required to supply man's basic needs. The average work week at the time of the Civil War was sixty-eight hours; by the turn of the century it had been reduced to sixty hours; today the ten-hour day and the six-day work week typical of about a half century ago has been generally replaced by the standard eight-hour day, five days weekly [17]. Thus, within the past one hundred years, the average person has gained nearly thirty additional hours of free time weekly which he may use in activities of his own choosing. Indications are that the work week will be further reduced in the future [20]. Young people, not yet faced with the problems of the workaday world, have an even greater amount of free time, for technological advances have also greatly prolonged the economic immaturity of the individual.

A more precise indication of the reduction of the work week coupled with an increase in individual production per man-hour since 1929 is given in the report by the Stanford Research Institute, as noted in Table 1-5. These data also point to further reductions in working hours in the future. Both management and labor are already giving serious consideration to this matter, as noted in a report in *Factory Management and Maintenance* for November, 1956 [3].

In addition to shortening the work week, technological progress has

[12] Methodist Episcopal Church, "The Doctrines and Discipline of the Methodist Episcopal Church in America," Parry Hall, Philadelphia, 1792, p. 68.

also broadened opportunities for extended vacation periods. This has had a strong bearing upon outdoor recreation, for more people are increasingly able to travel greater distances to points of particular interest.

IMPROVEMENT IN TRAVEL FACILITIES

In addition to the increase in leisure time, improvement in methods and facilities for travel have developed greatly. As a result, patterns of both work and play have changed materially. Our horizons, as well as our activities, are much broader than they once were.

Table 1-5. Average Weekly Hours and Gross Private Product per Man-Hour. Actual 1929–1952, Estimated 1960–2000

Year	Average weekly hours	Gross private production per man-hour, 1952 dollars	Year	Average weekly hours	Gross private production per man-hour, 1952 dollars
1929	48.5	1.45	1944	[illegible]	2.31
1930	47.0	1.42	1945	44	2.38
1931	47.0	1.41	1946	42.8	2.26
1932	45.3	1.36	1947	42.4	2.21
1933	46.0	1.33	1948	42.3	2.25
1934	44.2	1.44	1949	41.5	2.33
1935	43.5	1.54	1950	41.8	2.46
1936	44.2	1.62	1951	41.1	2.61
1937	44.9	1.63	1952	41.7	2.64
1938	43.1	1.68	....	....	....
			1960	40.1	3.01
1939	43.7	1.76	1965	39.1	3.24
1940	43.4	1.87	1970	38.1	3.46
1941	43.7	2.02	1975	37.1	3.65
1942	45.1	2.04	2000	35.0	4.33
1943	46.2	2.14			

SOURCE: "America's Demand for Wood, 1929–1975," a report by the Stanford Research Institute to the Weyerhaeuser Timber Company, Stanford, Calif., June, 1954.

The automobile has been the most vital factor in this development. As indicated in Table 1-6, automobile ownership began a marked acceleration about 1915. With the exception of the depression of the 1930s and World War II, this has continued unabated to the present day.

The travel radius of the average American family was phenomenally increased by the development of the automobile. Practically overnight, recreational journeys consisting of one-day trips to a picnic ground near the end of a streetcar line were broadened to weekends spent at points of interest many miles distant. The automobile also made possible extended trips to places which, because of the necessity of expensive, time-consuming rail journeys, had been previously inaccessible to the average citizen.

Table 1-6. Privately Owned Motor Vehicle Registrations in the United States

Year	Number	Year	Number	Year	Number	Year	Number
1895	4	1910	458,377	1925	17,439,701	1940	27,372,397
1896	16	1911	618,727	1926	19,220,885	1941	29,524,101
1897	90	1912	901,596	1927	20,142,120	1942	27,868,746
1898	800	1913	1,190,393	1928	21,308,159	1943	25,912,730
1899	3,200	1914	1,664,003	1929	23,060,421	1944	25,466,331
1900	8,000	1915	2,332,426	1930	22,972,745	1945	25,691,434
1901	14,800	1916	3,367,889	1931	22,330,402	1946	28,100,188
1902	23,000	1917	4,727,468	1932	20,832,357	1947	30,718,852
1903	32,920	1918	5,554,952	1933	20,586,284	1948	33,213,905
1904	54,590	1919	6,679,133	1934	21,472,078	1949	36,312,380
1905	77,400	1920	8,131,522	1935	22,494,884	1950	40,185,146
1906	105,900	1921	9,212,158	1936	24,108,236	1951	42,525,217
1907	140,300	1922	10,704,076	1937	25,390,773	1952	43,653,545
1908	194,400	1923	13,252,019	1938	25,167,030	1953	46,289,129
1909	305,950	1924	15,436,102	1939	26,139,526	1954	48,323,909

SOURCE: "Automobile Facts and Figures," 35th ed., Automobile Manufacturers Association, Detroit, 1955.

Development and wider use of motor vehicles by the public and the consequent interest in extended travel were soon reflected in improved and additional highways. Today, good roads span the length and breadth of our land. They penetrate to remote nooks and crannies and, except in rare instances, are available throughout the year.

The development of air travel gives promise of even greater impact on recreational travel habits in the future. The effects of this mode of transportation are already being felt, particularly in remote wilderness areas where lakes provide facilities for amphibious aircraft.

SUMMARY

Although recreation means many things to many people, it involves leisure-time activities which embody personal interest and enjoyment.

Constructive use of leisure time is of vital importance to the well-being of the individual, the community, and the nation, since the growth of an individual is determined as much by how he occupies his leisure hours as by the time spent upon his daily tasks. Technological progress has developed an essentially urban pattern of life, raised our standard of living, increased our leisure time, and expanded our transportation facilities. These factors, together with the growth and changing composition of our population, indicate that the future will witness increasing pressure on all existing recreational facilities. If the overcrowded conditions already typical of many recreational areas are to be alleviated and if the basic values of those lands are to be preserved, better land-use planning which gives adequate consideration to public recreational needs is required as is better technically trained recreational leadership. Additional recreational lands of diverse types adapted to a wide variety of interests —from municipal golf courses and children's playgrounds to remote wilderness areas—must be made available as needed. In particular, a greater number of certain types of recreational areas must be established in accordance with population patterns. Formation of the National Outdoor Recreation Resources Review Commission in 1958 is proof of growing public awareness of the need for adequate recreational planning with respect to the nation's future recreational needs. But regardless of enlightened planning and trained leadership, if spare-time interests of a steadily increasing number of people are to be served adequately, recreational activities of every kind will be subject to an increasing amount of regimentation. We may not like it, but in the future individual preferences will necessarily have to be tempered by consideration for the many.

SELECTED REFERENCES

1. Anonymous: Where Will U.S. Put 60 Million People? *U.S. News and World Report,* vol. 43, no. 6, pp. 46–54, Aug. 9, 1957.
2. Automobile Manufacturers Association: "Automobile Facts and Figures," 35th ed., Detroit, 1955.
3. Boyce, Carroll W.: The Four Day Week? *Factory Management and Maintenance,* vol. 114, no. 11, pp. 84–94, November, 1956.
4. Burns, C. D.: "Leisure in the Modern World," Appleton-Century-Crofts, Inc., New York, 1932.
5. Dana, S. T.: "Problem Analysis: Research in Forest Recreation," U.S. Forest Service, Washington, April, 1957.
6. Lord, Russell: "Forest Outings," U.S. Government Printing Office, Washington, 1940, pp. 17–36.
7. Menninger, W. C.: Recreation and Mental Health, *Recreation,* vol. 42, no. 8, pp. 340–346, November, 1948.
8. National Park Service: Recreational Use of Land in the United States, part

XI of "Report on Land Planning," prepared for the Land Planning Committee of the National Resources Board, Washington, 1938.

9. Neumeyer, M. H., and E. S. Neumeyer: "Leisure and Recreation: A Study of Leisure and Recreation in Their Sociological Aspects," A. S. Barnes and Company, New York, 1936.
10. Pack, Arthur N.: "The Challenge of Leisure," The Macmillan Company, New York, 1936.
11. Prendergast, Joseph: The Evolving National Recreation Pattern, *Planning and Civic Comment,* vol. 22, no. 4, pp. 1–6, December, 1956.
12. National Resources Committee: "The Problems of a Changing Population," Report of the Committee on Population Problems to the National Resources Committee, Washington, 1938.
13. Sarnoff, David: The Fabulous Future, *Fortune,* vol. 51, no. 1, pp. 82–83, January, 1955.
14. Stanford Research Institute: "America's Demand for Wood, 1929–1975," Report by the Stanford Research Institute to the Weyerhaeuser Timber Company, Stanford, Calif., June, 1954.
15. Stanford Research Institute: "America's Demand for Wood, 1929–1975," Summary of a report by the Stanford Research Institute to the Weyerhaeuser Timber Company, Stanford, Calif., 1954.
16. U.S. Congress: "Outdoor Recreation Resources Review Act, Public Law 85–470, S.846, June 28, 1958," 85th Congress, 1st Session, 1958.
17. U.S. Department of the Interior, National Park Service: "A Study of the Park and Recreation Problem of the United States," Washington, 1941.
18. U.S. Department of the Interior, National Park Service: "A Report on Our Vanishing Shoreline," n.p., n.d.
19. Vogt, William: Mankind at the Flood, *National Parks Magazine,* vol. 29, no. 122, pp. 109–110, July–September, 1955.
20. Wirth, Conrad L.: Is There a Need for a Comprehensive Recreation Program in the United States? *Planning and Civic Comment,* vol. 21, no. 2, pp. 1–9, June, 1955.
21. Wirth, Conrad L.: Basic Need for Land, *Planning and Civic Comment,* vol. 23, no. 4, pp. 22–28, December, 1957.
22. Wrenn, C. G., and D. L. Harley: "Time on Their Hands: A Report on Leisure, Recreation, and Young People," prepared for the American Youth Commission, American Council of Education, Washington, 1941.

CHAPTER 2 *Relationship of the Outdoors to Recreational Needs*

Outdoor recreation involves a multitude of interests pursued on a great variety of lands—municipal playgrounds, city and county parks, metropolitan park districts, numerous types of state and Federal lands, and areas owned and operated for various purposes by private enterprise. While all of these are important to outdoor recreation, this volume gives primary consideration to outdoor recreation of wild lands—areas characterized by a natural or largely unmodified character. Recreational lands which have been subjected to extensive modification through physical development, such as municipal parks and playgrounds, amusement parks, and the like, are only briefly mentioned. They are included largely to point out their relationship to recreation on wild land, as well as to broad public recreational needs.

VALUES OF OUTDOOR RECREATION ON WILD LANDS

Wild lands offer excellent opportunities for health-giving, outdoor, leisure-time pursuits. In addition they provide opportunity for development of physical and mental skills. To a large extent the individual engaged in recreational activity on wild land is on his own; his enjoyment is largely dependent upon his own resources. In a limited sense he must meet the physical demands of the outdoors as did his forebears, and the degree of success he attains is an indication of his self-reliance. Intellectually, too, his enjoyment of such areas depends upon his perception; in some cases the major recreational benefits can be achieved only from a combination of physical and intellectual abilities.

Physical values of recreation on wild land are derived primarily from such activities as fishing, hunting, hiking, riding, picnicking, camping, mountain climbing, skiing, boating, swimming, and the like. True, not only purely physical benefits are involved. To many fishermen, for instance, a full creel is but one of the rewards of a fishing trip; benefits other than exercise are derived from the ascent of a mountain; more than fresh air rewards those who camp in the outdoors. Such activities, however, can be enjoyed simply in their own right; physical pleasure is sufficient recreational reward for the effort involved.

FIG. 2-1. Recreation, if it fosters an understanding of nature's forces, such as those which were responsible for the formation of Delicate Arch in Arches National Monument, Utah, can be a cultural experience. (*National Park Service*)

Cultural or intellectual values are derived from such interests as photography, painting, handicrafts, nature study, scientific research, and even meditation, but these activities, in addition to being enjoyed for themselves alone, are remunerative in many other ways. The photographer who climbs a mountain to obtain a particular picture, or the entomologist who exerts great effort in searching for a particular specimen, frequently develops a high degree of physical skill. In such cases, however, necessary physical activity is a means to an end rather than an end in itself.

FIG. 2-2. In surroundings such as these a full creel is not the only reward of a fishing trip; Mirror Lake and Eagle Cap, Wallowa-Whitman National Forest, Oregon. (*U.S. Forest Service*)

NATURAL ENVIRONMENT VERSUS MAN-MADE ENVIRONMENT

Modern man's leisure-time interests are largely delineated by his essentially urban environment. He is often unfamiliar with the outdoors, a fact which prompts a lack of self-reliance and understanding which may cause annoying or even serious difficulties. Today many people must learn how to conduct themselves in the outdoors before they can expect to enjoy its opportunities fully. Assuming that one is physically able, maximum safety and personal enjoyment of varied recreational activities on wild land come only with an understanding of the interests and hazards involved. For instance, competent skiers recognize the signs of potentially dangerous slide areas; good hunters exercise caution in handling their weapons; and a knowledge of native plants and animals, or an understanding of geological processes, enhances the pleasures of a visit to the mountains.

Knowledge and understanding of a natural environment also foster good outdoor manners. Such awareness encourages participation in perpetuating the beauty of unspoiled surroundings; this is extremely important because outdoor recreational values are not inexhaustible and, in many cases, are very fragile. Careless treatment, whether by design or ignorance, reduces the worth of an area. Everyone knows of formerly attractive places ruined by thoughtless acts of vandalism.

It is not pleasant to camp or picnic amid an accumulation of cans, bottles, and assorted rubbish abandoned by previous visitors. A road flanked by blackened snags, the result of a man-caused forest fire, is anything but an asset to an area's scenic beauty. A significant feature such as Morning Glory Pool, in Yellowstone National Park, is not enhanced by candy-bar wrappers, film cartons, and other trash floating upon its surface; nor will a glance into its depths be conducive of any reaction other than one of disgust if an old automobile tire is seen lying beneath the surface.

Residents of large cities are not the only ones who lack an adequate understanding of the outdoors. Frequently that environment is equally unfamiliar and confusing to inhabitants of smaller towns. Today, by reason of radio, television, and almost universal distribution of newspapers and magazines, modern life tends to follow the pattern of metropolitan centers, even in many rural areas. In addition, small communities do not usually possess facilities such as museums, zoological gardens, and arboretums to foster public appreciation of many dramatic outdoor interests.

IRREGULAR DISTRIBUTION OF OUTDOOR RECREATIONAL RESOURCES

Today, in addition to timber, forage for livestock, minerals, water, and the like, inherent recreational interests of wild lands are generally recognized as an important natural resource; on many types of land they are of dominant value. But, like more tangible natural resources, recreational values are widely scattered without relationship to human need. Only rarely are recreational opportunities available in satisfactory variety close to large centers of population where their need is greatest.

Climate favorable to outdoor activities at different seasons, varied topography which is scenically interesting and which lends itself to different outdoor pursuits, water resources such as streams, lakes, and ocean frontage, and interesting floral and faunal associations are irregularly distributed about the country [17]. Countless numbers of people seeking expression for their spare-time interests in the outdoors must choose between relatively expensive travel to distant points and less dramatic but more readily available opportunities close at hand. The irregular distribution of recreational interests accounts for the differences in type and degree of outdoor recreational use of land, as well as for variations in recreational travel.

Irregular distribution of recreational resources emphasizes the need for careful planning in relation to present and future use of wild lands. We not only require more area set aside specifically for various recreational activities, but it should also be apparent that many forms of outdoor recreation are not incompatible with other forms of land use; wherever possible these should be coordinated. In any event only enlightened and perceptive management will foster the most logical recreational use by the greatest number of people, consistent with the perpetuation of all basic land values.

SOME LAND USES WHICH COMPETE WITH RECREATION

Recreational values of wild land are variously affected by most of man's other activities [17]. Industrial development and the growth of large urban centers have resulted in the pollution of streams, lakes, and ocean beaches. The erection of dams and the resultant formation of artificial lakes, although occasionally providing certain recreational opportunities, often destroy even more valuable recreational interests through the flooding of historical, archeological, or scenic areas, or the serious reduction in numbers of migratory fish. In the latter instance, not only do dams impede periodic upstream movements of certain sport fishes, but resultant development of large artificial lakes may raise water temperatures beyond the limit of tolerance for certain species. Improper methods in harvesting timber adversely affect scenic values and the same may be said of improper grazing; further, such ill-advised activities may have far-reaching adverse effects on the conservation of natural resources through the acceleration of upland erosion and silting of streams. Indiscriminate drainage of swamps and marshes greatly affects the numbers of migratory waterfowl, and the settlement and cultivation of marginal farm lands often lead to the disappearance of interesting or valuable birds and mammals. Private acquisition of choice recreational sites, particularly on lake shores and ocean beaches, has already eliminated a large part of such land from the possibility of general public use; on such high-premium recreational lands the needs of the masses should take precedence over the desires of the few.

It should be emphasized that these pages hold no brief for recreational management of wild lands at the expense of total exclusion of other uses of land which are vital to modern life. However, in the interest of public welfare it is apparent that in each specific case all aspects of human need must be carefully investigated before final decisions are made as to the type and character of that use. Except on areas which are clearly most valuable for recreation, administration and management of all natural resources, including recreation, should be properly coordinated wherever possible. No longer can we afford to act hastily or without due consideration for the future and correct the mistakes of ill-advised action later; too often such mistakes are irreparable.

AGENCIES IMPORTANT IN THE ADMINISTRATION OF RECREATIONAL LANDS

Most outdoor recreational areas are administered by various governmental agencies (Federal, state, county, or municipal) which control large tracts of land having recreational values. With few exceptions, private enterprise is not attracted to the management of lands for recreation, since such activity rarely returns a direct monetary profit commensurate with the necessary financial investment.

Recreation on Federal Lands. The principal types of Federal lands which are administered with varying recreational objectives are listed in Table 2-1.

Table 2-1. Principal Federal Agencies Administering Areas of Varied Recreational Interests

Area	Bureau or agency	Department
National parks, monuments, historical parks and sites, military and battlefield parks, and related areas	U.S. National Park Service	Interior
National forests	U.S. Forest Service	Agriculture
Game and bird refuges; fish hatcheries	U.S. Fish and Wildlife Service[a]	Interior
Reservoirs, artificial lakes	Bureau of Reclamation	Interior
Reservoirs, artificial lakes	Corps of Engineers	Army
Reservoirs, artificial lakes	Tennessee Valley Authority	
Public lands	Bureau of Land Management	Interior
Indian lands and reservations	Bureau of Indian Affairs	Interior

[a] In 1956 the U.S. Fish and Wildlife Service of the U.S. Department of the Interior (formerly the Bureau of Biological Survey, U.S. Department of Agriculture) was divided into two separate bureaus, the Bureau of Sports Fisheries and Wildlife and the Bureau of Commercial Fisheries, in charge of the Commissioner of Fish and Wildlife.

National parks and related areas (see Chapter 5), between 175 and 180 in number, with a total area of approximately 23 million acres [34], are administered on a single-use basis for a specific type of recreation. They are distinguished from other types of Federal recreational lands primarily by their unique character. Each of these areas is typified by nationally significant geological, biological, archeological, or historical interests; their administrative philosophy dictates that, in so far as possible, they be preserved in their natural condition for continuous public benefit and enjoyment.

In essence, national parks and related areas are outdoor museums. Maximum value and enjoyment are derived from these areas when a visitor has knowledge and understanding of their significant features. Public use requires the development of certain necessary facilities (e.g., roads, trails, campgrounds, hotels), but any development or activity which is not in keeping with the natural scene, or which detracts from

FIG. 2-3. National Park Service areas are nationally significant; one of the unique features of Mount Rainier National Park, Washington, is the large glacial system found upon the flanks of this volcanic peak. (*Photo by C. Frank Brockman*)

their outdoor-museum function, not only reduces their immediate value but impairs the character of their future public service.

In 1957 the number of visitors to areas administered by the National Park Service was almost 60 million (see Table 5-2); the prospect is for 80 million visitors in 1966 [18].

Other Federal lands are administered on a multiple-use basis with recreation assuming varying degrees of importance. Such multiple-use lands usually lack features of unique significance, or should such features be present, they are duplicated in more dramatic form on lands administered by the National Park Service. Their recreational policy is based upon a much more liberal philosophy, permitting many activities and types of development not suited to significant areas.

Recreational benefits of the national forests (see Chapter 6) are coordinated with their primary values. These include timber production, watershed protection, and grazing to a degree consistent with the development of maximum, over-all public benefits [14,15,16,29,30]. Aggregating an area of over 180 million acres, national forests are characterized by such important outdoor recreational potentials as spectacular scenery, abundant and varied native animal life, and forests of great interest and beauty [29]. National forests are extensively used for camping, picnicking, hiking, mountain climbing, horseback riding, skiing, and, in season, hunting and fishing. Facilities necessary to these activities are permitted under regulations of the U.S. Forest Service. Good highways make many sections of the national forests accessible, and trails tap many areas not available to motor travel. Exclusive of casual motorists, more than 60 million people used the national forests for various recreational pursuits in 1957 (see Table 6-2). It is predicted that this figure will be increased to 66 million by 1962 [31].

The U.S. Fish and Wildlife Service, primarily through its Bureau of Sports Fisheries and Wildlife is an important contributor to outdoor recreation through its program of research and varied activities concerned with the protection, management, and improvement of wildlife resources. Specifically, the U.S. Fish and Wildlife Service operates more than 250 wildlife refuges, with a total area of approximately 17.5 million acres, and about 100 game-fish hatcheries [8,10,22,23].

Wildlife refuges, although established primarily for research and protection of certain species, are becoming increasingly important for varied forms of recreation. They are operated on a multiple-use basis consistent with their primary purposes. Many of these areas are used for study and observation of birds and mammals; fishing is permitted on some refuges; others may be occasionally opened to limited hunting when it is necessary to reduce excess wildlife populations. Fish hatcheries operated by this agency, also open to the public, afford an excellent means of developing greater public interest in and understanding of technical problems concerned with the maintenance of our sport-fish resources. In 1955, according to the National Recreation Association, attendance at Federal wildlife refuges and fish hatcheries totaled nearly 7 million visitor days [23].

Artificial lakes, formed by waters impounded by dams built by the

U.S. Bureau of Reclamation, the Corps of Engineers, and the Tennessee Valley Authority, are of great importance for outdoor recreation (e.g., boating, swimming, fishing, picnicking, camping). Such projects are operated on a multiple-use basis with recreation officially recognized as an important adjunct of their primary purposes (e.g., irrigation, flood control, development of hydroelectric power, improvement of navigation, and the like). This radical change from the original concept of reservoir

FIG. 2-4. Artificial lakes, developed primarily for other purposes, often provide for a variety of public outdoor recreational activities; sailboating on Millerton Lake, California. (*Photo by Merritt S. Johnson, National Park Service*)

development, which neglected recreational values, resulted from increasing public recreational use of reservoirs and adjacent lands in spite of an earlier lack of adequate recreational facilities.

More than 100 reservoirs, aggregating a surface area of over 1 million acres, have been developed by the Bureau of Reclamation in seventeen western states. Many are located in arid areas lacking natural lakes. In 1955, according to the National Recreation Association, the number of visitors to these projects exceeded 9.5 million [23].

Since 1944 a cooperative agreement has existed between the Bureau of Reclamation and the National Park Service, providing that the National Park Service investigate the recreational potentials of reservoir projects, submit recommendations for their protection and use, and, on those having recreational values, prepare plans for their development. This agreement also provides that the National Park Service assume permanent administrative responsibility for recreational activities on such reservoirs—except those on national forests where recreational administration is handled by the U.S. Forest Service. On reservoirs deemed of national importance (e.g., Lake Mead and Lake Roosevelt) recreational resources are administered directly by the National Park Service; on reservoirs which are not of national importance the National Park Service may delegate administrative responsibility for recreation to some local agency; however, basic responsibility to the Bureau of Reclamation is retained by the National Park Service [22].

The U.S. Fish and Wildlife Service also cooperates by investigating fish and wildlife values on reservoirs developed by the Bureau of Reclamation.

The Corps of Engineers, by authority of the Flood Control Act of 1946, is empowered to construct, maintain, and operate public park and recreational facilities on reservoirs under control of the Department of the Army. Recreational potentials of such reservoirs are investigated by the National Park Service, on request of the Chief of Engineers. Minimum facilities (e.g., access roads, parking areas, sanitary needs, drinking water, camp and picnic areas) are provided by the Corps of Engineers. Various state and local agencies are encouraged to prepare plans for and to assume responsibility for additional needs.

In 1955 projects administered by the Corps of Engineers embraced a total area of 5.6 million acres, including approximately 3 million surface acres of water; in the same year these areas were host to about 62 million visitors [23]. Some idea of the growing popularity of these projects for recreation can be gained from the fact that 9 million, 10 million, 20 million, and 26 million visitor days were recorded, respectively, in 1929, 1949, 1950, and 1951 [22].

Various projects under control of the Tennessee Valley Authority, including twenty-six reservoirs with over 10,000 miles of shoreline and embracing more than one-half million acres of adjacent land above normal lake levels, are also heavily used for various forms of outdoor recreation. In 1954, for example, this independent Federal agency reported more than 25 million person-day recreational visits [26]; in 1955 this figure had increased to nearly 28 million [23].

Consistent with its primary responsibilities and statutory activities, TVA policy coordinates recreational values of its reservoirs and adjacent lands in a multiple-use program by which all varied resources may be developed for the greatest contribution to the economic and social welfare of the region. TVA acquires land for general reservoir purposes, including access, but does not acquire land specifically for recreation; neither does it develop or operate any recreational facilities or services. It does, however, transfer or convey land or land rights for a nominal consideration to Federal, state, and local governmental agencies for administration, development, and operation as public recreation areas of various types. In addition, land is leased, licensed, and sold for recreational purposes to quasi-public groups and organizations, or sold at public auction, leased, and licensed to private individuals and groups for summer residences, clubs, or commercial recreational establishments [27]. As a result, numerous parks—state, county, and municipal—as well as public access and wildlife areas now found in the Tennessee Valley, owe their origin to such procedures. Likewise, many camps sponsored by private organizations and groups, private summer-home sites, and a variety of commercial recreation businesses have been developed as a result of this policy.

By 1955 a total investment of nearly 50 million dollars had been made in recreational facilities and equipment on TVA lakes and lake shores by private individuals and organizations, and various public agencies other than TVA [26].

For some time the values inherent in the public recreational use of land have also been recognized by the Bureau of Land Management. This Federal agency is charged with the multiple-use administration of approximately 470 million acres of public land in the United States, including Alaska [4,21,22,23], which, in large part, was bypassed in the settlement and development of better or more accessible areas. In recent years, however, much of the area administered by the Bureau of Land Management has become increasingly valuable for various forms of recreation, and although no data are available on the extent of such use, it is constantly growing. As a result a formal recreational land-use policy formulated by the Bureau of Land Management was approved by the Secretary of the Interior in April, 1958 [31-*a*]. This policy outlines certain principles relative to public recreation on areas administered by this Bureau and provides the basic framework of procedures for their future use, development, and disposal for public recreational purposes.

Federal, state, or local governments, as well as private nonprofit organizations, are eligible to apply for the use or acquisition of such areas deemed most desirable for public recreation, as determined by the Bureau's land classification. Such land classification considers both potential as well as present recreational needs and values, consistent with other land-use requirements. Special attention is given to frontage along coast lands and inland waters and to their attendant access lands, to other lands of obvious recreational value, and to lands which provide access to recreationally useful areas.

The procedure for obtaining such use or acquisition varies, depending upon the land-use values of the area, the land status conditions, and the type of agency or organization involved in the request. Use or acquisition may be accomplished by special-use permit, lease, transfer, withdrawal, reservation, interagency agreement, or sale.[1] In certain instances provision is made for retaining such lands under Federal ownership, administering them through the Bureau of Land Management or some other Federal agency. In cases where Federal control is relinquished, certain terms and conditions may be imposed to ensure future public recreational use. The establishment of public recreation areas for state or local use and the provision of necessary public recreational facilities and services are ordinarily the responsibility of state or local agencies rather than the Bureau of Land Management, although the Bureau stands ready to facilitate such efforts.

To a lesser degree a number of other Federal agencies are concerned, directly or indirectly, with outdoor recreation [22,23]. The Bureau of Indian Affairs of the Department of the Interior is trustee for approximately 56 million acres of Indian lands which, although embodying important recreational potentials, are not yet widely used by the general public. On some Indian lands hunting and fishing is permitted by consent of the tribes concerned, and a few reservations provide limited accommodations for visitors interested in Indian arts and crafts.

State Lands Having Recreational Values. State lands such as parks, forests, and various types of wildlife and reservoir areas are becoming increasingly important in outdoor recreation. The state park movement in particular represents one of the most forceful recreational developments in recent years.

As outlined more fully in Chapter 4, forty-eight states now operate some form of state park system. Varying greatly in size and type, state parks include a multitude of typical state interests (e.g., attractive scenery, extensive natural areas, features of geological, biological, archeological, or historical significance), as well as facilities necessary to a variety of outdoor activities (e.g., picnicking, camping, hiking, riding, swimming, boating, fishing, and, in some cases, organized sports).

Although administered so that their particular interests may be preserved, state parks are usually accessible to centers of population and are developed to cater to the varied recreational needs of large numbers of people. In brief, state parks are generally larger and of more natural

[1] Recreational use of Revested Oregon and California Railroad and Reconveyed Coos Bay Wagon Road grant lands in Oregon, as well as public lands in Alaska, is governed by special provisions.

character than city or county parks, yet more readily accessible and usually more highly developed than such Federal lands as national parks and national forests which, to many people, are too remote for regular use. In 1957 the total area of state parks, numbering more than 2,000, was over 5 million acres; the total number of visitors in that year exceeded 200 million [35].

State forests with an aggregate area of nearly 5 million acres [22][2] are managed on a multiple-use basis to serve a variety of needs, including

Fig. 2-5. Many state parks embrace significant interests; a portion of the Dry Falls, Sun Lakes State Park, Washington. During the "ice age" this barren precipice, over 400 feet high and more than a mile wide, was the site of a great cataract. (*Washington State Parks and Recreation Commission*)

timber production, watershed protection, grazing, and recreation. According to the National Recreation Association, in 1955 the number of visitors to these areas, 180 in number, was nearly 5 million [23]. Practically all state forest lands are open to public hunting; in addition, especially in the East, they are widely used for many other forms of outdoor recreation. In New York, Pennsylvania, Massachusetts, Vermont, New Hampshire, Maine, Michigan, Wisconsin, Minnesota, Indiana, and Ohio, state forests are vital recreational areas used by a constantly increasing number of people. Similar lands in other states are destined to

[2] A total of 16.6 million acres is listed for state forest lands in the United States by Stanley G. Fontana in his article, State Forests, "Yearbook of Agriculture, 1949," pp. 390–394, U.S. Government Printing Office, Washington, 1949.

assume greater importance and more varied outdoor recreational use as recreational pressures increase.

Many state fish and game departments administer specifically designated wildlife areas (e.g., reserves, sanctuaries, game farms, fish hatcheries, public shooting grounds) as units in their broad program of regulating and improving hunting and fishing. Such areas are particularly interesting to hunters and fishermen, estimated in 1955 to be 25 million in number [36].

Municipal and County Parks. In 1955, according to the National Recreation Association, over 20,000 parks, playgrounds, and related recreational sites, aggregating an area of nearly 750,000 acres, were operated by municipalities, counties, and similar agencies throughout the United States. The foregoing figures do not include over 14,000 school

FIG. 2-6. Provision of tree-farm parks for free public use by private industrial forest-land owners fosters better understanding of modern forestry methods. (*Weyerhaeuser Timber Company*)

properties with a total area of over 100,000 acres, of which more than 7,500 areas totaling 50,000 acres were usable for recreation [23].

Because of their availability, municipal and county recreational areas naturally receive tremendous patronage. Although no recent data are available, some idea of the current use of these lands may be gleaned from the fact that in 1938 the total number of users was estimated to exceed 600 million annually [33]. That figure is greater than the current combined patronage of all other types of recreational lands.

To a much more limited degree certain public recreational activities are permitted on municipal power reservoirs, city forests, and, except in certain cases, watershed lands established as sources of municipal water supplies.

Public Recreation on Private Lands. In instances where private lands provide public recreational opportunities, such use usually takes one of several forms. Commercial amusement parks (e.g., Coney Island) make their appeal on manufactured amusement devices rather than upon natural values. Dude ranches, privately operated youth camps, and the like depend largely upon the interests of the surrounding region for a variety of planned outdoor activities. Such activities are usually carried out on nearby public lands; most private enterprises of this sort rarely own more than the minimum area necessary for housing and related physical facilities required by their patrons. Certain specialized recreational areas (e.g., Williamsburg and Mount Vernon) have philanthropic objectives; their management and maintenance are largely underwritten by private endowment. In addition, where such need is clearly demonstrated, a number of private power companies provide opportunity for fishing, boating, camping, picnicking, and related interests at their reservoirs. Finally, although many private timberlands have long been available, in season, to hunters and fishermen, recent years have witnessed the establishment of specially designated recreation areas on a number of industrial tree farms owned by commercial forest products firms.

A survey conducted by the American Forest Products Industries, Inc., completed in 1957, indicated that industrial forest land serves as an important recreational outlet for America's rapidly expanding population. This survey, first of its kind, embraced an area greater than 46 million acres controlled by 455 companies, or 74 per cent of commercial timberlands owned by various forest industries in the United States [5].

The survey revealed that more than 1,500,000 people, including hunters, fishermen, campers, picnickers, and skiers, used industrial forest land for various forms of recreation in 1956 [5]. Of the total area represented in the survey more than 92 per cent was open to hunting in season. Exclusive of game refuges, about 6 per cent of the area surveyed was closed to hunting [5]. The major portion of the area open to hunting is freely available,[3] although on 22.4 per cent of the area, hunting was limited by permit or was reserved for special groups. Special consideration to the requirements of game animals was given in cutting operations by 104 companies, and 44 companies actually engaged in planting of food species for game on 8,637 acres [5]. An annual average of 127,490 big-game animals were killed on lands of the 455 companies represented in the survey, and game-management specialists were employed by 31 companies [5]. Some companies, whenever possible, transport hunters to remote sections of their areas and haul deer killed to accessible public highways, without charge to the hunters.

The American Forest Products Industry survey also indicated that fishing was permitted on slightly more than 96 per cent of this industrial forest land. Although charges for this privilege were imposed by 18 companies, most of these firms made their lands freely available to fishermen.

[3] Certain areas may be closed during periods of extreme fire hazard [1,2].

Activities relative to the improvement of fishing were being taken by 41 companies, 22 companies actually stocked streams on their land, and a total of 228 artificial lakes were built by various industrial forestry firms [5].

The survey also revealed that by 1957, 65 companies operated 137 free public parks with an aggregate area of 3,432 acres. Most of these tree-farm parks were equipped with all necessary facilities and services. In addition to picnic tables, fireplaces, sanitary facilities, piped water, and free firewood, a number of these parks also have covered shelters or kitchens, children's playground equipment, boat ramps, swimming floats, bathhouses, and in some cases nature trails [5,38]. On 48 of these industrial tree-farm parks, swimming was an important recreational activity, and boating was featured on 34 areas. Even winter sports were not neglected; 6 areas made provision for skiing, 2 being equipped with lifts or tows, and ice skating was favored on 3 tree-farm parks [5].

In addition to the 65 companies which were operating tree-farm parks by 1957, 31 companies planned additional parks before the end of that year, and 69 companies had plans for parks beyond 1957 [5]. These tree-farm parks were made available to the general public without cost; the annual maintenance cost of $156,345 being borne by the companies involved [5]. Seven companies actually employed professional park planners to guide the development of these areas and to ensure best possible recreational use of such lands, consistent with their primary purpose of timber production [5].

Tree-farm parks are most important in the Pacific Northwest, where the idea originated. In 1955 nearly 100,000 visitors used Northwest tree-farm parks—91,512 as day visitors and 7,455 as overnight campers [7]. The not inconsiderable cost of public recreational programs on private forest lands is an investment in better public understanding of industrial timber-management programs, often misunderstood by laymen. Although a certain amount of vandalism accompanies public use of industrial forest lands, the cooperative activities of public recreational programs on private forest lands serve to minimize damage to timber reproduction by wildlife, reduce the fire hazard, and provide for more adequate control of growing recreational activities on such properties—including reduction of hazards to the public and possible damage to timber, equipment, and facilities [1,2,5,6,7,38].

RELATIONSHIP OF AREAS IMPORTANT IN OUTDOOR RECREATION

Almost any type of land has some recreational value. Whether the land is managed on a single-use basis strictly for some sort of recreation or on a multiple-use plan which, in varying degrees, considers other needs, depends upon the merits of each case. In the final analysis the kind of managment imposed hinges upon a great variety of factors, among which are the quality of interests possessed by an area, existing or potential public needs for the products or services it can provide, its adaptability to various types of development, the density of population, and the nature of travel facilities. Certain lands are of such character that the public welfare dictates some sort of exclusive recreational use. But values other than recreation must also be considered, since modern life requires an abundance of timber, minerals, hydroelectric power, agricultural crops, forage for livestock, water supply, and related products and services. Many areas must be managed on a multiple-use basis primarily for the production of utilitarian needs, with recreation assuming varying degrees of importance. In certain cases it may be necessary to exclude recreational use from consideration.

The ideal pattern of land use having all values properly balanced and in accord with one another has not been resolved. Doubtless it never will be, since the requirements of our expanding civilization are subject to continued development and inevitable change.

Recreational use versus utilitarian use has been the subject of many bitter land disputes. For instance, in the conflict over the boundary of the Olympic National Park recreationalists were pitted against lumbermen; and in the question of the Echo Park Dam, which would have resulted in the flooding of a large section of the Dinosaur National Monument, recreationalists were locked in battle with engineers. Even among recreationalists there is often disagreement over the type of recreational use on lands reserved exclusively for that purpose; some favor extensive development of roads, hotels, and related facilities, while others look with disfavor upon anything but completely natural conditions.

American history is studded with controversy over changing patterns of land use. Many of these arguments were extremely heated, and some, like the range wars of the old West, even involved bloodshed.

Single-use Recreational Areas. Single-use recreational areas, by reason of their features of interest or accessibility, are managed primarily for their recreational benefits. They are further divided into areas characterized by highly significant interests which are the most outstanding of their type and areas whose values cannot be so classified. Either of these land types may or may not be typified by scenic beauty; the criterion which determines their relationship to recreational needs is the presence or absence of features of national or regional significance.

Various types of significant recreational areas are fundamentally educational, cultural, or inspirational. In some cases topography may dramatically portray some chapter in the geological history of the world in which we live. In other instances the unique character of plant and animal life illustrates the complex interrelationship between all living things and their environment. Certain areas include important archeological remains which indicate how early man solved his problems of existence and survival. Finally, other lands bear a relationship with vital events of history and serve to impress one with the values of our historic heritage.

If the people are to obtain maximum benefit and enjoyment from the use of such areas there must be public understanding and appreciation of their significant features. For that reason one of the primary concerns in the management of such areas is the development of a public understanding of the values that are basic to the unique status of significant recreational lands. In certain types of such lands the objective is to preserve their natural or original character. Under these conditions lack of physical development serves as a limiting factor in their use; they appeal largely to people of perception or, in the case of wilderness areas, physical stamina. In other significant recreational areas certain types of development may be permitted. In any event, development of these significant areas should never be at the expense of the features of interest which prompted their establishment. Public interest and understanding of features contained in many significant recreational areas are often fostered by interpretive programs conducted by experienced staff members.

Areas administered by the National Park Service, certain specifically designated areas in the national forests, many state parks, and a few municipal, county, and private lands are essentially significant in their recreational appeal.

National parks, national monuments, national historic parks and sites, national battlefield parks and sites, and related areas administered by the National Park Service are of national, in some cases international, significance. Commercial exploitation of their varied interests, or the introduction of activities irrelevant to their purpose, is a form of desecration not unlike the introduction of jazz music in a great cathedral.

Although the national forests are administered on a multiple-use basis by the U.S. Forest Service, extensive sections within their boundaries, designated as wilderness or wild areas [29], actually operate as single-use recreational lands. These are relatively remote regions, usually at altitudes which make commercial production of timber impractical, typified by a total lack of development. They have been set aside primarily for the specific type of recreational activity which demands maximum self-reliance under primitive conditions.

Many state parks embody unique interests. Although they are not always of national importance, their features portray the story of dramatic events which are often of great significance on a state or regional level. Typical examples are the Ginkgo Petrified Forest State Park, a significant geological area in the state of Washington; the historic mother-lode town of Columbia, a unit in the California state park system; and Spring Mill State Park in Indiana.

Finally, certain units within city and county park systems (e.g., arboretums, zoological gardens, local historic sites) or on private land (e.g., Mount Vernon) are of significant interest.

The great majority of single-use recreational areas, however, although often interesting or beautiful, are not basically significant. Such lands provide for a more liberal approach to public outdoor recreational needs,

FIG. 2-7. Arboretums are examples of municipal areas of a specialized significant character; Azalea Way, University of Washington Arboretum, Seattle. (*Photo by E. F. Marten, University of Washington*)

permitting a greater variety of activities and necessary physical development.

Included among nonsignificant single-use recreational lands are most state parks, as well as parkways, campgrounds, picnic areas, and roadside attractions. Federal parkways (e.g., Blue Ridge Parkway in Virginia and North Carolina) might also be considered in this category. Most municipal and county parks, together with playgrounds, beaches, athletic fields, and picnic areas fall in this class. To complete the picture privately owned amusement parks must also be included. Since the recreational objectives of these areas are quite different, the degree to which natural conditions are protected and maintained depends upon their purpose and use. In some cases management is greatly concerned with the prevention of damage to natural interests and scenic beauty; in others (e.g., playgrounds and athletic fields) natural conditions must necessarily be sacrificed to other values.

Multiple-use Recreational Areas. On multiple-use lands recreation is coordinated with other uses. The degree to which recreation is emphasized is dependent upon its relative importance. Considerable emphasis is given to a wide variety of recreational activities in the administration of certain multiple-use lands, while on others recreation must necessarily be limited to a relatively few public activities and interests which interfere little with the primary management program.

Multiple-use lands under Federal, state, municipal, county, and private control are of varying importance in outdoor recreation. Outstanding among Federal areas of this type are the national forests, administered by the U.S. Forest Service, varied wildlife areas controlled by the U.S. Fish and Wildlife Service, and reclamation projects developed either by the Bureau of Reclamation, the Tennessee Valley Authority, or the Corps of Engineers of the United States Army. Miscellaneous public lands administered by the Bureau of Land Management and Indian lands handled by the Bureau of Indian Affairs are of lesser importance.

State multiple-use areas include state forests, reclamation projects, and various types of fish and game reserves. Similarly, municipal multipurpose lands embrace watersheds managed primarily to ensure a continuing supply of water for domestic and industrial needs, as well as forests managed for timber production. In some cases recreation is integrated with such primary functions. Even private lands are recreationally important; in addition to tree-farm parks specifically established by industrial timber-producing companies, general forest and agricultural areas provide for a large measure of public hunting and fishing.

Table 2-2 presents a visual picture of the general relationship between varied single-use and multiple-use lands of importance in public recreation.

SUMMARY

Since recreation involves a wide variety of interests and activities, some sort of recreational value is inherent in practically any type of land. Private as well as public lands of many kinds are involved. In particular, outdoor recreation is closely associated with wild land, for such an environment offers some of the most rewarding of recreational outlets, both from a physical and a cultural standpoint. For that reason, recreation, today, is generally recognized as one of our important wild-land resources; in some instances it is a dominant resource, and in many cases it is of major importance.

But like all natural resources recreational land values are widely and irregularly distributed throughout the nation without relation to human needs. Such irregular distribution, together with many wild-land uses which compete with recreation, necessitates the most careful planning and management if the varied, complex public needs of modern life are to be met and if all vital natural resources are to be used properly in a fashion which will ensure continued availability.

Table 2-2. Relationship of Various Types of Recreational Lands

	Single-use areas		Multiple-use areas
	Significant	Nonsignificant	
Federal	National Park Service areas Specific national forest lands (e.g., wilderness areas)	Parkways	National forests Reclamation projects Wildlife refuges; fish hatcheries Miscellaneous public lands Indian lands
State	State parks of unique quality or specialized interest	Most state parks Parkways Roadside markers; attractions Campgrounds Picnic areas	State forests Reclamation projects Wildlife refuges; fish hatcheries
Municipal and county	Arboretums, zoological gardens: other areas of specific interest	Most city and county parks; metropolitan park districts Playgrounds Beaches Picnic grounds	Municipal and county forests
Private	Areas of specific interest (e.g., Mt. Vernon, Williamsburg)	Commercial amusement parks	Industrial forests and tree farms: agricultural lands

The character and degree of recreational development of wild land are dependent upon the relative importance of all its inherent natural values. Certain areas must necessarily be reserved specifically for recreation on a single-use basis. Some single-use recreational lands embody features of such unique or significant value—geologically, biologically, archeologically, or historically—that their recreational use must be regulated carefully to preserve their basic interests; in such cases use should enhance public appreciation and understanding of their significant values. Other single-use recreational lands, lacking such unique qualities, are administered according to a more liberal policy; there consideration is given to a wider variety of activities, together with necessary physical facilities, not adapted to significant recreational lands.

But only a relatively small percentage of all land areas are of such importance for recreation that a policy of single-use recreational management is paramount. Many types of land, under both public as well as private control, are primarily valuable for the production of varied raw materials or services required by science and industry. When such lands embody recreational interests, multiple-use management should prevail, with recreation assuming varying degrees of importance.

SELECTED REFERENCES

1. Adams, Kramer A.: The Effects of Logging Old Growth Timber on Landowner-Sportsmen Relationships, *Proceedings of the Society of American Foresters Meeting*, Portland, Ore., Oct. 16–21, 1955, pp. 133–136, Washington, 1956.
2. Adams, Kramer A.: What Is the Future of Game in Relation to Land Use from the Timber Industry Viewpoint? *Meeting of the Western Association of State Game and Fish Commissioners*, Moran, Wyo., June 18, 1955, Weyerhaeuser Timber Company, Tacoma, Wash., n.d. (Mimeographed.)
3. Allen, Shirley W.: "Conserving Natural Resources," McGraw-Hill Book Company, Inc., New York, 1955, pp. 182–197.
4. Anonymous: Public Recreational Use of the Nation's Public Domain, *Planning and Civic Comment*, vol. 23, no. 1 pp. 12–13, March, 1957.
5. Anonymous: "Recreation on Forest Industry Lands in the United States," American Forest Products Industries, Inc., Washington, 1957. (Mimeographed.)
6. Billings, Frederick: Public Parks on Private Property, *Planning and Civic Comment*, vol. 22, no. 4, pp. 51–60, December, 1956.
7. Billings, Frederick: "Forest Industry Recreational Areas in the Northwest," Statement presented at meeting of Recreational Subcommittee, Columbia Basin Inter-agency Committee, Timberline Lodge, Ore., Sept. 14, 1956, Weyerhaeuser Timber Company, Tacoma, Washington, n.d. (Mimeographed.)
8. Butcher, Devereux: "Seeing America's Wildlife," The Devin-Adair Company, New York, 1955.
9. Carlson, S. T.: Recreation in Wildland Management, *Journal of Forestry*, vol. 44, no. 11, pp. 827–828, 1946.
10. Carson, Rachel L.: Guarding Our Wildlife Resources, *Conservation in Action*, no. 5, U.S. Fish and Wildlife Service, Washington, 1948.
11. Dufrense, Frank: Welcome Hunters! *Field and Stream*, vol. 61, no. 4, pp. 60–63, August, 1956.
12. Ely, Richard T., and G. S. Wehrwein: "Land Economics," The Macmillan Company, New York, 1940, pp. 315–350.

13. Ellison, Lincoln: Trends in Forest Recreation in the United States, *Journal of Forestry*, vol. 40, no. 8, pp. 630–638, 1942.
14. Forest Service, U.S. Department of Agriculture: Our National Forests, *Agriculture Information Bulletin*, no. 49, Washington, 1951.
15. Kenny, Nathaniel T.: Our Green Treasury, the National Forests, *National Geographic Magazine*, vol. 110, no. 3, September, 1956.
16. Lord, Russell: "Forest Outings," U.S. Government Printing Office, Washington, 1940.
17. National Park Service: Recreational Use of Land in the United States, part XI of "Report on Land Planning," prepared for the Land Planning Committee of the National Resources Board, Washington, 1938.
18. National Park Service, U.S. Department of the Interior: "Our Heritage: A Plan for Its Protection and Use," Washington, n.d.
19. National Recreation Association: "Recreation and Park Yearbook, Mid-century Edition: A Review of Local and County Recreation and Park Developments, 1900–1950," New York, 1951.
20. National Recreation Association: "The Recreational Resources of the United States: Their Conservation, Development and Wise Use," New York, December, 1953.
21. National Recreation Association: "The Role of the Federal Government in the Field of Public Recreation," New York, n.d.
22. National Recreation Association: "Agencies of the Federal Government Concerned with Recreation: Trends, Inadequacies, Needs," New York, January, 1954.
23. National Recreation Association: "1956 Recreation and Park Yearbook: A Nationwide Inventory of the Public Recreation and Park Services of Local, County, State and Federal Agencies for the Year Ending December 31, 1955," New York, 1956.
24. Renne, Roland R.: "Land Economics," Harper & Brothers, New York, 1947, pp. 300–324.
25. Society of American Foresters: Forests and Recreational Policies in New England: Report of Committee on Forest Policy, New England Section, *Journal of Forestry*, vol. 38, no. 5, pp. 397–400, May, 1940.
26. Tennessee Valley Authority, Division of Reservoir Properties: "Annual Report of Activities and Accomplishments, Fiscal Year Ending June 30, 1955," n.p., n.d.
27. Tennessee Valley Authority: "TVA Procurement Sources: Recreational Developments," n.p., July 1, 1956, pp. 242–252.
28. Tennessee Valley Authority: "Recreation on TVA Lakes," n.p., n.d.
29. U.S. Department of Agriculture: "Trees: The Yearbook of Agriculture, 1949," Washington, 1949, pp. 533–560, 855–892.
30. U.S. Department of Agriculture: The Work of the U.S. Forest Service, *Agriculture Information Bulletin*, no. 91, Washington, August, 1952.
31. U.S. Department of Agriculture, Forest Service: "Operation Outdoors: Part 1, National Forest Recreation," Washington, 1957.
31-*a*. U.S. Department of the Interior, Bureau of Land Management: "Secretary Seaton Approves Policy Statement by Bureau of Land Management on Recreational Land Use," Washington, April 16, 1958. (Mimeographed.)
32. U.S. Department of the Interior, National Park Service, in cooperation

with the National Recreation Association: "Municipal and County Parks in the United States, 1935," Washington, 1937.
33. U.S. Department of the Interior, National Park Service: "A Study of the Park and Recreation Problem of the United States," Washington, 1941.
34. U.S. Department of the Interior, National Park Service: "Areas Administered by the National Park Service, December 31, 1957," Washington, 1958.
35. U.S. Department of the Interior, National Park Service, Division of Recreation Resource Planning: "State Park Statistics, 1957," Washington, June, 1957.
36. U.S. Department of the Interior, Fish and Wildlife Service: "National Survey of Fishing and Hunting 1955," Washington, 1956.
37. Wagar, J. V. K.: Recreation in Relation to Multiple Land Use in the West, *Journal of Forestry*, vol. 41, no. 11, pp. 798–802, November, 1943.
38. Weyerhaeuser Timber Company: Tree Farm Parks for the Public, *Weyerhaeuser Magazine*, vol. 7, no. 6, pp. 4–6, June, 1955.

CHAPTER 3 *Development of Recreational Interest in the Outdoors*

Recreational values have always been inherent in the outdoors, but only in comparatively recent times have steps been taken to manage, preserve, and utilize them properly.

In one guise or another tracts of land have been reserved for park and recreational purposes since time immemorial. Such areas were not uncommon in the heyday of Babylon, Greece, and Rome, and during the Renaissance a revival of these ideas found expression largely in the development of formal gardens [31]. Although the establishment of the earliest of these areas stemmed largely from efforts of powerful rulers at self-aggrandizement, such acts nevertheless were indications of the need for such areas in early periods of man's development.

In hunting one finds even a closer affinity between primitive and modern concepts of outdoor recreation. True, to early man, hunting was a means of sustaining life, not a means of recreation, but various primitive peoples recognized their dependence upon a continuing supply of wild game and developed certain rules by which the taking of that game was guided. The modern science of wildlife management, which is the keystone of good hunting and fishing and thus an important aspect of recreation on wild land, has evolved from such practices which date from antiquity [18,30].

Modern recreation on wild land has a close relationship to medieval practices in Great Britain. In feudal England a forest was more important as a source of game than of timber, and certain lands were customarily reserved for hunting by the nobility. Such recreational privileges of the ruling classes, greatly extended by William the Conqueror and later Norman kings, were not modified until after the adoption of the Magna Charta in 1215 [18,30]. Today most of these medieval English preserves are but historical memories, but two areas exist as modern survivals of that period. Both the Forest of Dean, west of Gloucester, and New Forest, near Southampton, can trace their ancestry directly to the Norman period [19,20]. For example, in 1087 New Forest was decreed by William the Conqueror to be his royal domain, thus giving rise to the name of New Forest which has persisted to the present time. Today, by the slow processes of history, this area has become the common heritage of all Englishmen, administered by the British Forestry Commission for grazing, timber production, and public recreation. Its boundaries embrace 144 square miles of forest, meadow, and moor, of which about 100 square miles is publicly owned Crown land. The Forestry Commission, principal administrative agency of this and similar areas in England, is a direct descendant of the Lord Wardens appointed by the medieval kings to preserve their personal domain, and the principal administrative officer of the forest is still known by the ancient title of Deputy Surveyor [20].

RECREATION IN RELATION TO THE AMERICAN CONSERVATION MOVEMENT

In the United States the current extensive and growing interest in the recreational use of wild land is commonly regarded as having evolved from our general interest in the regulation of forests, wildlife, soils, water, and similar natural resources. However, an examination of the record will indicate that this is not entirely the case. True, progress in the conservation of other more tangible land values has, until recent years, been more obvious, but, rather than being an incidental facet of the broad conservation movement, interest in recreational value of wild land might be regarded as its nucleus. Evidence of this is contained in the fact that the first extensive areas of wild land to be reserved for public benefit were dedicated to an outdoor recreational objective. The Yosemite Grant (1864), the Yellowstone National Park (1872), and the Niagara Falls Reservation (1885) came into being well in advance of our national and state forests, Federal and state wildlife reserves, and similar areas of specifically dedicated public lands important to varied objectives of modern American conservation practices.

There were, of course, earlier manifestations of public interest in the regulation of natural resources in the United States, but these were significant largely in molding public opinion toward an acceptance of various conservation principles which first materialized in tangible fashion in the establishment of the three areas noted in the foregoing paragraph.

EARLY IMPORTANT CONSERVATION MILESTONES

The most important early milestones of the conservation movement in America included colonial laws relating to game and timber, the passage of the Great Ponds Act by the Massachusetts Bay Colony, the origination of the municipal park movement, and the reservation of lands surrounding the mineral springs in the Ouachita Mountains of Arkansas.

Early Laws Relative to Game and Timber. In spite of the fact that until recent years many people regarded the natural resources of our country as inexhaustible, certain early restrictions placed upon indiscriminate hunting and improper cutting of timber and the penalties imposed for setting forest fires imply obvious local depletion of forests and wildlife in the formative period of the history of America.

Initial game laws were put into effect soon after the first colonists established themselves along the Atlantic seaboard. The first of these laws, one which regulated seasons and prohibited export of game and hides, was passed by Connecticut in 1677 [18]. Except for Georgia, all of the original colonies had established closed seasons on deer by 1700, and similar restrictions were first placed upon the hunting of certain upland game birds by New York in 1708 [18]. The initial effort at enforcement of game laws is regarded as having occurred in 1739, when "deer wardens" were appointed in Massachusetts [18].

Examples of early restrictions concerning timber resources are equally revealing. In 1626, but six years after its establishment, the Plymouth Colony prohibited the cutting of trees on Colony lands without official consent [25]. In 1681 William Penn directed that for every 5 acres of forest land cleared in the Province of Pennsylvania, 1 acre was to be left intact [1]. The English sovereigns William and Mary, in establishing the Massachusetts Bay Colony in 1691, reserved trees of specific size, species, and quality for use by the British Navy, provisions that were later extended to other English colonies in North America [1]. Penalties for unlawfully setting woods on fire were first imposed in 1777 by North Carolina [25]. Following the American Revolution, from 1799 to 1831, Congress passed a series of bills concerning the conservation of live oak and other tree species for use in the construction of ships for the United States Navy and merchant marine [25], and for a short period, from 1828 to 1830, the Federal government actually engaged in an attempt to manage an area on the Santa Rosa Peninsula in Florida for the production of live oak timber for such purposes [1].

Early Municipal and County Parks in the United States. The common or green typical of many New England towns has its roots in the American colonial period, and although such areas were established for reasons other than recreation, their recreational values eventually assumed a dominant role as these communities grew. One of the most noteworthy examples of such early municipal public areas is the Boston Common, established in 1634, which has served the citizens of Boston for over three hundred years [27,45].

Recognition of the need for open spaces in town planning was expressed in somewhat similar fashion in other sections of the United States during its formative period. In accordance with Spanish custom a public square or plaza was reserved in the development of most early Spanish settlements in America. In 1682 William Penn reserved a number

FIG. 3-1. Central Park, New York City; first area acquired by a municipality specifically for public recreational use. (*Department of Parks, New York City*)

of tracts for public use within the city of Philadelphia [24]. James Edward Oglethorpe was guided by related ideas in developing the city of Savannah, Georgia, in 1793 [29], and open areas were provided for by Major Pierre Charles L'Enfant in planning Washington, D.C., in 1792.

One of the most significant of early municipal park areas of the United States is Central Park in New York City. Established in 1853,[1] it was the first area acquired by a municipality exclusively for public recreational use [3]. In addition, its early planning and administration were directed by Frederick Law Olmsted who, in 1864, played a major role in the establishment and early administration of the Yosemite Grant, forerunner of Yosemite National Park [23,24,40,41].

Another significant trend somewhat related to early municipal park

[1] Establishment of Central Park was first proposed by a group of prominent New York citizens in 1850; acquisition of land was begun in 1853 [3].

development was manifest about the third decade of the past century. This involved the growth of rural scenic cemeteries which were not uncommonly used for picnicking and related types of outdoor recreation. Mount Auburn, the first of such areas, was established near Boston in 1831 [23,24].

It will be noted from the foregoing paragraphs that our present extensive system of municipal and county parks has developed in little more than one hundred years. With the exception of the common or green typical of early New England towns and the plazas of pioneer Spanish settlements in North America, no city within the boundaries of our country had acquired land specifically for park purposes until the middle of the last century when Central Park was established in New York City. Once underway, however, city and county park development continued unabated to the present day. By 1877 about twenty cities had established parks, by 1892 the number of cities having such areas had increased to one hundred, and in 1902 positive steps had been taken along that line by nearly eight hundred municipalities [65]. Meanwhile, in 1895 the county park movement had originated in Essex County, New Jersey [36,65].

The greatest expansion in city and county park development has naturally occurred since the turn of the century. In 1950, according to the National Recreation Association, 1,338 cities and counties operated 17,142 park properties totaling 644,067 acres; two-thirds of this area (430,630 acres) consisted of city parks, while the balance (213,437 acres) was composed of county and regional lands [35]. Five years later the number of city and county parks, playgrounds, and related recreational sites in the United States (exclusive of school facilities) had increased to 20,000, with a total area of nearly 750,000 acres [38].

Early Reservation of Wild Land for Public Benefit. The Great Ponds Act, passed by the Massachusetts Bay Colony in 1641, was the first important milestone in the reservation of wild land for the public benefit. As such, it has a direct relationship to outdoor recreation.

The act decreed that about two thousand bodies of water, each exceeding 10 acres in size and aggregating an area of approximately 90,000 acres, were to remain as a public resource forever open to the public for "fishing and fowling" [39]. With the passing of time the great ponds lost much of their earlier utilitarian value and became more important and most generally used for recreational purposes. In 1923, when this trend from the original concept was questioned, the attorney general of Massachusetts ruled that the Great Ponds Act, permitting public access to and use of these waters, was still valid even though the character of such public use had changed [39].

The second major milestone in the history of American conservation, as it relates to outdoor recreation, occurred in 1832 when Congress passed an act reserving four sections of land in the Ouachita Mountains of Arkansas "for the future disposal of the United States" [49,63]. The act stated further that this reservation "shall not be entered, located, or appropriated, for any other purpose whatever" [49]. This area included a number of hot mineral springs whose waters were thus reserved for posterity and removed from the danger of private monopoly and exploitation.

The establishment of the Hot Springs Reservation was in direct response to an evident trend to capitalize upon its values. The springs had long been known to the Indians, who considered them as a communal resource. Early Spanish explorers had also recognized their values. About 1804 the first Americans visited the area, and in 1807 the first settler established himself there [59,63]. In 1830, prompted by the commercial possibilities embodied in growing general use of the springs, the first bathhouse was built [59,63]. It became obvious that, if nothing was done, this area would soon succumb to exploitation by private individuals; and since maintenance of this area in free public use was deemed desirable, public sentiment developed to the point where Congress was prevailed upon to take appropriate action.

Although the Hot Springs Reservation was not established because of its recreational values, these assumed increasing importance in later years. As a result, the hot springs area was incorporated into the national park system in 1921 as Hot Springs National Park [63,64].

EARLY COMMERCIAL RECREATIONAL FACILITIES

In passing one should not overlook the significance of early interest in general recreational travel and commercial recreational facilities in the outdoors. This trend was, naturally, first manifest in the East. Accommodations for visitors were available at Franconia Notch in the White Mountains as early as 1820 [24], and a hotel, later considerably enlarged in response to public patronage, was built in the Catskills in 1825 [23,24]. These were among the earliest of visitor accommodations in out-of-the-way places, although a number of health resorts and more readily accessible beach locations on the Atlantic had been utilized by the public for some time. Following the opening of the Erie Canal in 1827, canalboats, offering sleeping and eating facilities, began making trips through New York State to Lake Ontario, and for more than a decade this mode of travel was in high favor [23,24]. Soon thereafter travel to outlying areas was augmented by early railroads of the Eastern seaboard region [23,24].

These developments were the seeds from which our modern diversified and extensive tourist industry has grown. Slowly, as communities in various parts of the United States grew, developed, and achieved a sense of permanence, and as travel facilities improved, public interest in distant places expanded.

BIRTH OF THE NATIONAL PARK IDEA

As has been stated earlier in this chapter, the reservation of wild land for recreational purposes served as a potent force in the modern American conservation movement. Since the establishment of national parks figured prominently in such affairs, it is important that events bearing upon the formation of the earliest of such areas be understood.

First Proposal of a National Park. In 1833 the influential and widely circulated *New York Daily Commercial Advertiser* published a series of letters by George Catlin,[2] explorer and artist who had visited the Indian country of the upper Missouri in 1832 [23,24]. Catlin's experiences prompted his interest in the American Indian and caused him to ponder ways and means of preserving segments of such interests for the future. One of his letters included this significant observation [11]:

> . . . and what a splendid contemplation too, when one (who has traveled these realms and can duly appreciate them) imagines them as they might in the future be seen (by some protective policy of government) preserved in their pristine beauty and wildness, in a magnificent park, where the world could see for ages to come, the native Indian in his classic attire, galloping his wild horse amid the fleeting herds of elks and buffalos. What a specimen for America to preserve for her refined citizens and the world, in future ages. A nations park, containing man and beast, in all the wild and freshness of their nature's beauty. I would ask no other monument to my memory, nor any other enrollment of my name amongst the famous dead, than the reputation of having been the founder of such an institution.

This statement is highly significant in that it antedates by more than three decades the establishment of the first area of wild land for public benefit primarily because of recreational values (*Yosemite Grant,* 1864) and by nearly forty years the establishment of the first national park (*Yellowstone,* 1872). As Huth points out [23,24], initial negative American attitudes toward nature began to change early in the eighteenth century. Led by poets, writers, and artists who extolled nature's beauties, the many interests of the outdoors gradually became more meaningful. In Catlin's remarks one observes the dawn of an awareness of the great esthetic and cultural qualities inherent in significant segments of typical, primitive America and the need for their preservation. In a somewhat

[2] Catlin's letters, together with his drawings, were later published in book form (see bibliographical reference 11).

related vein Thoreau expressed man's need for wild places about the middle of the past century [42]. Such ideas, inexorably linked with the establishment of national parks, are also important in the designation of other types of wild land for various outdoor recreational purposes.

The Yosemite Grant. The Yosemite Grant, established in 1864, was the first extensive area of wild land to be set aside primarily for public

FIG. 3-2. Yosemite Valley, Yosemite National Park; this area comprised the major portion of the Yosemite Grant, established 1864, first extensive area of wild land set aside specifically for public recreational use. (*Photo by Ralph H. Anderson, National Park Service*)

recreational use. Although the Federal government did not then assume administrative authority for the Yosemite Grant, nor recognize its responsibility in that direction, interest in the unique character of the Yosemite Valley and the nearby Mariposa Grove of Big Trees (*Sequoia gigantea*) prompted the Federal government to entrust these parts of the public domain to the state of California "upon the express conditions that the premises shall be held for public use, resort, and recreation; shall be inalienable for all time . . . " [41,49].

The bill relative to the Yosemite Grant was introduced into Congress on March 28, 1864 by Senator John Conness of California who stated that its purpose was:

. . . to commit them [Yosemite Valley and the Mariposa Grove of Big Trees] to the care of the authorities of that State for their constant preservation, that they may be exposed to public view, and that they may be used and preserved for the benefit of mankind. . . . The plan [of preservation] comes from gentlemen of fortune, of taste, and of refinement. . . . The bill was prepared by the commissioner of the General Land Office, who takes a great interest in the preservation both of the Yosemite Valley and the Big Trees Grove [41].[3]

It was passed by the Senate on May 17, by the House on June 29, and signed by President Abraham Lincoln on July 1, 1864 [41].

This was a memorable event, especially when one considers that it occurred during the Civil War, one of the darkest periods of our history. It is also significant that the language of the bill establishing the Yosemite Grant paralleled the intent of later national parks. Further, Frederick Law Olmsted, planner and early administrator of Central Park in New York City, was one of those who supported the establishment of the Yosemite Grant; he also served as one of its original commissioners [8,41]. Olmsted had left New York City a few years earlier to undertake the management of the Mariposa Estate, a large tract of land owned by General Fremont and located in the foothill region near Yosemite [41]. Primarily because of his experience in landscape architecture and park planning, Olmsted assumed the major responsibility of the early administration of the Yosemite Grant and, in fact, served as its original custodian [8].

For more than forty years the Yosemite Grant was administered by a body of commissioners, appointed by the Governor of California, aided by a local resident custodian [7,8,41]. In 1906 the area was receded to the Federal government and incorporated into Yosemite National Park (established 1890), which surrounded it [41].

Development of interest in the Yosemite Valley is a significant item in Western history. The first civilized men to see the valley were American trappers, members of the Walker Expedition who viewed it from the north rim in the fall of 1833, while laboriously working their way westward across the Sierra Nevada [15,41]. In March, 1851, the valley was first entered by the Mariposa Battalion, a group of American citizen-soldiers organized to put down an Indian uprising that followed the discovery of gold in California [41]. The recalcitrant Yosemites, for whom the Mariposa Battalion named the valley, were pursued to this point.

The first "tourist party" visited Yosemite Valley in June, 1855 [41]. This journey was prompted by accounts of the earlier military expedi-

[3] Also see *Congressional Globe,* May 14, 1864, p. 2301.

tions, which appeared in San Francisco newspapers. One of these accounts mentioned a spectacular waterfall of prodigious height. James M. Hutchings, then publishing the *California Magazine* in San Francisco, became intrigued with the possibility of describing such a spectacle in his publication; with several companions, including an artist and two Indian guides, he made the long horseback journey into the Sierra and "spent five glorious days in scenic banqueting" in the valley [22]. As a result of publicity given Yosemite Valley by Hutchings, interest in the area quickly developed. Soon various well-known publications of the period began extolling the interests of the area, and prominent writers, artists, photographers, and public figures further enhanced this trend.

Coincident with developing interest in Yosemite Valley came the discovery of several groves of giant sequoia on the western slope of the Sierra, one of which was located just a few miles south of Yosemite Valley. Soon thereafter, in 1857 and 1858, the *Atlantic Monthly* and *Harper's Weekly* began agitating for the preservation of these groves [23,24].

Thus public opinion was molded by prominent leaders of the day, and the idea of preserving significant areas in their natural state for the enjoyment of present and future generations began to take form. Further, by 1864 there was need for immediate positive action; as part of the public domain Yosemite Valley was subject to entry, and several units of it had already been acquired by private individuals. The establishment of the Yosemite Grant gave priority to public rights in the area, and after considerable litigation, claimants to certain lands in the valley were favored with a financial settlement [41].

Public awareness of the need for conservation in all its aspects developed greatly in the three decades following the establishment of the Yosemite Grant. Between 1864 and 1900 the first state parks were established,[4] the national park idea was born, and five of our national parks came into being. During that same period a number of states

[4] The movement to preserve an area about Niagara Falls, initiated in 1867, bore fruit in 1885 when the Niagara Falls Reservation was dedicated [23,24,39].

The year 1885 also witnessed the transfer of an obsolete military reservation on Mackinac Island from the Federal government to the state of Michigan. Previous to its acquisition by the state of Michigan it had a brief existence as a national military park [31,39,43].

Minnesota established the first portion of Itasca State Park in 1891; two historical areas were also established by that state about the same time, Birch Coulee in 1889 and Camp Release in 1895 [39].

In 1885 the State Legislature of New York established the Adirondack Forest Preserve. Since cutting of timber was forbidden in that area in 1897, as well as on state lands in the Catskills in 1899, both the Adirondack and Catskill areas assumed the essential character of state parks. In addition, the famous Palisades Interstate Park of New York and New Jersey had its origin in 1895, when the first lands of that area were acquired [39].

formed forestry commissions and state forests, the first Federal forest reserves, now known as national forests, were formed, and the nucleus of the U.S. Forest Service evolved.

The momentum developed during this period continued beyond the turn of the century and, despite resistance and occasional reverses, resulted in the expansion and refinement of the entire program of natural-resource conservation in the United States.

The First National Park. Yellowstone National Park, established March 1, 1872 [49,64], was the first area of its kind in the United States, as well as the first national park in the world.

The history of events leading to the establishment of Yellowstone National Park begins with the first exploration of that region by John Colter, a member of the Lewis and Clark Expedition, in 1807 and 1808 [12]. Colter had become interested in the upper Missouri region during the expedition's westward trek to the Pacific in 1805. In 1806, upon the expedition's return to the Missouri, he was released at his own request in order to conduct personal explorations of that area. His journeys resulted in the discovery of the geysers and other evidences of hydrothermal activity in the Yellowstone, but his reports of these phenomena were received by the outside world with derision. As a result, the Yellowstone country was known for many years as "Colter's Hell" [12].

Other adventurers followed in Colter's foosteps. Joseph Meek, one of a number of "mountain men" engaged in the fur trade, visited Yellowstone in 1829 [12]; Warren A. Ferris, clerk of the American Fur Company, penetrated the area on several occasions in the 1830s and 1840s [12]; and James Bridger, fur trader and "mountain man," made numerous visits to the Yellowstone previous to 1850 [12]. Like Colter, all these early explorers expounded on the wonders which they had observed only to be met by public skepticism. Bridger embellished accounts of his observations with the wildest fancies of his imagination, and his tall tales of the Yellowstone have earned him a unique place in the folklore of the early American West [12].

Finally these unbelievable stories aroused official curiosity. In 1859 and 1860 a government expedition under command of Captain W. F. Raynolds skirted but, unfortunately, never entered the area now included in the park [12]. In September, 1869, the Folsom-Cook-Peterson Expedition spent a month in the Yellowstone area; Folsom's account of that trip appeared in the *Western Monthly*, a Chicago publication, in July, 1870 [12].

The most significant exploration of the Yellowstone was conducted in 1870 by a group of nine prominent Montana citizens, led by Henry D. Washburn and Nathaniel P. Langford, with a military escort of five cavalrymen under the command of Lt. G. C. Doane [12,28]. Our first national park resulted from the efforts of this group. The idea emerged from a discussion about their campfire at the junction of the Firehole and Gibbon Rivers, their last camp in what is now Yellowstone National Park. Since the area was in the public domain at that time, anyone had the privilege of establishing a claim in accordance with the law governing such action and eventually establishing ownership of the desired property. However, Cornelius Hedges, a lawyer from Helena, Montana, proposed that the group forego personal claims and favor the establishment of a national park to be protected forever and available to all the

FIG. 3-3. Junction of the Firehole (*left*) and Gibbon (*right*) Rivers, Yellowstone National Park, birthplace of the national-park idea; location of the historic 1870 campfire is on riverbank at edge of the forest at left. (*National Park Service*)

people. Except for one dissenter, his suggestion met with general favor [28,43,48].

Immediately upon their return to Helena, Hedges and Langford took steps to achieve that goal. They enlisted William H. Clagett, newly elected delegate to Congress from Montana, in their cause. Later, in Washington, Clagett and Langford drew up the Yellowstone bill which was introduced into the House by the Montana delegate on December 18, 1871 [12].

During the summer of 1871 two government parties made additional studies of the Yellowstone region, one under the leadership of Dr. F. V. Hayden of the United States Army Engineer Corps, who became an ardent supporter of the proposed park [12]. In the Hayden party was W. H. Jackson, pioneer photographer, who made a remarkably fine series of Yellowstone photographs, samples of which were placed in the hands of all senators and congressmen by Dr. Hayden. Following a favorable opinion by the Secretary of the Interior, the Yellowstone bill was adopted by the House on January 30, 1872, passed by the Senate on February 27, and received the signature of President Grant on March 1, 1872 [12,49].

Other Early National Parks. In 1890 the Sequoia, General Grant (incorporated into Kings Canyon National Park in 1940), and Yosemite National Parks were established [64]. In the case of Yosemite, Federal park lands surrounded the state-controlled Yosemite Grant, which was not receded to the Federal government until 1906 [41,64]. Just before the turn of the century, on March 2, 1899, Mount Rainier National Park, the fifth of these areas, came into being [9,64].

Sequoia and General Grant National Parks owe their existence largely to the efforts of George W. Stewart, editor of the *Visalia Delta* [43]. Beginning in 1879, in cooperation with a group of public-spirited citizens, Stewart conducted an active campaign for the preservation of those areas which contain extensive representative stands of giant sequoia.

Yosemite National Park is a monument to John Muir. Muir arrived in Yosemite in 1868 [68]. For several years he lived and worked in the Yosemite Valley and the adjacent Sierra Nevada area, studying that region and observing the despoliation of its natural resources. His enthusiasm and knowledge, gained through personal investigation, soon brought him into national prominence as a writer. His first article appeared in the *Sacramento Record-Union* on February 2, 1876 [41]. Later writings, based upon a hiking trip south from Yosemite in 1875, were concerned with the need for preserving the magnificent groves of giant sequoia. These writings aided Stewart and his associates in their efforts to establish Sequoia and General Grant National Parks. Muir soon attracted the interest of Robert Underwood, editor of *Century Magazine*, and in 1889 he became a regular contributor to that publication [43,68]. His work was to influence thousands of people on matters pertaining to the preservation and wise use of our natural resources.

The establishment of Mount Rainier National Park resulted from the combined efforts of the National Geographic Society, the American Association for the Advancement of Science, the Geographical Society of America, the Sierra Club, and the Appalachian Mountain Club [9,33]. Although the original bill, introduced into Congress by Senator Watson Squire of the state of Washington in 1894, did not receive favorable action, a revised bill passed both houses of Congress in 1899 and, on March 2 of that year, was signed by President McKinley [9,49,64].

EARLY INTEREST IN FOREST CONSERVATION

As early as 1867 the states of Michigan and Wisconsin formed fact-finding committees for the purpose of studying and reporting upon the destruction of their forest resources. Similar action was taken by Maine in 1869 and, within a few years, by a number of other Eastern states. By 1885 the states of New York, California, Colorado, and Ohio had formed forestry commissions. However, since the forestry commissions of the latter three states soon became inoperative, New York has the distinction of having the oldest continuous record of official forestry activities [1,25].

The first tangible interest in forest conservation by the Federal government was manifest in 1876 when Dr. Franklin B. Hough was appointed as a forestry agent in the Department of Agriculture [25]. Hough's appointment, resulting from official interest in an address which he gave at the annual meeting of the American Association for the Advancement of Science in 1873, was the seed from which the U.S. Forest Service grew [1]. Today this agency administers the important recreational resources of the national forests as part of its multiple-use program.

Hough's speech was an indication of a growing awareness on the part of many informed individuals of weaknesses in our public-land program of the period, a program handled by the General Land Office of the Department of the Interior which sought to encourage the development of unsettled territory, but which had been subject to much abuse. By authority of such legislation as the Preemption Act of 1841, the Homestead Act of 1862, the Timber Culture Act of 1873 (together with later modifications), and the Desert Land Act of 1877 individuals could acquire specified areas of public lands for personal use and benefit, either by purchase at a nominal price, or without cost by fulfilling certain requirements of residence and development. Other legislation passed by Congress during that period granted specific lands to states in the interest of education, and to railroads in order to encourage development of badly needed transportation facilities. Vast areas of land, including much valuable timber, were disposed of by such means. Although this program contributed greatly to the development of the country, it was not generally accompanied by careful evaluation of the natural resources involved, and it was typified by many irregularities—not infrequently, by fraud [2,14,21,25].

Two other dates are noteworthy in the early development of public awareness to the need for conservation of natural resources. In 1872 Arbor Day was instituted in Nebraska. Designed primarily to encourage tree planting in the prairie region, this idea soon gained headway in other states [2,16]. Three years later, on September 10, 1875, the American Forestry Association was organized in Chicago for the purpose of promoting forestry [2]. This association was a strong influence in initial forest-conservation activities in the United States; it has continued to exert its influence in matters pertaining to forest-land management to the present day.

By 1881, as a result of the activities of Franklin B. Hough and supporters of his program, Federal interest in forestry matters was broadened. In that year the Division of Forestry was established in the Department of Agriculture [1,25]. However, the purpose of this Division was purely advisory. It was not until 1891 that the first federally controlled forest, known as the Yellowstone Timberland Reserve, was established from the public domain [1]. For more than a decade the administration of this forest reserve was vested in the General Land Office of the Department of the Interior [25]. The Division of Forestry, elevated to the status of a bureau in 1901 [1,25], continued to serve in an advisory capacity in the management of this and other later forest reserves. It was 1905 before the Federal forest reserves were placed under control of Federal foresters of the Bureau of Forestry; soon thereafter the name Bureau of Forestry and forest reserve were changed, respectively, to U.S. Forest Service and national forest—designations by which they are known today [1].

The amalgamation of Federal foresters and Federal forest lands under a unified administration and the organization of the U.S. Forest Service in approximately its present form resulted largely from the efforts of Gifford Pinchot, dynamic early forestry leader. Pinchot, who had become affiliated with the Division of Forestry during the early stages of its development, was placed in charge of its activities in 1898 [1] and immediately instituted a militant campaign to correlate Federal forestry activities. When these efforts bore fruit in 1905 he continued as chief of the U.S. Forest Service and greatly strengthened and broadened the organization of this bureau. To this end he received the cooperation of Theodore Roosevelt, then President of the United States, whose interest in varied phases of natural-resource conservation was manifested in many ways. In particular, President Roosevelt materially increased national forest acreage and, in 1908, called a conference of political, business, and scientific leaders for the purpose of considering interrelated problems concerned with the conservation of natural resources. This conference, known as the National Conservation Conference of Governors [1], had far-reaching effects. In addition to fostering a meeting of important people it was responsible for the establishment of many state conservation commissions. Further, a National Conservation Commission was appointed by the President with Pinchot as chairman [1]; this commission developed an inventory of the nation's natural resources and suggested plans for their proper use.

Although Pinchot resigned as Chief of the U.S. Forest Service during the administration of President William Howard Taft as a result of a controversy with Secretary of the Interior Ballinger over public-land-management questions, he organized the U.S. Forest Service along the fundamental lines which continued to serve as keystones of the programs of his successors [1].

It will be noted that early proponents of forest conservation did not consider recreation as an important natural resource of forest land. The

FIG. 3-4. Gifford Pinchot, first Chief of the U.S. Forest Service. (*U.S. Forest Service*)

establishment of forest reserves and, later, the organization of the U.S. Forest Service was motivated by interest in the sustained yield of other values such as timber, forage, water, and the like. For many years the two major facets of natural-resource conservation, one concerned with the preservation of significant or scenically beautiful areas in parks and the other revolving about proper use of more tangible needs in forest reserves, were considered as separate entities having little in common and being largely incompatible. Early forestry leaders could not, of course, envisage today's great public interest in outdoor recreation; in their time there was little indication of modern diversified outdoor recreational needs requiring extensive use of national forest areas. Nevertheless, as will be noted later, legislation by which the original forest reserves were established provided for eventual broadening of the program of multiple use of national forest resources to include recreation.

THE ANTIQUITIES ACT

June 8, 1906 marked another important milestone in the history of American conservation. On that date the Act for the Preservation of American Antiquities, introduced into Congress by Representative John F. Lacey, received the signature of President Theodore Roosevelt and became law [43,64]. This act empowered the President of the United States to set aside, as national monuments, areas of federally controlled land containing historic landmarks, historic or prehistoric structures, or other objects of historic or scientific interest. The Antiquities act is designed to protect and preserve such interests for the benefit of future as well as present generations; it is similar in general purpose to legislation establishing national parks, except that Presidential proclamation rather than congressional action is required.[5] It had the support of numerous archeologists, historians, and scientists who had recognized the need for such action as a result of gross vandalism at many significant yet unprotected sites. Within one year after passage of the Antiquities act, five of our present series of more than four-score national monuments had been established.[6]

A number of national parks (e.g., Carlsbad Caverns, Grand Canyon, Olympic, Zion, and Bryce) were originally national monuments [64]. In such cases protection was given those areas until legislation necessary for their redefinition as national parks could be prepared and passed by Congress.

Although an area receives more lasting protection as a national park than as a national monument, considerable time is often required before the support of a majority of the members of Congress can be obtained for the establishment of a national park. In such cases there is danger that efforts may become mired in a morass of legal and political technicalities. Further, forewarned by public interest in an area, those having selfish interests might take advantage of the time lag, legally establish

[5] In later years a number of national monuments have been established by congressional action.

[6] Devils Tower, Wyoming—Sept. 24, 1906; El Morro, New Mexico—Dec. 8, 1906; Montezuma Castle, Arizona—Dec. 8, 1906; Petrified Forest, Arizona—Dec. 8, 1906; Chaco Canyon, New Mexico—Mar. 11, 1907.

Casa Grande National Monument, established Mar. 2, 1889, was administered as a national park until Aug. 3, 1918, when it was changed to national monument status [64].

themselves and destroy, or at least greatly modify, the value of the area in question. Since establishment of a national monument involves action by but one man—the President—it can usually be accomplished with greater dispatch. Although national monuments can be decreased or increased in area by Presidential proclamation, only Congressional action can eliminate them. Thus, although the degree of protection given these areas is not as absolute as is that given national parks, it renders them inviolate so long as they retain a satisfactory area or, as has been desirable in several cases, until they are redefined by Congressional action as national parks.

NATIONAL PARK SERVICE FORMED

The establishment of the National Park Service as a bureau in the Department of the Interior was a singular event in the development of public interest in the recreational use of wild land. The National Park Act, passed by Congress in 1916 and signed by President Woodrow Wilson on August 25 of that year, coordinated the administration of the national parks then in existence, as well as that of certain national monuments, under a central, specialized authority and laid down certain basic tenets for their proper management and use [43,49,59,60,64].

The establishment of the National Park Service, representing the culmination of events over a period of more than forty years, was prompted by numerous difficulties in national park administration which developed as the number of such areas increased. These difficulties were manifest almost immediately after the establishment of Yellowstone National Park in 1872, for in the designation of that area Congress made no provision for financial support of an adequate administrative program. This important consideration was also largely neglected in relation to many national parks established at a later date. As a result there developed a disjointed relationship between various national parks, and this lack of a cohesive administrative authority showed signs of undermining the concept upon which the parks had been founded and of impairing the public services which they could render.

The early administration of Yellowstone National Park was complicated by many serious difficulties. During the first five years of the existence of the park Congress failed to provide funds for the park's protection, development, or administration, and N. P. Langford, who served as superintendent during that period, did so without remuneration [43]. Further, the protection of wildlife in Yellowstone was generally ignored during its early years in national park status; not until 1894, after a particularly flagrant violation involving hunting in the park, did Congress provide formal law-enforcement machinery, including a definition of park offenses with specific penalities designed as punishment for such acts [43]. In addition many applications for leases and concessions of various kinds were received from people who lacked understanding of national park objectives, and some of the early superintendents who followed Langford not only lacked appreciation for the basic concept of the national park idea but even became unwisely involved in irregular practices concerning the operation of facilities for visitors [43]. This untenable situation eventually prompted action. In 1883 a bill was passed by Congress permitting the Secretary of the Interior to request the War Department to assign troops to Yellowstone National Park for the purpose of patrolling the area [43]. Soon thereafter such a request was made, and from 1886 to 1918 various units of cavalry protected Yellowstone National Park; their commanding officers served as acting superintendents. This period also witnessed the construction of the park's basic highway system by the Army Engineer Corps [12,43].

From 1901 to 1914 Sequoia, General Grant, and Yosemite National Parks were also protected by United States Cavalry [7,41,43]. As in the case of Yellowstone the officers who served as acting superintendents left an outstanding record of achievement.

For a number of years several national parks, such as Mount Rainier National Park in the state of Washington [9], and many national monuments which were adjacent to or surrounded by national forests were administered by the U.S. Forest Service. In such cases the forest supervisor also acted as the principal administrative officer of the national park or national monument.

Such irregular divisions of responsibility in the field had a counterpart in the lack of unified authority in the office of the Department of the Interior in Washington, D.C. There responsibility for the national parks was assigned to various officials of the Interior Department who handled such matters in addition to their regular duties [43].

A national parks bureau was first suggested by Dr. Horace McFarland, President of the American Civic Association, and Charles Evans Hughes, Governor of New York, during the National Conservation Conference of Governors in 1908 [43]. Although nothing tangible resulted from the suggestion, McFarland, with the backing of the American Civic Association, continued to work toward that goal. The U.S. Forest Service, which the dynamic Gifford Pinchot had welded into a coordinated whole in 1905, served as his example. In 1910 McFarland found official support in Secretary of the Interior Richard A. Ballinger who, in his report to the President in 1910, advocated a national parks bureau with an adequate, qualified staff [43].

In 1911 Walter L. Fisher became Secretary of the Interior. He had a deep interest in the national parks and, backed by the railroads and the

American Automobile Association, he immediately called a meeting of national park officials and other interested individuals in Yellowstone National Park [43]. A similar conference was held in Yosemite National Park in 1912. Thus, for the first time friends and officials of the national parks joined in a discussion of common problems; on both occasions a national parks bureau was advocated. These meetings had the personal blessing of President William Howard Taft who, in a speech before the American Civic Association in 1911, stated that he was keenly aware of the unsatisfactory administrative status of the national parks [43].

During this period W. B. Aker, an assistant attorney in the Department of the Interior, served as liaison officer for the national parks in addition to a number of other duties [43]. Although required to concern himself with only the fiscal affairs of the national parks, Aker's sincere interest in these areas prompted attention to all aspects of national park matters. He rendered a service far greater than could normally have been expected from anyone in a similar position.

By 1912 the need for a national parks bureau was so obvious that President Taft, on February 2 of that year, sent a special message to Congress in which he stated [43]:

> I earnestly recommend the establishment of a Bureau of National Parks. Such legislation is essential to the proper management of these wonderful manifestations of nature . . . . The first step in that direction is the establishment of a responsible bureau, which shall take upon itself the burden of supervising the parks and of making recommendations as to the best method of improving their accessibility and usefulness.

Although Congress failed to take action on the President's suggestion, the idea continued to ferment. In 1913 Franklin Lane became Secretary of the Interior, and in lieu of a national parks bureau, he broadened the responsibilities of the position of Assistant to the Secretary and filled that post with Adolph C. Miller, professor of economics at the University of California [43]. Miller, to whom specific responsibility for the national parks was delegated, supervised work on appropriate bills relative to the establishment of a national parks bureau; in addition, he set up the framework for better correlation between national parks then in existence by appointing Mark Daniels as Superintendent of National Parks [43].

Before Miller had completed six months of service, he was "drafted" by President Wilson for a post concerned with the Federal Reserve Act [43]. Daniels continued as Superintendent of National Parks, but the problem of finding a suitable replacement for Miller was not solved until the following year. At that time Secretary Lane received a letter of complaint relative to the administration of the national parks, signed by Stephen T. Mather. Lane knew this man well. He was a friend and former classmate at the University of California, a successful Chicago businessman who had been making regular summer pilgrimages into the Western mountains for years, a member of the Sierra Club of California, the Prairie Club of Chicago, and the American Civic Association. Lane asked Mather to assume responsibility for the administration of the national

FIG. 3-5. Stephen T. Mather, first director of the National Park Service. (*Photo by Hileman, courtesy of National Park Service*)

parks, and at a considerable financial sacrifice, Mather accepted. On June 21, 1915 [43] he was sworn in as Assistant to the Secretary. Horace Albright, who had come to Washington with Miller the previous year, was assigned to work with Mather [43]. These two men continued in intimate association from that day until the time of Mather's resignation shortly before his death on January 22, 1930.

Soon after his appointment as Assistant to the Secretary, Stephen T. Mather vigorously attacked the problem of establishing a bureau of national parks. With the help of Horace Albright he enlisted the aid of Congressmen William Kent and John Raker, Dr. Horace McFarland, Frederick Law Olmsted, Robert S. Yard, Robert B. Marshall, Enos Mills, Henry A. Barker, Richard E. Watrous, and Gilbert Grosvenor. All of these men were vitally interested in the national parks. Among them a well-knit park service bill was prepared which was finally passed by both the House and the Senate. On August 25, 1916 the act establishing the National Park Service was signed by President Woodrow Wilson [43,49]. Stephen T. Mather was named Director of the fledgling bureau.[7]

At the time of its establishment the National Park Service was given jurisdiction over fifteen national parks then in existence,[8] as well as twenty-one national monuments [59]. Since that time additions to the national park and monument system, as well as such legislation as the Reorganization Act of 1933 and the Historic Sites Act of 1935, have greatly increased the responsibilities of this organization.[9] As noted in Chapter 5, the National Park Service now administers between 175 and 180 areas in a variety of categories [64]. In addition, by means of inter-bureau agreement, the National Park Service has administrative responsibility for recreational development and use of certain artificial lakes formed as a result of federally sponsored reclamation developments [64].

[7] In addition to Mather, who resigned Jan. 12, 1929, a little more than one year before his death on Jan. 22, 1930, five men have served as Director of the National Park Service—Horace Albright (1929–1933), Arno B. Camerer (1933–1940), Newton B. Drury (1940–Mar. 31, 1951), Arthur E. Demeray (Apr. 1, 1951–Dec. 8, 1951), and the present Director, Conrad L. Wirth [9,48].

[8] National parks under the jurisdiction of the National Park Service upon its establishment on Aug. 25, 1916 were Casa Grande Ruin (established 1889), Crater Lake (established 1902), General Grant (established 1890), Glacier (established 1910), Hawaii (established Aug. 1, 1916), Lassen Volcanic (established Aug. 9, 1916), Mesa Verde (established 1906), Mount Rainier (established 1899), Platt (established 1906), Rocky Mountain (established 1915), Sequoia (established 1890), Sully's Hill (established 1904), Wind Cave (established 1903), Yellowstone (established 1872), and Yosemite (established 1890) [59].

In addition to the aforementioned national parks, the Hot Springs Reservation was also placed under National Park Service administration [59].

Casa Grande Ruin, established Mar. 2, 1889, was reclassified as a national monument on Aug. 3, 1918 [61]. Sully's Hill National Park was abolished and turned over to the Biological Survey, now the U.S. Fish and Wildlife Service, for a game preserve on Mar. 3, 1931 [62]. General Grant National Park was incorporated into Kings Canyon National Park upon the establishment of that area on Mar. 4, 1940 [64].

[9] By authority of the Reorganization Act of 1933, President Franklin D. Roosevelt consolidated under National Park Service administration all national parks and monuments, national military parks, national battlefield parks and sites, national memorials, certain national cemeteries, and the National Capital Parks [64].

The Historic Sites Act of Aug. 21, 1935, provided for the establishment of national historic sites [64].

IMPETUS TO STATE PARK PROGRAMS

Establishment of the National Park Service and the resultant development and improvement of areas in its charge soon focused public interest and attention upon these areas, resulting in constantly increasing numbers of visitors. It became evident that the term "national park" embodied commercial magic which was reflected in the economy of adjacent communities. A veritable flood of proposals for the establishment of additional national parks developed; many of these proposed areas, largely sponsored by biased interests, were unworthy of national park status. In 1916, alone, sixteen areas were proposed for inclusion in the National Park System [43,59].

Stephen T. Mather, Director of the National Park Service, recognizing the danger of diluting national park standards through the addition of areas lacking in significant features of outstanding national interest, also knew that many areas other than national parks possessed recreational values which were needed, and which would be increasingly valuable in later years. He diverted this pressure for additional national parks into proper channels by calling a conference of interested parties for the purpose of planning the extension and development of state park systems [34].

Des Moines, Iowa was selected as the convention site and about two hundred delegates from twenty-five states gathered there in January, 1921. As a result, a permanent organization known as the National Conference on State Parks was formed [34,43]. Since that time this body has met annually for purposes of discussing common state park problems and furthering mutual interests. Much of the recent progress in the development of state parks stems from activities of this organization.

DEVELOPMENT OF RECREATIONAL USE OF NATIONAL FOREST LANDS

National forests today, in addition to being an important source of timber, forage and other tangible natural resources, are vital units in our outdoor recreational program. The U.S. Forest Service is doing an exceptionally fine job of developing the recreational potential of areas in its charge, as well as in integrating that potential with other important values of the national forests and with recreational services of other important recreational lands. But the current interest in recreation as a resource of national forest lands was not typical of the initial years of the forest-conservation movement in the United States. Early foresters could not envisage the great public interest in the recreational values of the national forests typical of the present day; at that time few people did. There was little indication of the eventual need for our present extensive system of varied outdoor recreational areas. Consequently, although a few forestry leaders began calling attention to growing public interest in and use of national forests for outdoor recreation about 1910, official U.S. Forest Service recognition of recreation as a valid part of national forest management did not develop for more than a decade. Further, for many years many foresters exhibited a negative attitude toward such use.

The reasons for this early negative attitude are not difficult to understand. In their formative period the national forests were largely undeveloped; their boundaries were not clearly defined, the nature and abundance of their varied natural resources were not fully inventoried nor understood, road and trail development was meager, and when it existed, the technical training of limited personnel was largely based upon European standards which had to be reevaluated to meet American conditions. These and related difficulties were slowly corrected as appropriations increased and as experience developed.

In addition, foresters are trained largely in technical matters pertaining to the production, harvesting, and utilization of tangible forest products, while recreation poses problems of a very different and more intangible nature.

The early negative attitude of foresters toward recreation was further influenced by unfortunate personality clashes between forestry leaders and exponents of complete preservation, relative to controversies over jurisdiction of certain lands. One of the earliest of the controversies involved the damming and subsequent flooding of Hetch Hetchy Valley in Yosemite National Park, a struggle which began about the turn of the century when the city of San Francisco began searching for reservoir sites in the Sierra Nevada as a source of water for her expanding population [43,68]. Gifford Pinchot, then Chief of the U.S. Forest Service, favored the development of the Hetch Hetchy project. He was violently opposed by a group led by John Muir, famous writer and naturalist. The issue was not resolved until 1908 when access to the Hetch Hetchy Valley was granted the city of San Francisco [41]. Construction of the dam and development of the reservoir resulted.

Later, a number of areas which qualified for national park status were withdrawn from the national forests and placed under a separate administration as national parks [43]. Several of these transfers evoked bitter debate over the priority of land use; these disagreements further embittered foresters, delaying their understanding of the value of recreational land use.

Although interest in other values of forest land prompted the establishment of the first Federal forest reserves, early legislation relative to these areas can be interpreted as providing for public recreational use. The act of June 4, 1897,[10] which outlined the broad policy of management for the forest reserves, included the following provisions [57]:

He [the Secretary] may make such rules and regulations and establish such service as will insure the objects of such reservations, namely, to regulate their occupancy and use and to preserve the forests thereon from destruction. . . .

Nor shall anything herein prohibit any person from entering upon such forest reservations for all proper and lawful purposes. . . . *Provided,* that such persons comply with the rules and regulations covering such forest reservations.

The act of February 28, 1899[11] opened the door still wider for the public utilization of recreational values in the national forests, as indicated in this passage [57]:

The Secretary of the Interior . . . hereby is authorized, under such rules and regulations as he from time to time may make, to enter or lease to responsible persons or corporations applying therefor suitable spaces and portions of ground near, or adjacent to, mineral, medicinal, or other springs, within any forest reserves established within the United States, or hereafter to be established, and where the public is accustomed or desires to frequent, for health or pleasure, for the purpose of erecting upon such leased ground sanatoriums or hotels, to be opened for the reception of the public.

It should be pointed out that the early negative attitude toward recreation on national forest lands was not shared by all members of the forestry profession. Many of these men, notably Aldo Leopold[12] and Robert Marshall,[13] were responsible for many advances in recreational use of national forest lands which are of primary importance today.

One of the first employees of the U.S. Forest Service to publicly recognize the recreational values of the national forests, and the trends of public interest in them, was Treadwell Cleveland, Jr. In an article, National Forests as Recreation Grounds, published in 1910 by the American Academy of Political and Social Science, Philadelphia, Cleveland made this statement [13,32]:

Fortunately, the objects for which the National Forests were created and are maintained, will guarantee the permanence of their resources and will bring about their fullest development for every use. . . .

So great is the value of national forest area for recreation, and so certain is this value to increase with the growth of the country and the shrinkage of the wilderness, that even if the forest resources of wood and water were not to be required by the civilization of the future, many of the forests ought

[10] 30 Stat. 35, sec. 551, title 16, U.S.C., and 30 Stat. 36, sec. 482, title 16, U.S.C.

[11] 30 Stat. 908, sec. 495, title 16, U.S.C.

[12] See *Journal of Forestry,* vol. 46, no. 8, pp. 605–606, August, 1948.

[13] See *Journal of Forestry,* vol. 38, no. 1, pp. 61–62, January, 1940; also *The Living Wilderness,* vol. 16, no. 38, pp. 10–23, Autumn, 1951.

certainly be preserved, in the interest of national health and well-being, for recreation use alone.

Recognition of the recreational values of the national forests at the highest level is noted for the first time in the annual report of the Chief of the U.S. Forest Service (Henry Solon Graves) for the fiscal year ended June 30, 1912, as follows [50]:

> With the construction of new roads and trails the forests are visited more and more for recreation purposes, and in consequence the demand is growing rapidly for sites on which summer camps, cottages, and hotels may be located. In some of the most accessible and desirable locations the land has been divided into suitable lots of from 1 to 5 acres to accommodate as many visitors as possible. The regulations of this department for handling this class of business seem to be entirely satisfactory. Permits are issued promptly and on conditions with which permittees willingly comply.
>
> Some objection is heard to the fact that the permit is revocable in the discretion of the department. If occupancy of lots wanted for summer camps, cottages, and hotels for a period of years could be authorized, more substantial buildings than are now being erected would probably be put up.

Less than three years later the act of March 4, 1915, authorized the Secretary of Agriculture to issue, for periods not exceeding thirty years, permits to responsible citizens for sites, not to exceed 5 acres, needed for recreation and public convenience [57].

Increasing use of national forests for recreation prompted this statement from Chief Forester Graves in his report for the fiscal year ending June 30, 1917 [51]:

> The use of some of the National Forests for recreation purposes is growing to such importance as to be one of the major activities. Upon the Angeles National Forest permits for 814 residences, 26 hotels and 28 summer resorts were in force at the end of the fiscal year. It is believed that the use of the National Forests along this line, as shown by the foregoing figures, represents only a promising beginning of the development which is to follow.

Finally, in 1918, the U.S. Forest Service employed F. A. Waugh to make a five months' field investigation of the recreational values of national forest lands [32]. Waugh's recommendations were outlined in a small booklet, "Recreation Uses on the National Forests," published by the U.S. Government Printing Office in 1918 [66]. This was the first official Forest Service study of recreation; it is important in that it recognized recreation as one of the major uses of the national forests. Recreation, however, was not given specific financial support by the U.S. Forest Service until 1922. Previous to that year limited recreational facilities had been provided without special allotments for that purpose, largely as a matter of expediency and primarily as a means of protecting public health and property. Since the number of people using the national forests for recreation was constantly increasing, such procedure could not continue indefinitely; as a result annual reports of the Chief Forester began urging official recognition of recreation as a valid resource of the national forests. Excerpts from these reports for the fiscal years ended June 30, 1920, 1921, and 1922 follow:

As an important use it [recreation] bids fair to rank third among the major services performed by the National Forests, with only timber production and stream flow regulation taking precedence of it [52].

Outdoor recreation ranks today as one of the major resources or utilities of the National Forests, not because of anything the government has done to facilitate or increase this form of use, but because of the demonstrated belief of several millions of people that the Forests offer a broad and varied field of recreational opportunity [53].

. . . failure to develop recreational possibilities would mean withholding a form of public service which, though intangible in value, ranks in social and indeed economic importance with the timber, forage and waterpower values of these properties. Public welfare dictates an aggressive policy of ascertaining, developing, and offering the recreational opportunities in the national forests [54].

The act of May 11, 1922 (Agricultural Appropriation Bill) provided $10,000 for recreational development in the national forests [32], a sum largely earmarked for improvement of existing campgrounds. That meager appropriation, infinitesimal by present-day standards,[14] is significant in that it was the first tangible support given recreational use of the national forests. It initiated a trend which soon established recreation as a recognized national forest resource, along with timber, forage, water supply, and related tangible resources. Today, on some national forests recreation is regarded as of dominant importance.

Even in its early stages development of an active recreational program on national forest lands was recognized as being advantageous to forestry as well as to the general public. In an article published in the *Ames Forester* in 1922, Robert G. Schreck of the U.S. Forest Service made this statement [32]:

The recreational movement in the National Forests has done what years of propaganda could never have accomplished. For years the Forest Officers have tried to interest the public in their work and the great necessity for adequate fire protection.

The insertion of recreation into our Forests has and is accomplishing more for the interest of conservation than any other method resorted to. It has not

[14] The five-year program of the U.S. Forest Service for the years 1958–1962, a program known as Operation Outdoors and aimed at the rehabilitation, improvement, and expansion of recreational facilities on the national forests, calls for an expenditure of 85 million dollars [58].

only converted the local people to fire protection, game preservation and reforestation, but it is acting as a stimulant to increase and arouse interest in the good things that the U.S. Forest Service stands for.

Colonel William B. Greeley, Chief Forester of the U.S. Forest Service from 1920 to 1928, included these paragraphs in his reports for the fiscal years ending June 30, 1924 and 1925:

> The coordination of outdoor recreation with timber production is wholly germane to the practice of forestry, and is an essential part of any sound plan of national forest administration [55].
>
> Recreation use, under proper safeguards and supervision, is wholly compatible with timber production and watershed protection and may properly be planned for in systematic forest management [56].

Thus, as implied by Colonel Greeley's words, increasing recreational use of the national forests prompted the U.S. Forest Service to prepare, for the first time, a formal policy to guide the development of such activities. Formulated in 1925 by E. A. Sherman, Associate Forester, this policy [44] has since been greatly expanded. To a large degree the good name that the U.S. Forest Service enjoys has resulted from contacts which the people have had with the national forests through various outdoor recreational activities.

SIGNIFICANT DEVELOPMENTS IN WILDLIFE CONSERVATION PERTINENT TO OUTDOOR RECREATION

The history of tangible steps relative to the conservation of native wildlife species in the United States by the Federal government embraces a period of approximately seventy-five years, dating from 1871 when Congress passed the act establishing the Commission of Fish and Fisheries [10,17], later the Bureau of Fisheries of the Department of Commerce. In 1886 Congress passed another act establishing the Division of Economic Ornithology and Mammalogy, later the Bureau of Biological Survey of the Department of Agriculture [10]. Although these two Federal agencies were originally concerned only with research and investigation, their scope in later years was gradually broadened to encompass matters pertaining to the protection and management of native wild-animal species. In 1939 the Bureau of Fisheries of the Department of Commerce and the Bureau of Biological Survey of the Department of Agriculture were, by authority of the Reorganization Act of 1933, amalgamated into one organization known as the U.S. Fish and Wildlife Service and placed in the Department of the Interior [10].[15]

[15] Since 1956 the U.S. Fish and Wildlife Service has been comprised of two separate bureaus, the Bureau of Sports Fisheries and Wildlife and the Bureau of Commercial Fisheries, under the Commissioner of Fish and Wildlife.

Between 1871 and 1939 a number of other important steps were taken by the Federal government in the interest of wildlife protection and management. The Lacey Act, passed in 1900 [10,17], was designed to halt indiscriminate slaughter of native birds and mammals. In 1918, following the ratification in 1916 of a treaty between the United States and Great Britain relative to the protection of birds migrating between the United States and Canada, the Migratory Bird Treaty Act was passed. This act was later amended to fulfill requirements of a migratory bird treaty with Mexico, ratified in 1937 [10,17].

The Federal program of refuge acquisition and development, although originating in 1903 with the establishment of the first Federal wildlife refuge,[16] first assumed major importance in 1929 when the Migratory Bird Conservation Act was passed [10]. This legislation is the cornerstone of our present extensive system of Federal wildlife refuges.

More recent legislation includes the Migratory Bird Hunting Stamp Act of 1934, amended in 1939, and the Federal Aid in Wildlife Restoration Act of 1937 [10]. The former provided for the annual purchase of a duck stamp by all migratory-bird hunters for the purpose of financing research in waterfowl management, as well as for the acquisition of waterfowl sanctuaries; the latter levied an excise tax on hunting arms and ammunition for the purpose of developing a special fund to be used in aiding the states in various wildlife projects.

The Federal wildlife program has had an obvious impact on the recreational use of wild land. Its influence is not only felt by sportsmen; in addition, limited recreational facilities are now provided on many Federal refuges primarily for the convenience of those who wish to observe or study their interesting native animal inhabitants.

The impressive Federal wildlife conservation program is greatly enhanced by similar activities on the state level which, as noted earlier in this chapter, have a much older history. Today every state is engaged in some sort of game- and fish-conservation program. Further, many state game and fish departments have acquired lands for refuges, sanctuaries, and public shooting grounds. The scope of such activities, as well as the nature of their administration, naturally varies with different states [17]. Some are characterized by highly efficient programs, based upon sound research and directed by trained biologists; others are not so efficiently organized. Nevertheless, while the impact of varying state political fortunes is manifested to a degree in some instances, public interest in the importance of this natural resource, plus a growing awareness of its economic values, has fostered an intelligent approach toward varied state wildlife problems.

[16] Pelican Island National Wildlife Refuge, a 5-acre area on the east coast of Florida, was established in 1903 by Executive order of President Theodore Roosevelt; it protects a favorite nesting site of the brown pelican [10].

DEVELOPMENT OF INTEREST IN THE RECREATIONAL POTENTIAL OF RECLAMATION PROJECTS

Artificial lakes and reservoirs resulting from the construction of dams by such Federal agencies as the Bureau of Reclamation, Corps of Engineers of the United States Army, and the Tennessee Valley Authority have been officially recognized in recent years as having great recreational value.

Development of the recreational potential of varied projects of the Tennessee Valley Authority, recognized by that agency at the time of its inception in 1933, has been guided by a carefully formulated recreational policy adapted to its broad multiple-use program [38,46,47]. Since 1944 the Bureau of Reclamation has given its official blessing to public recreational use of those areas under its jurisdiction [37,38]. Since 1946, by authority of the Flood Control Act of that year, the Corps of Engineers of the United States Army has been authorized to construct, maintain, and operate public recreational facilities, or to permit suitable state or local agencies to provide for such needs, on reservoirs, artificial lakes, and stabilizing pools developed by that agency [37,38].

TREE-FARM PARKS

The provision of public recreational facilities on privately owned industrial forest lands is one of the most recent innovations in the recreational use of wild land. The tree-farm-park movement was originated by the Weyerhaeuser Timber Company in 1941 in the state of Washington [5]. Following World War II that company revitalized and expanded its recreational program, and the idea was adopted by a number of other industrial-forest landowners in that section of the country. By 1955, for instance, thirteen forest-products firms in Washington, Oregon, Idaho, and Montana were operating thirty-five specifically designated public parks with an aggregate area of 150 acres which had necessitated a total investment of $124,000 [6]. Since its inception in the Pacific Northwest, the tree-farm-park movement has also interested certain forest-land owners in other sections of the country [67]. A survey of public recreational use of private industrial forest lands in the United States, completed by the American Forest Products Industries, Inc., in 1957, indicated that over 46 million acres of forest land controlled by 455 forest-products firms were being made available to the public for various types of recreation, primarily hunting and fishing. The survey also revealed that by 1957 sixty-five companies were operating 137 tree-farm parks with an aggregate area of 3,432 acres [4].

This extension of the multiple-use principle of forest-land management on private forest land is highly significant. Without doubt the tree-farm-park movement is destined to expand as public recreational pressures develop.

APPROVAL OF BUREAU OF LAND MANAGEMENT RECREATIONAL LAND-USE POLICY

Another recent development of note was the Secretary of the Interior's approval, in April, 1958, of a formal public recreational land-use policy, prepared by the Bureau of Land Management. Although the Bureau of Land Management had informally recognized the values in public recreational use of land for a number of years and had taken certain steps to provide for such use when it was obviously in the public interest, this action gave added stature to public recreational use of lands under the administration of this Federal agency.

THE NATIONAL OUTDOOR RECREATION RESOURCES REVIEW COMMISSION

Establishment of the National Outdoor Recreation Resources Review Commission by authority of Public Law 85-470, approved June 28, 1958, is the most noteworthy of recent developments in the recreational use of wild land [49-*b*]. Establishment of this Commission, more completely outlined in Chapter 1, is of singular importance since it represents the first tangible effort on a national level toward the study, planning, and coordination of varied public recreational needs and resources so that future as well as present Americans may be assured of outdoor recreational opportunities of adequate quality, quantity, type, and distribution.

This Commission is of such recent origin that the effects of its activities are not yet readily apparent. However, one may confidently expect new developments to take form in the field of outdoor recreation as a result of its work. Further, although the Commission's activities are scheduled for completion in 1961, its studies and recommendations will certainly influence this form of wild-land use and management in many ways for many years.

PROPOSED NATIONAL WILDERNESS-PRESERVATION SYSTEM

Another movement indicative of growing public interest in the recreational use of wild land is the effort toward establishment of a national wilderness-preservation system. Several bills with that objective were prepared for introduction into Congress [49-*a*,49-*c*], but because of strong opposition from various quarters, they failed to achieve their goal.

Proponents of this program envisage a national wilderness-preservation system involving those federally owned or controlled lands in the United States, its territories, and possessions which are still in a primitive condition, including areas within national parks and monuments, national forests, wildlife refuges, and similar public lands. Policies relative to the establishment, administration, and use of areas selected for inclusion in the proposed wilderness system have been outlined in various drafts of wilderness bills.

It is of interest to note that this is the first attempt to provide for the establishment of specifically designated wilderness areas by congressional action. True, various types of wilderness areas have existed in the national forests for many years and these are officially recognized by the U.S. Forest Service as an important feature in its multiple-use management program; however, wilderness areas in the national forests are not established by Congress (see Chap. 6). Further, within the National Park System national monuments are established primarily by Presidential proclamation; national parks, although established by Congress and managed so that their primitive characteristics may, in large part, be preserved, are not specifically designated solely for wilderness use (see Chap. 5).

SUMMARY

Use of wild land for outdoor recreation is rooted in the democratic American concept that public rights transcend private interests on certain areas. This is indicated in the reservation of the great ponds by the Massachusetts Bay Colony in 1641, the creation of the Hot Springs Reservation by the Federal government in 1832, and the establishment of original municipal areas, set aside by early American towns for varied public needs, which eventually evolved into public parks.

The Yosemite Grant, established in 1864, was the first tangible manifestation of public interest in the recreational values of wild land in the United States. It touched off a series of events which, by the turn of the century, had developed a firm foundation for the entire American conservation movement. Yellowstone, our first national park, came into being in 1872, and before the turn of the century four additional reservations of similar character were formed—Yosemite, Sequoia, and General Grant[17] National Parks in 1890, and Mount Rainier National Park in 1899. The last decades of the past century were equally significant in other ways. Those years witnessed the establishment by several states of a number of recreational areas which were destined to become the nucleus of our varied state park systems; further, the beginnings of the U.S. Forest

[17] Incorporated into Kings Canyon National Park in 1940.

Service stem from initial Federal interest in forest conservation in 1876 and the establishment of the first Federal forest reserve in 1891. Federal interest in wildlife conservation was also first manifested in that period.

Since the beginning of the twentieth century, conservation activities in the United States have been greatly expanded. The U.S. Forest Service, an agency important in the management of lands that are now widely utilized for a variety of outdoor recreational interests, was organized in its present form in 1905. In 1906 the passage of the Act for the Preservation of American Antiquities provided a legal basis for the establishment of national monuments, and ten years later (1916) the National Park Service was formed.

The National Conference on State Parks, organized in 1921, sparked a revival of interest in the development of state park programs. In addition, as a result of growing recreational use of the national forests, this period marked official Forest Service recognition of recreational values as a resource of national forest lands, followed by the development of an established recreational policy by that organization whereby this form of use was incorporated into its program of multiple-use forest management.

In more recent years further expansion and refinement of our outdoor recreational program resulted from continued public interest in and need for a wide variety of recreational outlets. The National Park Service, organized in 1916 for the purpose of correlating the administration of an expanding series of national parks, was given additional responsibilities in 1933 when, by authority of the Reorganization Act, the administration of all national parks, national monuments, national military parks, and related significant areas was placed under its aegis. Two years later (1935) passage of the National Historic Sites Act provided for the establishment of national historic sites; these areas are also under National Park Service administration.

Wildlife-conservation activities on both Federal and state levels, greatly expanded over the past several decades, now embrace many refuges, sanctuaries, and public shooting grounds which loom large as outlets for a variety of recreational pursuits. In addition, numerous states have developed strong forestry programs and, in many instances, state forests are now being managed with due regard for the preservation and use of outdoor recreational interests. Further, varied agencies concerned with reclamation projects, with particular emphasis on TVA, the Bureau of Reclamation, and the Corps of Engineers of the United States Army, have recognized recreation as one of the public benefits of such developments. An official recreational policy was formulated by TVA in 1933, by the Bureau of Reclamation in 1944, and by the Army Corps of Engineers in 1946. In addition, since 1941, even certain owners of industrial forest lands have provided for public recreational use of such areas in the establishment of tree-farm parks. Finally, in the spring of 1958, a formal recreational land-use policy was officially adopted by the Bureau of Land Management. Two months later an event which holds much promise for the future occurred: on June 28, 1958, the Outdoor Recreation Resources Review Act (Public Law 85-470) was approved. This act provides for the establishment of the National Outdoor Recreation Resources Review Commission, which has been charged with making an inventory of the nation's outdoor recreational resources and with planning for their most adequate distribution, development, and use. Interest has also developed in the establishment of a national wilderness-preservation system.

SELECTED REFERENCES

1. Allen, Shirley W.: "An Introduction to American Forestry," McGraw-Hill Book Company, Inc., New York, 1950.
2. American Forestry Association: "American Conservation in Picture and Story," Washington, 1946.
3. Anonymous: "An Outline History of Central Park," City of New York, Department of Parks, n.d. (Mimeographed.)
4. Anonymous: "Recreation on Forest Industry Lands in the United States," American Forest Products Industries, Inc., Washington, 1957. (Mimeographed.)
5. Billings, Frederick: Public Parks on Private Property, *Planning and Civic Comment*, vol. 22, no. 4, pp. 51–60, December, 1956.
6. Billings, Frederick: "Forest Industry Recreational Areas in the Northwest," Statement presented at meeting of Recreational Subcommittee, Columbia Basin Inter-agency Committee, Timberline Lodge, Ore., Sept. 14, 1956, Weyerhaeuser Timber Company, Tacoma, Wash., n.d. (Mimeographed.)
7. Brockman, C. Frank: Administrative Officers of Yosemite, *Yosemite Nature Notes*, vol. 23, no. 6, pp. 53–57, June, 1944.
8. Brockman, C. Frank: Principal Administrative Officers of Yosemite: Frederick Law Olmsted, *Yosemite Nature Notes*, vol. 25, no. 9, pp. 106–110, September, 1946.
9. Brockman, C. Frank: "The Story of Mount Rainier National Park," Mount Rainier National Park Natural History Association, Longmire, Wash., 1952.
10. Butcher, Devereux: "Seeing America's Wildlife in Our National Refuges," The Devin-Adair Company, New York, 1955.
11. Catlin, George: "The Manners, Customs, and Condition of the North American Indians," vol. 1, George Catlin, London, 1841, pp. 261–262.
12. Chittenden, H. M.: "Yellowstone National Park" (revised by Eleanor Chittenden Cress and Isabelle Story), Stanford University Press, Stanford, Calif., 1954.
13. Cleveland, Treadwell: National Forests as Recreation Grounds, *The Annals of the American Academy of Political and Social Science*, vol. 35, no. 2, pp. 241–247, March, 1910.

14. Coyle, David Cushman: "Conservation: An American Story of Conflict and Accomplishment," Rutgers University Press, New Brunswick, N.J., 1957.
15. Farquahar, Francis: Walker's Discovery of Yosemite, *Sierra Club Bulletin*, vol. 27, no. 4, pp. 35–49, August, 1942.
16. Forest Service, U.S. Department of Agriculture: "Highlights in the History of Forest Conservation," Washington, January, 1948. (Mimeographed.)
17. Gabrielson, Ira N.: "Wildlife Management," The Macmillan Company, New York, 1951.
18. Graham, E. H.: "The Land and Wildlife," Oxford University Press, New York, 1947.
19. Great Britain, Forestry Commission: "Forest of Dean: National Forest Park Guides," His Majesty's Stationery Office, London, 1947.
20. Great Britain, Forestry Commission: "New Forest: Forestry Commission Guide," Her Majesty's Stationery Office, London, 1951 (reprinted 1952).
21. Hibbard, Benjamin H.: "A History of the Public Land Policies," Peter Smith, New York, 1939.
22. Hutchings, James M.: "In the Heart of the Sierras," Pacific Press, Oakland, Calif., 1886.
23. Huth, Hans: Yosemite: The Story of an Idea, *Sierra Club Bulletin*, vol. 33, no. 3, pp. 47–78, March, 1948.
24. Huth, Hans: "Nature and the American," University of California Press, Berkeley, Calif., 1957.
25. Illick, Joseph S.: "An Outline of General Forestry," Barnes & Noble, Inc., New York, 1939.
26. Ise, John: "The United States Forest Policy," Yale University Press, New Haven, Conn., 1924.
27. Korn, Jerry: Boston's Uncommon Common, *Collier's Magazine*, vol. 128, no. 7, pp. 26–27, August 18, 1951.
28. Langford, N. P.: "The Discovery of Yellowstone National Park, 1870," J. E. Haynes, St. Paul, Minn., 1923.
29. Lee, Clermont H.: The Squares of Savannah, *Planning and Civic Comment*, vol. 17, no. 1, p. 24, March, 1951.
30. Leopold, Aldo: "Game Management," Charles Scribner's Sons, New York, 1947.
31. Lieber, Richard: "America's Natural Wealth," Harper & Brothers, New York, 1942.
32. Maughan, Kenneth O.: Recreational Development in the National Forests, *Technical Publication*, no. 45, New York State College of Forestry, Syracuse University, Syracuse, N.Y., 1934.
33. Meany, Edmond S.: "Mount Rainier: A Record of Exploration," The Macmillan Company, New York, 1916.
34. National Conference on State Parks: "25th Anniversary Yearbook: Park and Recreation Progress," Washington, 1946.
35. National Recreation Association: "Recreation and Park Yearbook, Mid-century Edition: A Review of Local and County Recreation and Park Developments, 1900–1950," New York, 1951.
36. National Recreation Association: "The Recreational Resources of the United States: Their Conservation, Development, and Wise Use," New York, December, 1953.
37. National Recreation Association: "Agencies of the Federal Government

Concerned with Recreation: Trends, Inadequacies, Needs," New York, January, 1954.

38. National Recreation Association: "1956 Recreation and Park Yearbook: A Nationwide Inventory of the Public Recreation and Park Services of Local, County, State, and Federal Agencies for the Year Ending December 31, 1955," New York, 1956.
39. Nelson, Beatrice W.: "State Recreation," National Conference on State Parks, Washington, 1928.
40. Peet, Creighton: Central Park: New York's Big Back Yard, *American Forests Magazine*, vol. 60, no. 7, pp. 8–12, July, 1954.
41. Russell, Carl P.: "100 Years in Yosemite," University of California Press, Berkeley, Calif., 1947.
42. Saylor, John P.: Saving America's Wilderness, *The Living Wilderness*, vol. 21, no. 59, pp. 1–12, Winter–Spring, 1956–1957.
43. Shankland, Robert: "Steve Mather of the National Parks," Alfred A. Knopf, Inc., New York, 1951.
44. Sherman, E. A.: "Outdoor Recreation on the National Forests," U.S. Forest Service, Washington, May, 1925. (Mimeographed.)
45. State Street Trust Company: "State Street: A Brief Account of a Boston Way," Boston, 1906.
46. Tennessee Valley Authority, Division of Reservoir Properties: "Annual Report of Activities and Accomplishments: Fiscal Year Ending June 30, 1955," n.p., n.d.
47. Tennessee Valley Authority: "TVA Procurement Sources: Recreational Developments," n.p., July 1, 1956, pp. 242–252.
48. Tilden, Freeman: "The National Parks: What They Mean to You and Me," Alfred A. Knopf, Inc., New York, 1951.
49. Tolson, Hillory A.: "Laws Relating to the National Park Service, the National Parks and Monuments," U.S. Government Printing Office, Washington, 1933.

49-*a*. U.S. Congress: "Hearings of the Senate Committee on Interior and Insular Affairs, National Wilderness Preservation Act, S.1176, June 19–20, 1957," 85th Congress, 1st Session, 1957.

49-*b*. U.S. Congress: "Outdoor Recreation Resources Review Act, Public Law 85-470, S.846, June 28, 1958," 85th Congress, 1st Session, 1958.

49-*c*. U.S. Congress: "Hearing of the Senate Committee on Interior and Insular Affairs, National Wilderness Preservation Act, S.4028, July 23, 1958," 85th Congress, 2d Session, 1958.

50. U.S. Department of Agriculture, Forest Service: "Report of the Forester for 1912," Washington, 1912.
51. U.S. Department of Agriculture, Forest Service: "Report of the Forester," Washington, 1917.
52. U.S. Department of Agriculture, Forest Service: "Report of the Forester," Washington, 1920.
53. U.S. Department of Agriculture, Forest Service: "Report of the Forester," Washington, 1921.
54. U.S. Department of Agriculture, Forest Service: "Report of the Forester," Washington, 1922.
55. U.S. Department of Agriculture, Forest Service: "Report of the Forester," Washington, 1924.

56. U.S. Department of Agriculture, Forest Service: "Report of the Forester," Washington, 1925.
57. U.S. Department of Agriculture: The Principal Laws Relating to the Establishment and Administration of the National Forests and to Other Forest Service Activities, *Miscellaneous Publication*, no. 135, Washington, 1939.
58. U.S. Department of Agriculture, Forest Service: "Operation Outdoors," Washington, 1957.
59. U.S. Department of the Interior, National Park Service: "Annual Report of the Superintendent of National Parks to the Secretary of the Interior for the Fiscal Year Ended June 30, 1916," Washington, 1916.
60. U.S. Department of the Interior, National Park Service: "Annual Report of the Director of the National Park Service to the Secretary of the Interior for the Fiscal Year Ended June 30, 1917," Washington, 1917.
61. U.S. Department of the Interior, National Park Service: "Annual Report of the Director of the National Park Service to the Secretary of the Interior for the Fiscal Year Ended June 30, 1918," Washington, 1918.
62. U.S. Department of the Interior, National Park Service: "Annual Report of the Director of the National Park Service to the Secretary of the Interior for the Fiscal Year Ended June 30, 1931," Washington, 1931.
63. U.S. Department of the Interior, National Park Service: "Hot Springs National Park, Arkansas," Washington, 1950.
64. U.S. Department of the Interior, National Park Service: "Areas Administered by the National Park Service, December 31, 1957," Washington, 1958.
65. U.S. Department of Labor, Bureau of Labor Statistics: Park Recreation Areas in the United States, *Miscellaneous Publication*, no. 462, Washington, 1928.
66. Waugh, F. A.: "Recreation Uses on the National Forests," U.S. Government Printing Office, Washington, 1918.
67. Weyerhaeuser Timber Company: "Miscellaneous Notes: Public Recreational Use of Industrial Forest Land," Tacoma, Wash., Mar. 9, 1956. (Mimeographed.)
68. Wolfe, Linnie M.: "Son of the Wilderness: The Life of John Muir," Alfred A. Knopf, Inc., New York, 1947.

CHAPTER 4 *Recreation in State Parks of the United States*

State parks are among our most popular recreational areas. They are second only to municipal areas in number of visitors, and they have an annual recreational patronage that is far greater than the combined total for national parks and national forests. In 1957 (see Table 4-1) they were host to over 200 million people.

This tremendous use is due to several factors. State park systems are best developed in states having large populations and, therefore, are of particular importance in the East. With few exceptions geographic loca-

FIG. 4-1. The heavy patronage typical of many state parks in the United States is illustrated by this view of Jones Beach State Park, Long Island, New York. (*Division of Parks, New York Conservation Department*)

tion plays a vital role in the selection of areas for state parks, for the availability of varied outdoor recreational interests to large numbers of people is one of the keystones of state park administration. In addition, most state parks are of such character that development of facilities and provision of services designed for use by large numbers of people are permissible; except in specific cases, absolute maintenance of undisturbed natural conditions is not a primary consideration.

RELATIONSHIP OF STATE PARKS TO PUBLIC OUTDOOR RECREATIONAL NEEDS

Public outdoor recreational needs in a given region will be most adequately and economically served if all types of recreational areas are integrated to provide the greatest variety of recreational services with a minimum of duplication. Properly planned state park systems are vitally

Table 4-1. State Park Attendance, 1941–1957

Year	No. areas reporting[a]	Total	Day visitors	Overnight visitors	Cabins and hotels[b]	Organized camps[c]	Campers[c]
1941	100[d]	97,488,528	94,570,487	2,918,041	466,673	818,065	1,628,795
1946	67	92,506,662[e]	88,922,733	3,138,929	1,083,169	1,000,737	1,055,023
1951	78	120,722,423	114,024,207	6,698,216	1,345,054	1,351,846	4,001,316
1952	77	149,255,417[e]	139,577,727	7,812,163[e]	1,507,347	1,683,872	4,618,194
1953	80	159,255,417[e]	148,188,609	8,347,055[e]	1,523,836	1,537,526	5,134,919
1954	81	166,427,274[e]	155,817,374	9,472,400	1,480,915	1,582,956	6,408,529
1955	82	183,187,643[e]	169,123,466	11,056,660[e]	1,575,639	1,696,939	7,649,847
1956	89	199,118,881[e]	183,739,033	12,642,073[e]	1,727,204	1,809,019	9,105,850
1957	89	216,780,226	201,880,919	14,899,307[e]	1,835,921	2,208,621	10,571,039

[a] The same park agencies have not always reported each year.

[b] Guest days.

[c] Camper days.

[d] Includes reports partially covering state forests, wildlife areas, waysides, etc., that have not been included in subsequent tabulations.

[e] Totals do not equal the sum of component parts because some agencies reported no breakdown of the total figure.

SOURCE: "State Park Statistics, 1956 and 1957," National Park Service, Division of Recreation Resource Planning, Washington, June, 1957, 1958.

important to such a well-integrated program, for in addition to having the advantage of relative accessibility, they are generally adapted to considerable flexibility in development and use.

State parks not only foster the preservation of noteworthy or significant interests on a state level but also provide for necessary outdoor recreational activities not adapted to, desirable, nor possible on other types of recreational lands. Further, because they are more readily accessible than national parks and national forests and because they are usually larger than municipal or county parks, state parks offer at least a semblance of wild or wilderness conditions for people who are unable to utilize more remote recreational areas conveniently.

No longer do municipal parks completely serve the nation's outdoor recreational needs. Nor can national parks and national forests alone absorb the impact of increased public recreational use without serious damage to their principal interests. Despite the fact that national parks and national forests are too distant for regular use by millions of people, many of these areas already suffer from overcrowding. In addition, many national parks and national forest recreational areas also suffer from public pressure for undesirable facilities and activities, a pressure which comes largely from a misinterpretation of the primary values of such areas. Properly developed state park systems can materially alleviate such conditions by providing for recreational outlets not adapted to national parks and national forests.

State parks, then, stand midway between municipal parks and the more remote Federal recreational areas, supplementing and accentuating public outdoor recreational opportunities to varying degrees in different sections of the country.

State park systems are usually of minor importance in states having relatively small population and a preponderance of federally owned land of recreational value (e.g., Arizona, Colorado, Idaho, Montana, Nevada, New Mexico, Utah, Wyoming); conversely, where the population is large and where federally owned land is limited or nonexistent (e.g., Florida, Indiana, Illinois, Kentucky, Michigan, Minnesota, New York, Ohio, Pennsylvania, Tennessee, Wisconsin) well-developed state park systems assume a major role in outdoor recreation. A number of states (e.g., California, Oregon, Washington) have both sizable federally owned acreage as well as large urban populations; in such cases, state park development parallels recreational use of Federal lands.

Except for the fundamental concept of providing a variety of outdoor recreational opportunities in relatively wild settings for large numbers of people there is little unity in organization or management between various state park systems; each state develops its state park program in accordance with its particular needs. Consequently, state park systems differ widely in the number of areas and their aggregate acreage; the size, character and complexity of their administrative organization; the source, background, and training of their personnel; methods of land acquisition; the nature and reliability of financial support; and their general policy of development and management.

EXTENT OF STATE PARK SYSTEMS

Throughout the United States there are more than 2,000 state parks (see Table 4-2). These vary in size from small historic sites or waysides of less than an acre to extensive units like Baxter State Park in Maine, which embraces over 190,000 acres [37].

Forty-eight states have some form of park system. Statistics compiled by the Division of Recreational Resource Planning of the National Park Service indicate that, in 1957, the most extensive of these systems were in New York and California. New York, including 2,485,170 acres of state forests administered essentially as state parks, had 129 areas aggregating over 2.5 million acres; California possessed 147 state parks with a total area of more than 606,000 acres [37]. Other state park systems noteworthy for their size in 1957 [37] were those in Maine, Michigan, and Pennsylvania (150,000 to slightly more than 200,000 acres each); Minnesota, Ohio, and South Dakota (75,000 to 100,000 acres each); Florida, Missouri, Oklahoma, Oregon, Tennessee, Texas, and Washington (50,000 to 75,000 acres each); and Alabama, Georgia, Illinois, Indiana, Iowa, Massachusetts, Nebraska, New Hampshire, North Carolina, South Carolina, Virginia, and West Virginia (25,000 to 50,000 acres each).

BASIC CHARACTERISTICS OF STATE PARKS

In spite of their wide variety, state parks can be grouped logically into three principal classes.

1. *Utilitarian areas*, developed primarily to foster physically active recreational interests (e.g., swimming, boating, picnicking, camping, winter sports, and the like), in which significant interests are generally lacking. A great number of state parks are in this class.

2. *Significant areas*, containing unique or important geological, biological, archeological, or historical features typical of a particular state. Such state parks are designed to foster public understanding of the primary interests of such areas; physical facilities are usually held to a minimum. State parks such as Ginkgo Petrified Forest (Washington), John Day Fossil Beds (Oregon), Spring Mill (Indiana), and Valley Forge (Pennsylvania) fall in this class.

3. *Scenic or dual purpose areas*, which, owing to their larger size, often combine the qualities of the two former types. Generally they offer opportunity for varied outdoor recreational activities (e.g., hiking, camping, horseback riding, boating, and the like) in a scenically attractive and usually natural setting. Development of necessary physical facilities is conducted with regard to preservation of scenic beauty and natural in-

Table 4-2. Areas, Acreages, and Land Acquisition in State Parks, 1941–1957

Year	No. of agencies reporting[a]	Total no. of areas	Aggregate acreage	Land acquisition				Acreage disposed
				By purchase, acres	By gift, acres	By other means, acres	Total acreage acquired	
1941	100[b]	1,335[c]	4,259,899[c]	......	......	......	81,656	
1946	67	1,531	4,634,365	46,255	1,415	73,920	121,590	
1951	78	1,750	4,877,178	15,510	3,236	29,745	48,491	12,729
1952	77	1,818	4,927,806	11,312	8,392	16,980	36,684	4,049
1953	80	1,879	4,875,666[d]	14,258	2,716	4,017	20,991	8,570
1954	81	1,969	5,005,237	29,892	31,322	31,001	92,215	983
1955	82	2,034	5,085,951	13,750	35,724	20,674	70,148	2,996
1956	89	2,100	5,165,125	30,850	16,055	14,639	61,544	3,967
1957	89	2,216	5,247,682	29,119	9,851	24,419	63,398	1,789

[a] The same park agencies have not always reported each year.

[b] Includes reports partially covering state forests, wildlife areas, waysides, etc., that have not been included in subsequent tabulations.

[c] Area and acreage figures for 1941 shown here, as well as those for subsequent years, do not include state forests, wildlife refuges, and waysides not administered by state park agencies.

[d] The acreage figure reported for 1953 is lower than those reported for 1951 and 1952 owing to reexamination of park-acreage figures in some states.

SOURCE: "State Park Statistics, 1956 and 1957," National Park Service, Division of Recreation Resource Planning, Washington, June, 1957, 1958.

terests. Such state parks as Moran (Washington), Fall Creek Falls (Tennessee), Matthiesson (Illinois), Turkey Run (Indiana), Bear Mountain (New York), and Custer (South Dakota) are of this class.

Some states place greater emphasis on one type of development than on others. In many states, such as Kansas, Nebraska, Arkansas, Iowa,

FIG. 4-2. Significant historical interests are important in many state park systems; Fort Pickens State Park, Santa Rosa Island, Florida. (*Florida Park Service*)

Fig. 4-3. Fall Creek Falls (236 feet), highest waterfall in eastern United States, is a highlight of Fall Creek Falls State Park, Tennessee. (*Photo by Paul A. Moore, Tennessee Conservation Department*)

Rhode Island, Connecticut, Delaware, and Maryland, state parks are basically utilitarian in character; they serve heavily populated sections of the country or offer recreational interests otherwise lacking in their particular region; for instance, many state parks in some of the Great Plains states feature artificially developed lakes which provide welcome opportunity for water sports. State parks in North Dakota are of a significant character with emphasis on local history. State park programs are of limited importance in the Rocky Mountain region where public outdoor recreational needs are largely satisfied by extensive Federal lands in national forests and national parks. Some state park systems, however, are noted for their great diversity, including areas of a utilitarian, significant, and dual-purpose character; this is the case in such states as California, Illinois, Indiana, Michigan, Minnesota, New York, Oregon, and Washington.

ADMINISTRATION OF STATE PARKS

Since most outdoor recreational interests and activities are closely related to forests and wildlife, it is natural that this affinity should be reflected in the organization of state activities of that nature; although there are variations in specific details, twenty-eight states administer their state parks in conjunction with either, or both, state forestry and state fish and game activities. As noted in the following paragraphs, administrative organizations of different state park systems may be broadly classified into six principal categories [22,23,37].

1. *State parks, forests, and game administered as separate units within a common department.* In fifteen states (Alabama,[1] Illinois, Indiana, Iowa, Kansas, Massachusetts,[2] Michigan,[3] Minnesota, Nebraska, New Jersey,[4] New York,[5] Ohio,[6] South Dakota, West Virginia, and Wisconsin[7]) state park, state forest, and state fish and game affairs are handled by distinct divisions within one major department. For example, state parks in Indiana are administered by the Division of State Parks, Lands and Waters of the Department of Conservation, which also includes the Division of Forestry and the Division of Fish and Game [19].

2. *State parks and state forests administered under a common author-*

[1] Mound State Monument is administered by the Alabama Museum of Natural History [37].

[2] In Massachusetts eight independent commissions administer a like number of reservations with an aggregate area of about 14,000 acres; in addition, several public beach areas are independently managed by the Division of Public Beaches [37].

[3] Mackinac Island State Park is administered by the Mackinac Island State Park Commission [37].

[4] That portion of the Palisades Interstate Park located in New Jersey, 1,900 acres, is under the authority of the Palisades Interstate Park Commission [37].

[5] In New York seven state forest areas, with a total of 2,485,170 acres, are administered as state parks by the Division of Lands and Forests; in addition the Department of Education administers twenty-one historic sites, with an aggregate acreage of 629 acres [37].

[6] The Ohio Historical Society administers nearly 60 areas totaling more than 4,000 acres; one area of 1,573 acres is managed by the Akron Metropolitan Park District [37].

[7] In Wisconsin the State Historical Society independently administers several historical areas [37].

Fig. 4-4. Among noteworthy areas in the California State Park system are those typified by the coast redwoods (*Sequoia sempervirens*). (*Division of Beaches and Parks, California Department of Natural Resources*)

ity, with fish and game administration separate. Thirteen states (California, Connecticut, Kentucky, Maryland,[8] New Hampshire, North Carolina, Oklahoma,[9] Pennsylvania,[10] South Carolina, Tennessee, Utah, Vermont, and Virginia[11]) consider fish and game as a separate entity,

[8] One small area is under the supervision of the Maryland Tercentenary Memorial Commission [37].

[9] The Will Rogers Memorial in Oklahoma is managed by the Will Rogers Memorial Commission [37].

[10] In Pennsylvania several recreation areas are managed by independent agencies, and a number of historical sites are under the authority of the Pennsylvania Historical and Museum Commission [37].

[11] One of fourteen areas in Virginia administered by the Breaks Interstate Park Commission [37].

controlled by a specific administrative organization, while state parks and forests are administered by subdivisions of another major department. In California, for example, the Division of Beaches and Parks, which administers state parks, and the Division of Forestry are included as separate units within the Department of Natural Resources; fish and

FIG. 4-5. Many of Oregon's state parks are located along the Pacific shoreline; Canon Beach and Hay Stack Rock, Ecola State Park. (*Oregon State Highway Commission*)

game matters are administered by an independent Department of Fish and Game.

3. *Administration of state parks by a distinct department.* Fourteen states (Arizona,[12] Colorado,[13] Delaware,[14] Florida, Georgia,[15] Louisiana,

[12] Arizona established a State Park Board in 1957 [5]; previously two areas of state land, considered as state parks, were administered by the Arizona Game and Fish Commission [23].

[13] Colorado established a State Park and Recreation Board in 1957 [6]; five small historical areas in Colorado are administered by the State Historical Society [37].

[14] In Delaware two of five state recreation areas are managed by the State Highway Department [37].

[15] Georgia's Jekyll Island State Park, 11,000 acres, is managed by the independent Jekyll Island Park Authority [37].

Maine,[16] Mississippi, Missouri, Nevada, New Mexico, Texas,[17] Washington, and Wyoming[18]) have independent state park organizations, distinct from forestry, fish and game, or any other state agency. For example, in the state of Washington the independent State Parks and Recreation Commission manages state parks, the equally independent Department of Game is concerned with sports fisheries and wildlife, and the highly important state forestry program is administered by the Department of Natural Resources.

4. *State parks administered by a state park division within the highway department.* This system is used in Montana and Oregon [37]. It is considered to be conducive of efficient and economical maintenance of state park areas by existing highway department personnel skilled in and equipped for such activities.

5. *State parks administered by historical bodies.* In North Dakota, state parks are largely of historical interest and the State Historical Society has been designated as the administrative agency [37].

6. *Miscellaneous.* State parks in Arkansas are administered by the State Publicity and Parks Commission; in Idaho by the Department of Public Lands; in Rhode Island by the Department of Public Works [37].

ACQUISITION OF STATE PARK LANDS

In many states development of state park systems has been characterized by considerable difficulty. The states, except Texas, do not possess public-domain lands;[19] further, private acquisition of extensive areas within the states had been largely accomplished before the state park movement developed. Consequently, lands in most state park systems have been obtained in a great variety of ways (see Table 4-2), including acquisition by gift, purchase from proceeds of bond issues, purchase with funds secured through tax levy, exchange of school lands, purchase by authority of legislative action and appropriation, transfer of Federal lands, and purchase with funds derived from a percentage of fish and game receipts [29,36].

[16] Baxter State Park in Maine, 193,254 acres, is administered by the independent Baxter State Park Authority [37].

[17] Two of the fifty-eight state parks of Texas are managed by independent commissions [37].

[18] In Wyoming two small historical sites are under authority of the Historical Landmark Commission [37].

[19] Public-domain lands are the property of the Federal government, subject to sale or other transfer under Federal laws; most national parks and national forests were established from the public domain either by congressional action or Presidential proclamation. Unoccupied and unappropriated lands within the present boundary of Texas, following its annexation, remained as public lands of that state instead of becoming part of the public domain [8,16].

Significant portions of almost every state park system were acquired through gifts, varying from small contributions of money from numerous individuals, accumulated for the purchase of specific areas, to extensive acreage given by one person. Gifts involving extensive land areas have been important in the development of state parks in New York, Michigan, Texas, Iowa, Washington, Wisconsin, Minnesota, Kentucky, and Indiana [29].

In numerous instances Federal lands have been transferred to the states for park purposes [29]. Outstanding examples of such transfers include the Yosemite Grant, entrusted to the state of California by the Federal government in 1864, and Mackinac Island, acquired by the state of Michigan from the Federal government in 1885 [29]. Originally such transfers had to be accomplished by specific congressional action, but in 1927 Congress passed the Recreational Act,[20] eliminating that necessity in connection with such transfers. Later, additional laws passed by Congress relative to the disposal of surplus Federal lands provided further assistance in the development of state recreational systems. Of greatest significance was the amending, in 1948, of the Surplus Property Act of 1944. As amended, this act provided for the transfer of Federal lands declared surplus previous to July 1, 1948, at 50 per cent of their fair, appraised value, to states and local governments for use as public parks and recreational areas [12]. The amended Surplus Property Act of 1944 also made possible the transfer, without monetary consideration, of lands having historic value, provided such lands were to be administered as historic sites [12]. A number of state parks came into being as a result of the opportunity thus afforded.

State parks have also been formed through exchange of school lands [29] originally given by the Federal government to all but the original thirteen states, as well as the states created from them, and Texas. Many of these school sections were scattered throughout the Western national forests. To promote efficient administration of the national forests Congress authorized the U.S. Forest Service to negotiate with the states for the exchange of school sections within national forest boundaries for a consolidated, equivalent national forest area within the same state. Some exchanges of this nature were prompted by the recreational values of lands derived from the U.S. Forest Service. Custer State Park in South Dakota was formed largely in this manner [29].

In Missouri, Nebraska, and Kansas a percentage of fish and game receipts is reserved for purchase of state park lands [29], and in a number

[20] The Recreational Act permits a discount by the Bureau of Land Management of up to 70 per cent for land only; timber involved must be acquired at full value. This act also permits a 50 per cent discount for land and timber by the General Services Administration (personal communication, Mar. 17, 1958, from Charles DeTurk, Park Planner, Washington State Parks and Recreation Commission, Seattle).

of other states (e.g., New York, Illinois, New Hampshire, Rhode Island, California) the purchase of land for state park use has been accomplished through the sale of bonds, a procedure justified on the basis of the relationship of outdoor recreation to public health and welfare. Some states, however, do not view this latter method of fund raising for park purposes with favor. In Indiana, for instance, statutory provisions prohibit the sale of bonds by the state for such purposes [19,29]. However, the Indiana Division of State Parks will assume responsibility for development and administration of lands purchased by individual counties, through county bond issues, for state park purposes. This procedure is based upon the philosophy that local demonstration of interest in state parks is indicative of the need of such areas, since citizens of various counties assume the financial burden involved in the acquisition of necessary area.

Finally, although it is difficult to convince many state legislators of the advisability of direct legislative appropriation for purchase of state park lands, that method has occasionally had some success. A number of state parks in Iowa, Massachusetts, and Washington owe their origin to funds provided by special legislative appropriation [29].

FUNDS FOR OPERATION AND ADMINISTRATION OF STATE PARKS

Funds required for the management of state parks are derived primarily from legislative appropriations (see Table 4-3). Additional revenue is obtained from fees, permits, and services, including payments by operators of concessions, entrance and parking fees, charges for campground use, and, when operated by state park organizations, returns from the sale or rental of equipment (see Table 4-4). In addition, miscellaneous income is derived from special leases (e.g., air beacons and radio or television towers erected on state park land) and the sale of special products (e.g., sand, gravel, coal, and salvage timber).

As noted in Tables 4-3, 4-4, and 4-5, the phenomenal growth in public use of state parks in recent years has necessarily been reflected in increased appropriations as well as greater revenue from operations. However, cost of operation, per visitor, has become fairly stabilized. The gross operating cost of state park systems in 1957 was about 34 cents per visitor,[21] with net operating cost[22] per visitor between 11 and 12 cents [37].

While most state park systems make moderate charges for overnight campground use and exact certain charges for concession rights, only

[21] About 19 cents for operation and 15 cents for capital improvements.

[22] Net cost per visitor computed by deducting operational revenue (about $16 million) from operational costs (approximately $41 million).

Table 4-3. Funds Available for Expenditure in State Parks, 1941–1957

Year	No. agencies reporting[a]	Total funds	From appropriations	From other sources
1941	100[b]	$ 10,372,213	$ 7,093,234	$ 3,278,979
1946	67	20,710,995	17,123,148	3,587,847
1951	78	62,859,125	37,290,456	25,568,669
1952	77	60,885,828	37,220,623	23,665,205
1953	80	68,791,159	43,746,161	25,044,998
1954	81	64,058,815	37,032,471	27,026,344
1955	82	69,075,185	43,382,441	25,692,744
1956	89	88,254,728	49,609,999	38,644,729
1957	89	124,076,912[c]	89,308,782	33,049,009

[a] The same park agencies have not always reported each year.

[b] Includes reports partially covering state forests, wildlife areas, waysides, etc., that have not been included in subsequent tabulations.

[c] Total does not equal sum of component parts because some agencies reported no breakdown in total figures.

SOURCE: "State Park Statistics, 1956 and 1957," National Park Service, Division of Recreation Resource Planning, Washington, June, 1957, 1958.

Table 4-4. Revenue from Operations in State Parks, 1941–1957

Year	No. areas reporting[a]	Total revenue	Operated facilities	Concessions	Entrance and parking fees	Other sources
1941	100[b]	$ 3,176,504[c]	$1,091,033	$ 298,636	$ 625,386	$ 105,360
1946	67	4,117,906[c]	1,585,743	681,513	305,194	365,477
1951	78	7,652,243	4,128,149	1,530,787	1,016,839	976,468
1952	77	9,349,423[c]	5,239,988	1,779,255	1,224,950	1,024,060
1953	80	10,775,957	6,342,187	1,854,808	1,529,086	1,049,876
1954	81	13,098,735	7,186,878	1,915,863	2,545,266	1,450,728
1955	82	13,816,924	7,512,696	2,086,426	2,695,419	1,522,383
1956	89	14,927,567	8,473,557	2,240,498	2,854,292	1,359,220
1957	89	15,986,646	9,390,305	2,404,832	2,727,781	554,124

[a] The same park agencies have not always reported each year.

[b] Includes reports partially covering state forests, wildlife areas, waysides, etc., that have not been included in subsequent tabulations.

[c] Totals do not equal the sum of component parts because some agencies reported no breakdown of the total figure.

SOURCE: "State Park Statistics, 1956 and 1957," National Park Service, Division of Recreation Resource Planning, Washington, June, 1957, 1958.

a few systems impose an admission charge to state parks. In Indiana[23] the theory is that visitors who use and enjoy state parks should pay a slightly higher share of the cost. The Indiana state park organization also feels that people will display greater appreciation and exert more care for such areas if a small charge is made.

Since 1949 support of the state park system in the state of Washington has been based largely upon revenue derived from automobile licenses. Of the $4 fee collected every two years from each operator of a motor vehicle in that state, $2.20 is reserved for state parks. In addition, Washington state parks receive approximately 25 per cent of fines derived from violation of the state highway code laws of 1937.

Table 4-5. State Park Expenditures, 1941–1957

Year	No. areas reporting[a]	Total	Salaries and wages	Supplies and equipment	Lands	Improvements
1941	100[b]	$10,022,146[c]	$ 4,186,433	$ 2,755,702	$1,559,721	$ 1,449,319
1946	67	15,144,880[c]	5,556,029	3,160,649	3,204,384	2,303,636
1951	78	38,545,051[c]	15,141,739	7,698,854	3,314,161	12,390,297
1952	77	40,468,523	17,862,034	8,277,449	2,754,793	11,574,247
1953	80	49,565,425[c]	20,194,346	9,962,999	5,696,225	12,812,437
1954	81	49,133,791[c]	21,174,310	10,446,764	5,217,544	12,142,069
1955	82	55,093,278[c]	22,673,339	11,350,681	5,523,426	15,293,114
1956	89	65,843,582[c]	24,705,841	13,304,603	5,987,080	21,520,424
1957	89	74,008,146[c]	27,844,296	13,778,686	4,809,278	27,526,153

[a] The same park agencies have not always reported each year.

[b] Includes reports partially covering state forests, wildlife areas, waysides, etc., that have not been included in subsequent tabulations.

[c] Totals do not equal the sum of component parts because some agencies reported no breakdown of the total figure.

SOURCE: "State Park Statistics, 1956 and 1957," National Park Service, Division of Recreation Resource Planning, Washington, June, 1957, 1958.

ADMINISTRATIVE POLICIES OF VARIOUS STATE PARK SYSTEMS

A clear, concise, well-defined policy is the basis of good state park administration. Such a policy, in addition to outlining the scope and purpose of areas most desirable to a particular system, indicates the nature and extent of necessary development. With few exceptions, well-established state park systems operate within the bounds of these well-defined policies which, although they vary in detail owing to differences in local conditions, are somewhat similar to the policy of the National Park

[23] No admission charge for children under eight years of age ([29], also personal correspondence, Feb. 3, 1954).

Service. Statements relative to the administration of representative state park systems follow.

California state parks are administered by the Division of Beaches and Parks, established in 1928, and guided by a State Park Commission of five members which was set up in 1927. This division is one of several in the Department of Natural Resources [3]. The objectives of the California state park program[24] are the acquisition and development of the best recreation areas of state-wide importance, the preservation for public enjoyment and education of outstanding scenic areas of the state, and the acquisition, restoration, and preservation of significant historic sites and buildings [3]. State parks in California must have one or more of the following attributes [3]:

1. Natural scenery of unusual beauty.
2. Natural objects of unique beauty or scientific value, such as rare kinds and combinations of trees, plants and wildlife; and rare forms of earth, rock and water.
3. State wide historical interest.
4. Adaptability to such activities as camping, hiking, swimming, fishing, and other forms of simple outdoor recreation inspiring to the mind and refreshing to the body.

In Florida the Board of Parks and Historic Memorials was established by the state Legislature on July 1, 1929. As noted in section 12 of Senate Bill 441, the policy under which the board operates is as follows [14]:

To promote the state park system for the use, enjoyment and benefit of the people of Florida and visitors; to acquire typical portions of the original domain of the state which will be accessible to all of the people, and of such character as to emblemize the state's natural values; conserve these natural values for all time; administer the development, use and maintenance of these lands and render such public service in so doing, in such manner as to enable the people of Florida and visitors to enjoy these values without depleting them, to contribute materially to the development of a strong mental, moral and physical fibre in the people; to provide for the perpetual preservation of historic sites and memorials of statewide significance and interpretation of their history to the people; to contribute to the tourist appeal of Florida.

In Illinois the first state park was established in 1903. In 1918 the administration of the state parks of Illinois was delegated to the Division of Parks and Memorials,[25] originally established as a unit in the Department of Public Works and Buildings, and later combined with the Department of Conservation. Its policy is as follows [44]:

[24] In 1956 the California State Park Commission reaffirmed these basic principles [4].
[25] Personal communication, Jan. 21, 1949.

To preserve the most important historic sites and events which are connected with early pioneer or Indian history . . . as a part of the education of present and future Illinois citizens.

To set aside as public reservations those locations which have unusual scenic

Fig. 4-6. Moss-festooned bald cypress (*Taxodium distichum*) add interest to Hillsborough River State Park, Florida. (*Florida Park Service*)

attractions . . . These areas should be large in size and whenever practical shall not be less than 1,000 acres in extent.

To preserve large forested areas and marginal lands along rivers, small water courses, and lakes for recreational use different from that given by the typical city park, and so that these tracts may remain unchanged by civilization, so far as possible, and be kept for future generations.

Indiana's well-developed state park system is administered by the Division of State Parks, Lands and Waters of the Department of Conservation, established in 1919, and adheres to the following policy [19]:

> The chief function of this Division is to conserve for all time for the use and enjoyment of the people of Indiana certain areas of typical Hoosier scenery in its original state. Such areas of outstanding beauty, unusual formations, historical settings and places closely related to early Indiana development were thought worthy of preservation. In addition to this, it had long been known that a state, as a unit of government, had a definite obligation to its citizens; it should protect and preserve such areas, and in so doing provide access to them, provide means for their fullest and most complete enjoyment by the people, and also provide without detracting from their natural appeal, such outdoor recreations and facilities as were compatible with the surroundings.

The state park system of Tennessee was developed largely through interest in outdoor recreational activities related to lakes formed after construction of dams by the Tennessee Valley Authority. The first state parks of Tennessee, together with their central administrative body, the Division of State Parks of the Department of Conservation, were established at the same time. Tennessee state park policy is implied in the following statement [35]:

> In the selection of state park sites, some insist that high priority be given to the acquisition of sites having an outstanding scenic and historical significance. Others contend as strongly in behalf of selection of adequate sites bearing a definite relationship to major concentrations of state population . . . in view of the present needs of the people of Tennessee and the status of development of its state park system at this time, priority both at present and during the next few years must be placed on the acquisition and development of areas suitable in character and in location best to serve the varied recreational needs of the state and its neighbors.

State park facilities in the Lake states are typified by those in Wisconsin. There state recreational areas are in four categories: state parks, state forests, state historic and memorial parks, and wayside or roadside parks.

Roadside parks are located along principal highways and provide picnic and camping facilities for travelers who wish to stop for relatively short periods. Historic parks are related to interesting events in Wisconsin's past. State forests are extensive areas which, in addition to their value for timber production, are widely used for recreation; a network of forest roads makes them accessible. State parks are relatively large scenic areas, each with a distinctive feature of state-wide importance; all may be reached by good highways, and they provide facilities and opportunity for a wide variety of recreational interests.

These lands are administered by the Forests and Parks Division of the

Wisconsin Conservation Department, which has defined state park policy in these words [45]:

> The primary purpose of state parks is to preserve the unusual and unique scenic or historic places of the state for all time, in a manner consistent with the legitimate use of such areas by the public. This fact makes it imperative that the use of these parks can only be had in accordance with prescribed regulations which aim to preserve those things that have made these areas of value for state park purposes.

Although the foregoing policy statements are representative of only a few state park systems, they are characteristic of the general theme upon

FIG. 4-7. One of the objectives of many state park systems is the preservation of representative examples of typical flora; Anza Desert State Park, California. (*Division of Beaches and Parks, California Department of Natural Resources*)

which such systems are operated. Broadly speaking, it is apparent that such statements indicate:

1. A definite recognition of the value of preserving areas containing typical state scenery.
2. A definite recognition of the value of preserving significant historical, geological, or biological interests characteristic of the state.
3. That development of state parks be carried out under a carefully considered plan, and that their public use be governed by regulations which will ensure perpetuation of the values which make them interesting.

4. That, consistent with the preservation of inherent interests, development of state parks should be guided by the policy that, if such development is not compatible with public use of certain state parks, other areas adapted to such needs should be provided.

5. That a definite minimum size limit exists for state parks having interesting or unique scenic values.

6. That, wherever possible, accessibility to centers of population be given adequate consideration in selection of various types of state park lands.

7. That, while the greater effort will be made for citizens of a particular state, the interests of out-of-state visitors should not be neglected.

STATE PARK PERSONNEL

The success and efficiency of any organization are a reflection of its personnel. This is particularly true of agencies administering state parks, for they are one of the more recent manifestations of recreational land use. In the past many state park organizations have been plagued with difficulty in developing and maintaining an adequate staff of well-trained, enthusiastic individuals, for such organizations were beset by conditions responsible for low salary schedules, job insecurity, and lack of public or official recognition of personal initiative. To varying degrees such conditions still exist, although they are not as typical of older and better established organizations as of those in primary stages of development.

Employees of only a few state park systems are under civil service; in too few cases are applicants for positions judged primarily upon aptitude, experience, or training, or upon the results of an adequate examination designed to bring out the qualities required for state park work. In fact, except in certain technical fields, such as engineering, architecture, and landscape architecture, opportunities for adequate academic training are limited.

But state parks have shared in the gradual awakening of public interest in the values of outdoor recreation. The rapid expansion of state park systems and the greatly increased use of such areas have necessitated higher standards of performance on the part of personnel, and a greater understanding of all factors which bear upon the planning, development, protection, and use of recreational lands.

Today, most forward-looking state park organizations are striving to correct situations which militate against the development and retention of competent personnel. Attempts are being made to place salary scales in line with experience and ability required in specific jobs; in many instances civil service programs have been established or are being considered as a means of protecting the job security of capable employees against changes in the political fortunes of the state; and there is a definite trend toward the development of a career outlook in state park work by filling openings in the upper echelons of state park organizations with qualified members of the current staff whenever possible. The growing importance of training institutes [1,15] and in-service programs designed primarily for regular park personnel, and the enthusiastic manner in which such efforts have been received, imply recognition of the need for academic training specifically adapted to the management of recreational lands. The relatively few schools now offering such training will undoubtedly be augmented by others as opportunities in this field develop [9].

It is obvious that history is repeating itself in the state parks. The initial years of the U.S. Forest Service and the National Park Service

Table 4-6. State Park Personnel, 1941–1957

Year	No. areas reporting[a]	Total	Year round	Seasonal	Year	No. areas reporting[a]	Total	Year round	Seasonal
1941	100[b]	5,486	2,630	2,856	1953	80	12,936	5,030	7,906
1946	67	6,650	2,771	3,879	1954	81	12,404	5,105	7,299
1951	78	11,313	4,376	6,937	1955	82	13,637	5,657	7,980
1952	77	12,116	4,753	7,363	1956	89	14,932	6,048	8,884
					1957	89	15,442	6,301	9,141

[a] The same park agencies have not always reported each year.

[b] Includes reports partially covering state forests, wildlife areas, waysides, etc., that have not been included in subsequent tabulations.

SOURCE: "State Park Statistics, 1956 and 1957," National Park Service, Division of Recreation Resource Planning, Washington, June, 1957, 1958.

were characterized by somewhat similar personnel difficulties. The training and background of numerous early employees of both these organizations often left much to be desired; nevertheless, many of these individuals were admirably equipped with vision and enthusiasm by which they grew in stature. Today the eminent position which is enjoyed by both the U.S. Forest Service and the National Park Service is largely the result of the perseverance of those men who dedicated themselves to an ideal.

The number of state park employees is too small for adequate handling of increasing administrative responsibilities resulting from expanding state park patronage and acreage. As noted in Table 4-6, there were approximately 15,000 employees in 1957, with the greater number employed on a seasonal basis. It will also be apparent that, between 1941 and 1957, the percentage of increase in year-round staff was less than that of seasonal personnel. This, of course, is a reflection of the nature of state park patronage which, being largely confined to a portion of the year, places greatest pressures on the need for increased staff during the peak period.

However, there is tangible evidence that the inadequate state park personnel situation is showing definite signs of improvement. Data compiled by the Division of Recreational Resource Planning of the National Park Service [37] bear this out. State park employees are not only increasing in number, but the quality of personnel is also being enhanced. Since 1941 the number of state park employees has expanded at a much more rapid rate, percentagewise, than has travel to state park areas.[26] Of particular interest is the trend toward a larger number of professionally trained employees. Although the number of professional employees is small, data for 1957 [37] indicated a 20 per cent increase in this group over the previous year, whereas during the same period, the total number of state park employees increased by only about 3 per cent.

MISCELLANEOUS ADMINISTRATIVE PROCEDURE IN STATE PARK SYSTEMS

Since population patterns, as well as economic and political factors, vary in different states, the fundamental concepts of state park policy in different states are interpreted differently, in accordance with local conditions.

Most state park organizations exercise direct supervision of field operations from a central headquarters. State parks of New York, however, are organized on a regional basis with nine regions, each essentially autonomous, under the supervision of the Division of Parks in the Conservation Department [30,31]. Custody and direct operation of the state parks of New York in each region is the responsibility of several regional park commissioners, together with their staff. The chairman of each regional commission is, by law, a member of the State Council of Parks which is a planning, policy-making, and budget-making authority. The various regional commissions report to the Conservation Department through that body. In addition, nearly 2.5 million acres of state forest lands are designated as recreational areas; they are under the supervision of the Division of Lands and Forests, a different division in the Conservation Department. The Director of the Division of Lands and Forests is also a member of the State Council of Parks.

[26] During the past eleven years, however, the percentage of increase in number of employees has been approximately that of the percentage of increase in state park patronage [37].

The goal of most states is to have state parks located so that no citizen will be more than 50 miles distant from at least one of these areas; Connecticut has established an objective of 25 miles.[27] New York, however, frowns upon such a closely defined policy; establishment of parks in the latter state is judged purely upon local needs.

Necessary size of state parks is not easily reduced to a standard since this depends upon desired use, geographical location, topography, inherent interests, and related factors. Nevertheless, there is fairly common agreement among most state park executives that scenic state parks must necessarily encompass large tracts of land. This policy recognizes that basic scenic values cannot be maintained under pressure of great public use unless the size of an area is sufficient to cushion the impact of such use by proper dispersal of recreational activities within its boundaries. The term "large tract" is itself a relative matter, subject to a variety of interpretations. Although many state parks are much greater in size, certain states have established a minimum of 1,500 acres for scenic state parks. Other state park organizations, reflecting local attitudes and conditions, place a different interpretation on the term "large tract" and are satisfied with a much smaller minimum size for parks in this category.

It is also generally recognized that development of physical facilities must proceed from a carefully prepared plan, and that development of an area must be completed before it is opened to the public. Most state park executives also feel that where fairly extensive public facilities (e.g., hotels, campgrounds, and related features) are required, such development should be confined to a relatively small section of the park so that the basic interests of its major portion may not be greatly altered.

Gifts of land are not accepted for park purposes unless such areas adhere to state park standards. Further, most state park organizations consider neither gifts nor purchases if the development of such lands for state park purposes necessitates excessive expenditures. Kansas, however, since it is not blessed with natural recreational areas to the same extent as other states, takes a more liberal view of any such gifts or purchases. In Kansas, where there is but one natural lake, considerable emphasis is laid on the development of facilities for water sports of various kinds.[27] Similar objectives prevail in Oklahoma and Iowa.[27]

A number of states prohibit the acquisition of lands within the corporate limits of municipalities for state park purposes.

Certain state park organizations, with the interpretive program of the National Park Service as a model, give considerable attention to the development of facilities and the provision of services designed to develop public understanding of significant state park interests. Outstanding in

[27] See Grant Sharpe, "A Survey of the State Parks of the United States . . . ," manuscript, March 17, 1953.

this respect is the state park system of California [2,21], which employs a number of year-round and seasonal interpretive personnel. The well-developed interpretive program carried out in certain Indiana state parks is conducted by seasonal employees.[28] In Washington a year-round employee, together with an advisory board of especially qualified individuals, guides the development of significant state park interests, with emphasis on historical features [2]. Naturalists are employed seasonally in certain Minnesota state parks through cooperation of the Division of State Parks, the State University, and the Natural History Museum.[28] To a more limited degree, interpretive activities are conducted on a seasonal basis in the state parks of Maine, Missouri, and North Carolina.[28] In Louisiana daily lectures are given at Longfellow-Evangeline State Park, while Pre-Historic State Park includes a museum.[28] Guided trips are conducted in Caverns State Park in Florida,[28] and a similar service is available in Lewis and Clark Cavern in Montana.[28] At Bear Mountain State Park in New York the American Museum of Natural History has cooperated in the development of several trailside museums which are leaders in their field.[29]

State park development in the South provides separate systems for white and Negro races. In 1955, however, a decision affirmed by the Supreme Court, with specific reference to Sandy Point State Park in Maryland, outlawed the principle of segregation in these areas.[30]

SUMMARY

Rapidly expanding interest in outdoor recreation has prompted the development of state park systems in forty-eight of the states. Although these systems are administered differently, state parks are generally dedicated to the basic principle of providing a wide variety of outdoor recreational activities in pleasant, attractive, and largely natural surroundings; they are also important in the preservation of significant state interests (e.g., geological, biological, archeological, historical). Thus, in the field of outdoor recreation, state parks occupy a place midway between the more remote and relatively unaltered Federal recreational lands (e.g., national parks and national forests) and the more artificially developed municipal and county parks. Their patronage, in excess of 200 million visits annually, indicates that they are among the most generally used public recreational areas in the United States.

[28] *Ibid.*

[29] See William H. Carr, Trailside Museums and Nature Trails in Parks, "1940 Yearbook: Park and Recreation Progress," U.S. Government Printing Office, Washington, 1940.

[30] *Dawson v. Mayor and City Council of Baltimore City,* 220 Fed. 386 (4th Cir. 1955), *aff'd per curiam,* 350 U.S. 877 (1955).

Per-visitor cost of operating state parks has remained fairly static in recent years. However, increases in attendance, which, barring some major economic or political catastrophe, give evidence of continuing, indicate higher over-all operating costs in the future. This trend also implies a need for increased personnel with greater emphasis upon various types of professional training.

SELECTED REFERENCES

1. Albrecht, George J., A. T. Wilcox, and J. V. K. Wagar: College Training for Park Administration and Planning, *Planning and Civic Comment,* Part II, vol. 18, no. 4, pp. 23–30, December, 1952.
2. Brockman, C. F., and Albert Culverwell: "Panel on Interpretive Programs in State Parks," American Planning and Civic Annual, American Planning and Civic Association and National Conference on State Parks, Washington, 1954, pp. 73–78.
3. California Department of Natural Resources, Division of Beaches and Parks: "California State Park System Five Year Master Plan: July 1, 1956 to June 30, 1961," Sacramento, Mar. 1, 1956.
4. California State Park Commission: California Announces State Park Criteria, *Planning and Civic Comment,* vol. 23, no. 1, pp. 50–51, March, 1957.
5. Carithers, J. F.: State Parks for Arizona, *National Parks Magazine,* vol. 31, no. 130, p. 120, July–September, 1957.
6. Colorado State Park and Recreation Board: "General Policy Statement," Denver, Jan. 16, 1958.
7. Cougill, K. R., and others: Suggested Criteria for Evaluating Areas Proposed for Inclusion in State Park Systems, *Planning and Civic Comment,* vol. 20, no. 4, pp. 51–57, December, 1954.
8. Coyle, David C.: "Conservation: An American Story of Conflict and Accomplishment," Rutgers University Press, New Brunswick, N.J., 1957.
9. Cox, Laurie D., and Philip H. Elwood: Academic Training for Park Planning, "1940 Yearbook, Park and Recreation Progress," U.S. National Park Service, Washington, 1940, pp. 67–70.
10. DeTurk, Charles A.: State Park Records and Financing, "1940 Yearbook, Park and Recreation Progress," U.S. National Park Service, Washington, 1940.
11. Elmer, Arthur C.: Michigan's Extensive Recreational Development, *Proceedings of the Society of American Foresters Meeting,* Minneapolis, Minn., Dec. 17–20, 1947, pp. 159–163, Washington, 1948.
12. Emerson, Ralph W.: Disposal of Surplus Federal Property for Parks and Recreation, "1949 Yearbook, Park and Recreation Progress," National Conference on State Parks, Washington, 1949.
13. Eppley, Garrett G.: In-service Education, "1949 Yearbook, Park and Recreation Progress," National Conference on State Parks, Washington, 1949, pp. 8–9.
14. Florida State Senate: "The Collins Bill," Senate Bill 441, 1949.
15. Great Lakes Park Training Institute: *Proceedings,* 1956: *Tenth Anniversary,* Indiana University, Department of Recreation, Bloomington, Ind., 1956.

16. Hibbard, B. H.: "A History of the Public Land Policies," The Macmillan Company, New York, 1939.
17. Huppuch, Matt C.: Administrative Organizations for State Park Systems, "1938 Yearbook, Park and Recreation Progress," U.S. National Park Service, Washington, 1939, pp. 48–50.
18. Illinois Department of Conservation, Division of Parks and Memorials: "Illinois State Parks and Memorials," Springfield, Ill., n.d.
19. Indiana Department of Conservation, Division of State Parks, Lands and Waters: "Description of Properties and Facilities," n.d. (Mimeographed.)
20. Ise, John: "The United States Forest Policy," Yale University Press, New Haven, Conn., 1920.
21. Jenkins, H. O.: "Report on the Interpretive Service of the State Parks of California," California Department of Natural Resources, Division of Beaches and Parks, Sacramento, Calif., November, 1952.
22. Kauffman, Erle (ed.): "The Conservation Yearbook, 1954," The Conservation Yearbook, Washington, 1954.
23. Kauffman, Erle (ed.): "The Conservation Yearbook, 1955–1956," Cornwell, Inc., Washington, 1956.
24. Maine State Park Commission: "Report of the State Park Commission," June, 1950.
25. Maine State Park Commission: "Preliminary Report on State Park and Related Recreational Planning," January, 1952.
26. McKeever, Kermit: Purpose of State Parks, *Journal of Forestry,* vol. 48, no. 10, p. 721, October, 1950.
27. National Conference on State Parks: Suggested Statements of State Park Policy: Wildlife Policy for State Parks, State Park Policy on Vegetation Management, and Suggested Park Management Standards and Practices in Historical and Archeological Areas, *Planning and Civic Comment,* vol. 22, no. 2, pp. 54–61, June, 1956.
28. Nebraska Legislative Council: "Report of the Nebraska Legislative Council Committee on the Development and Administration of State Parks in Nebraska," Committee Report 48, July, 1954. (Mimeographed.)
29. Nelson, Beatrice: "State Recreation," National Conference on State Parks, Washington, 1928.
30. New York Conservation Department, Division of Parks, State Council of Parks: "New York State Parks: Thirtieth Anniversary, 1924–1954," Albany, N.Y., n.d.
31. New York Conservation Department, Division of Parks, State Council of Parks: "Principles Governing the Establishment, Extension, and Development of the Park and Parkway System of New York State," Albany, N.Y., 1944.
32. North Dakota State Parks Committee: "State Parks and Historic Sites in North Dakota," State Historical Society, Bismarck, N. Dak., 1950.
33. Oregon Highway Department, State Division of Parks: Unique Set-up Puts State Parks under Highway Division, *Park Maintenance,* vol. 6, no. 11, pp. 5–7, November, 1953.
34. Schulz, W. F.: "Conservation Law and Administration: A Case Study of Land and Resource Use in Pennsylvania," The Ronald Press Company, New York, 1953.
35. Tennessee State Planning Commission and Department of Conservation,

Division of State Parks: "State Parks: A Proposed Plan for Tennessee," no. 243, November, 1952.

36. U.S. Department of the Interior, National Park Service: "A Study of the Park and Recreation Problem of the United States," Washington, 1941.
37. U.S. Department of the Interior, National Park Service, Division of Recreation Resources Planning: "State Park Statistics, 1957," Washington, June, 1958.
38. Vanderwell, E. J.: "Historical Background of the Wisconsin State Park System," Wisconsin Conservation Department, Madison, Wis., Feb. 10, 1953.
39. Vanderzicht, John: Forest Recreation on the State Level, *Proceedings of the Society of American Foresters Meeting,* Portland, Ore., Oct. 16–21, 1955, pp. 99–102, Washington, 1956.
40. Vermont State Board of Forests and Forest Parks: "Biennial Report, 1951–1952," Vermont Forest Service, Montpelier, Vt., n.d.
41. Virginia Department of Conservation and Development, Division of Parks: "Virginia State Parks," n.p., n.d.
42. Wagner, H. S.: What May Be Considered Adequate State Park Standards? *Landscape Architecture,* vol. 22, no. 1, pp. 1–6, 1931.
43. Whitnall, C. B.: Relationship of Municipal, County, and State Recreational Systems, "1940 Yearbook, Park and Recreation Progress," U.S. National Park Service, Washington, 1940, pp. 32–38.
44. Williams, G. W.: Wise Laws Gave Impetus to Illinois Park System, *Illinois Public Works,* vol. 4, no. 2, pp. 18–19, Summer, 1946.
45. Wisconsin Conservation Department: "Among the Wisconsin State Parks and Forests," no. 400–54, Madison, Wis., n.d.

CHAPTER 5 *Outdoor Recreation in National Park Service Areas*

The National Park Service, a bureau in the U.S. Department of the Interior, is charged with the administration of the national parks and related areas by authority of the act establishing the National Park Service. This act, passed by Congress and signed by President Woodrow Wilson on August 25, 1916 [27,31,41], was designed to unify the administration of the national parks and national monuments then under the jurisdiction of the Department of the Interior. It stated that [31]:

> The service thus established shall promote and regulate the use of the Federal areas known as national parks, monuments, and reservations hereinafter specified by such means and measures as conform to the fundamental purpose of said parks, monuments, and reservations, which purpose is to conserve the scenery and the natural and historic objects and the wild life therein and to provide for the enjoyment of the same in such manner and by such means as will leave them unimpaired for the enjoyment of future generations.

EXTENT OF THE NATIONAL PARK SYSTEM

The National Park System includes more than 175 areas with a total of approximately 23 million acres (see Table 5-1). National parks, although best known and having the greatest aggregate acreage, are but one of several categories in this system.

In addition, by virtue of interbureau agreements, the National Park Service also has the responsibility for recreational development and use of several large reclamation projects of national interest, known as national recreation areas.[1]

[1] These include Franklin D. Roosevelt Lake in the state of Washington, formed by Grand Coulee Dam, Lake Mead on the Arizona-Nevada border, formed by Hoover Dam, and Shadow Mountain Lake and Lake Granby, adjacent to Rocky Mountain National Park, Colorado. These projects were developed by the Bureau of Reclamation [41].

Table 5-1. Summary of Areas of the National Park System, December 31, 1957

Type of area	No.	Federal land, acres	Non-Federal lands within exterior boundaries, acres	Total lands within exterior boundaries, acres
National parks	29	13,136,239.13	416,493.11	13,552,732.24
National historical parks	8	31,968.32	5,455.60	37,423.92
National monuments	83	8,974,660.89	160,219.59	9,134,880.48
National military parks	11	24,450.04	2,329.24	26,779.28
National memorial park	1	68,679.72	1,694.58	70,374.30
National battlefield parks	3	5,516.25	2,177.84	7,694.09
National battlefield sites	5	188.63	547.35	735.98
National historic sites	10	1,354.07	2.12	1,356.19
National memorials	12	4,428.90	58.13	4,487.03
National cemeteries	10	215.10	5.00	220.10
National seashore recreational area	1	24,705.23	3,794.77	28,500.00
National parkways	3	85,558.59	27,256.85	112,815.44
National Capital Parks, includes 792 units	1	38,518.31	1,446.30	39,964.61
Total	177	22,396,483.18	621,480.48	23,017,963.66

SOURCE: "Areas Administered by the National Park Service, December 31, 1957," U.S. National Park Service, Washington, 1958.

LEGAL STATUS OF AREAS IN THE NATIONAL PARK SYSTEM

The great diversity of types of areas in the National Park System, coupled with the nature of various titles applied to these lands, occasionally leads to some confusion as to the relationship of various categories involved. Differences in title do not imply a degree of relative importance, significance, or size. Each unit in the National Park System has specific interests which are generally most typical of that area; each is nationally important in its own right, and size is irrelevant. For instance, certain national monuments are much larger than a number of national parks.

All areas of the National Park System are administered in accordance with the same basic principles, as stated in the National Park Act of 1916. Differences between these areas relate primarily to the method of their establishment; in short, their legal status. The following paragraphs are indicative of the basic differences between the principal categories.

1. *National parks* are established only by specific act of Congress; likewise enlargement or reduction of national parks is possible only by act of Congress.

Fig. 5-1. Old Faithful Geyser, one of several thousand evidences of hydrothermal activity in Yellowstone National Park. (*Photo by George A. Grant, National Park Service*)

2. *National monuments.* Most areas in this category have been established by Presidential proclamation, by authority of the Act for the Preservation of American Antiquities which became law on June 8, 1906. The Antiquities act authorized the President to set aside, as national monuments, lands owned or controlled by the United States which contained historic landmarks, historic or prehistoric structures, and other objects of historic or scientific interest. Similarly, national monuments may be

enlarged or reduced in size by Presidential proclamation, though only Congress can abolish them. A number of national monuments, however, have been established through direct action by Congress.

3. *National military parks, national battlefield parks and sites, national memorials and cemeteries, many national monuments, and the national capital parks* were originally administered by a variety of government agencies. On June 10, 1933, these areas were consolidated under National Park Service administration by President Franklin D. Roosevelt, by authority of the Reorganization act, which became law earler in the same year.

4. *National historic sites.* The Historic Sites Act of August 21, 1935, provided for the establishment of national historic sites to be protected and preserved for public inspiration and enjoyment.

Specific legislation has also provided for the acquisition, development, and administration by the National Park Service of such areas as national parkways and the national seashore recreational area. In addition, the act of June 23, 1936, authorized the National Park Service to conduct studies of park, parkway, and recreational area programs, and the Surplus Property Act of 1944, as amended, authorized the National Park Service to cooperate with the General Services Administration in investigating surplus properties for public park and recreation purposes.

SUMMARY OF VARIED SIGNIFICANT INTERESTS OF THE NATIONAL PARK SYSTEM

Although there are differences in their legal status and their principal features of interest, various areas of the National Park System possess a common characteristic; each is nationally unique and significant, either from a geological, biological, archeological, or historical viewpoint. For instance, the historical events that occurred at Gettysburg National Military Park are as significant to Americans as are the geological and biological wonders of Yellowstone, Sequoia, and Grand Canyon National Parks, or the evidences of early man in the United States, as noted in Mesa Verde National Park and other archeological sites. This ability of National Park Service areas to portray in dramatic, inspirational fashion some significant chapter in the story of our country serves as the matrix which unifies them under the same administration and qualifies them for a similar type of management.

Because of their unique significance, public use of areas in the National Park System must necessarily be guided by criteria that are quite different from the managerial objectives of lands which most logically can be made to serve our material needs. Most people realize that commercial exploitation of timber, minerals, hydroelectric power potentials, and the like cannot be condoned in National Park Service areas. It is not as generally recognized, however, that development of recreational facilities, or the encouragement of recreational activities, that are at variance with national park objectives is equally damaging and undesirable on National Park Service lands.

The National Park System embodies a national resource of tremendous value and importance; it represents a resource of culture and knowledge which will retain its value only so long as we protect and utilize it properly. The principal value of a visit to areas in the National Park System is derived from an understanding of the great truths of natural and human history which they portray, and which not only bear upon the nature of our own existence but will continue to exert an influence on the lives of future generations. Such a visit is a cultural experience, one in which elements of compulsion typical of general processes of learning are lacking. Instead, we are challenged to fathom the apparent mysteries about us; irrespective of our experience and background, we must seek, with whatever tools we possess, our own means of answering the questions that present themselves in these superlative settings. Finding the answers to these questions on that basis is a test of one's initiative and ability; from that process one derives tremendous satisfaction and enjoyment, which most adequately justifies the effort involved and makes a visit to one of these areas most rewarding.

Much has been written about the national parks and their companion areas. Numerous superbly illustrated books present an adequate outline of the basic interests found in various segments of the National Park System; a host of technical papers and pamphlets which deal with specific areas or fields of interest sketch in the details of the national park story. Some of these publications are noted in the bibliography. Any attempt to duplicate such efforts in these pages, even if it were physically possible would be unnecessary. But in the interest of completeness, and because the national park story is sufficiently commanding to warrant constant repetition, a brief summary of the values contained in these areas follows.

Some Geological Interests of the National Park System. Yellowstone National Park, with about 3,000 geysers and hot springs [41], is preeminent in the world as a region of hydrothermal activity. It was primarily because of these phenomena that this area was established as our first national park in 1872. Only two other areas, one in Iceland and the other in New Zealand, can remotely compare with Yellowstone in its principal characteristic [27,30,43].

Mount Rainier, rising 14,410 feet[2] above sea level and with a base that

[2] The height of Mount Rainier was redetermined to be 14,410 feet on Aug. 8, 1956, by the U.S. Geological Survey; previous to that date its elevation was considered to be 14,408 feet.

covers approximately 100 square miles of territory, is our greatest volcanic cone. It was formed by successive flows of lava and outbursts of volcanic ash and, although never in active eruption within the record of modern man, is one link in a chain of volcanic mountains that rims the Pacific [25]. Several other areas of the National Park System are also links in this series of Pacific volcanoes—Lassen Peak in Lassen Volcanic National Park and Lava Beds National Monument in California, Mauna Loa and Kilauea in Hawaii National Park in the Hawaiian Islands, and

FIG. 5-2. Crater Lake, principal feature of Crater Lake National Park, Oregon, occupies the caldera of a prehistoric volcano. (*Photo by George A. Grant, National Park Service*)

Crater Lake in Crater Lake National Park in Oregon. Eruptions of Mauna Loa and Kilauea are not infrequent [7,17,30]. The rugged terrain of Lava Beds National Monument, pitted with cinder cones, small craters, and fumeroles, and scored with deep, tortuous lava trenches, attests to the tempestuous past of this area [7,39]. Lassen Peak is unique in being the only recently active volcano in the United States [7,27,30,44]. The spectacular blue waters of Crater Lake are found in the *caldera* of a former volcanic cone, thought to have been more than 12,000 feet high; christened Mount Mazama, it decapitated itself in a great eruption during prehistoric time [7,27,30,45].

In sharp contrast to such volcanic areas are the rugged peaks of Glacier National Park, Montana. These mountains, as indicated by their layered appearance, are of sedimentary origin. Ages ago the numerous layers of sandstone, slate, and shale which compose them were sand, mud, and limy ooze on the floor of an ancient sea; later these sediments were folded, lifted, and changed to their present character by powerful forces accompanying the shrinkage of the earth's crust. In fact, so great were these pressures that these sedimentary layers were torn asunder and one section was pushed northeastward 15 to 18 miles over the adjoining portion [7,10,27,30]. As a result one may observe older rocks overlying more recent geological strata, a feature that is world famous to geologists as the Lewis Overthrust [7,10,27,30].

Equally interesting are the peaks of the central Rockies along the Continental Divide in Rocky Mountain National Park, and in the Sierra Nevada of California, as seen in Yosemite, Sequoia, and Kings Canyon National Parks. The mountains in these areas are composed largely of granite, rocks formed from once-molten lava which cooled and solidified very slowly beneath a former surface which originally was at least one mile thick and which has since been largely destroyed by erosion. The granite peaks of Rocky Mountain National Park originally formed a portion of the core of a great dome of overlying sedimentary materials, uplifted by pressure from the sides. Remnants of these overlying sedimentary strata may be observed in the foothills as one approaches Rocky Mountain National Park [16]. By contrast the Sierra Nevada is composed of a great granite block, approximately 800 miles long, which was tilted bodily to the west. The precipitous eastern escarpment of this great range, together with its gradual westward slope, attests to the nature of this upheaval [19,30].

In each of these specific examples the constructive forces which built these mountains were counteracted by destructive forces of erosion, such as running water, glacial ice, freezing and thawing, and the like which, over long periods of time, fashioned these areas into their present configuration.

As successive eruptions built Mount Rainer's cone to greater heights, the moisture-laden winds from the Pacific, forced into cooler upper-air strata in passing over the Cascades, deposited great quantities of snow upon its flanks. This snow eventually compacted into ice and began moving slowly downward as glaciers [18,25,27]. In various ways glacial ice modified the appearance of Mount Rainier, forming large natural amphitheaters known as cirques, giving rise to a myriad of small but beautiful lakes known as tarns, developing numerous broad U-shaped valleys, and depositing masses of rock debris known as moraines. The numerous glaciers found on Mount Rainier today are remnants of Rainier's greater ice fields of the past [18,25]. Many of these glaciers still persist in downward movement; one finds many evidences of this, both past and present, in Mount Rainier National Park. The surface of "living" glaciers is scored by many deep crevasses, many exposed rock surfaces are highly polished and striated, and in summer streams emerging from the glaciers are milky in color because of their burden of finely pulverized rock known as "glacial flour" [25].

FIG. 5-3. Layers of sandstone, slate, and shale composing the mountains of Glacier National Park, Montana, were once layers of sand, mud, and limey ooze on the floor of an ancient sea; in addition, broad U-shaped valleys and numerous lakes—including Upper St. Mary Lake, pictured here—are evidence of past glacial erosion. (*National Park Service*)

Although lacking the extensive glacial system of Mount Rainier, the scenery of Glacier National Park, with its many-faceted peaks, broad U-shaped valleys, and spectacular lakes, is the result of erosive action of former glaciers on relatively soft sedimentary rocks [7,10,30]. One finds small remnants of that region's once extensive glacier system nestled at the base of great cirques at high altitudes [10,27].

Similarly, the effects of past glacial erosion in granite, a much harder material than either the sedimentary rocks of Glacier or the extrusive volcanic material of Rainier, may be noted in Rocky Mountain National Park [7,16,27]. Its scenery is replete with broad U-shaped valleys, glacial tarns, morainal deposits, and precipitous cliffs flanking glacial-carved cirques.

Perhaps the best known and most significant example of the erosive power of stream and ice action in granite is to be found in Yosemite National Park. The world-famous Yosemite Valley, principal topographic feature of this area, is noted for its level floor, its near-vertical granite cliffs over one-half mile high, numerous waterfalls of great beauty, and such oddly shaped landmarks as Half Dome. These and related topographical characteristics are indelibly linked with the westward tilting of the Sierra block and the resultant acceleration in speed and erosive power of the prehistoric Merced River, as well as later erosion by glaciers which widened and deepened the previously formed V-shaped river-cut canyon to its present configuration [19]. The nature of erosion in the Yosemite granite was determined by the manner in which this material fractured as it slowly cooled and solidified, long before it was exposed by removal through erosion of the original overlying material [19]. Since the fractures in the Yosemite Valley region were largely vertical, many of Yosemite's cliffs, including the northern face of Half Dome, monumental El Capitan, and the cliff over which upper Yosemite Falls pours, are similarly formed. Where the fractures were horizontal or diagonal, greater resistance to erosion prompted the formation of ledges of various widths and sizes. Such differences in the fracture pattern are responsible for the "step" between the upper and lower Yosemite Falls[3] and the angled appearance of the Three Brothers. A number of trails by which one may climb from the valley floor to the rim also follow diagonal fracture patterns in the granite. The level floor of Yosemite Valley resulted from the filling of a lake which occupied the valley following the retreat of the glacier; sand, silt, and similar river-borne materials were carried into this lake by the Merced River and other streams [19].

That portion of the Grand Canyon of the Colorado River in Grand Canyon National Park, Arizona, which many regard as one of the world's most stupendous natural spectacles, presents still another significant example of the erosive power of running water. This great gorge, 217 miles long, 4 to 18 miles wide, and approximately 1 mile deep, was cut by the Colorado River as the vast plateau upon which it is located was slowly elevated above the surface of an ancient sea [27,30]. Numerous layers of differently colored sedimentary rocks, once beds of mud, silt, or sand on a prehistoric ocean floor, reacted differently to the forces of erosion, accounting for the irregular pattern of numerous buttes, pinnacles, towers, and shelves which comprise the chaotic scene as viewed from vantage points on the rim. Some idea of the erosive power of the

[3] Yosemite Falls, 2,565 feet high, consists of an upper fall of 1,430 feet, a lower fall of 320 feet, and an intermediate cascade of 815 feet [19].

Colorado River can be obtained from the fact that it carries past any given point an average of nearly 1 million tons of sand and silt every twenty-four hours [40]!

But the story of the Grand Canyon has other equally interesting facets.

FIG. 5-4. The appearance of Yosemite Falls, Yosemite National Park, was determined by the fracture pattern in the granite and its effect upon the nature of erosion by stream and ice action. (*National Park Service*)

We may also learn something of the nature of plants and animals that existed there in past ages [7,30,40]. Along several trails by which one descends from the rim to the Colorado River one may observe fossilized remains of plants and see footprints of a prehistoric lizardlike animal, originally made in the sand along an ancient seashore, preserved in stone.

Colorful Zion Canyon of Zion National Park in southern Utah is also unique as an example of water erosion on sedimentary rocks, though the rocks of Zion National Park are of more recent geological origin than the strata which comprise the Grand Canyon [7,30]. Also in the same general vicinity is Bryce Canyon National Park, noteworthy for its multitude of fantastically eroded pinnacles, spires, and minarets in a variety of colors.

FIG. 5-5. This view of the Grand Canyon of the Colorado River, Grand Canyon National Park, Arizona, portrays one of the world's most spectacular examples of stream erosion in sedimentary rock. (*National Park Service*)

These features resulted from the disintegration of still more recently formed sedimentary rocks by running water, rain, frost, wind, and chemical agencies [7,27,30]. In the formations of Grand Canyon, Zion, and Bryce Canyon National Parks one may read the story of the geological past encompassing a period of one billion years [38].

Erosion by underground water on limestone was responsible for the formation of Carlsbad Caverns National Park, New Mexico, and Mammoth Cave National Park, Kentucky [7,27,30,41]. Fantastically beautiful stalactites and stalagmites found in these huge caverns are the result of later deposits of limestone on the ceiling and floor by percolating water.

Some Biological Interests of the National Park System. Equally significant are the varied biological interests contained in the National Park System. Best known of these are the forests of giant sequoia (*Sequoia gigantea*) found in Sequoia National Park, California.[4] The age of many of these arboreal giants, popularly regarded as the largest living things, is estimated at between 3,000 and 4,000 years [27,41], thus the largest and oldest of individual specimens date from the days of the Egyptian

FIG. 5-6. Erosion by rain, running water, frost, wind, and chemical agencies formed the fantastic pinnacles in the colorful sedimentary rocks of Bryce Canyon National Park, Utah. (*National Park Service*)

Pharaohs. Regarded as the greatest of these magnificent botanical specimens is the General Sherman tree which measures 101.6 feet in circumference at the base, has an average basal diameter of 36.5 feet, and is 272.4 feet tall [27]. Its first limb, 130 feet above the ground, is 6.8 feet in diameter, a sizable tree in its own right.

As attested to by numerous fossilized specimens found in various parts of the globe, many species of sequoia were once widely distributed throughout various sections of the world [24]. Today only two species

[4] Groves of giant sequoia are also noteworthy features of interest in Yosemite and Kings Canyon National Parks.

exist—the giant sequoia (*Sequoia gigantea*), found only in a series of groves on the western slope of the Sierra Nevada, and the coast redwood (*Sequoia sempervirens*), native only to the coast of northern California and extreme southwestern Oregon [24]. Within the National Park System the latter species is found in Muir Woods National Monument, just north of San Francisco [7,30,41].

FIG. 5-7. Mammoth Cave, Mammoth Cave National Park, Kentucky, is one of several National Park Service areas which are unique as examples of underground water erosion in limestone. (*National Park Concessions, Inc., photo by W. Ray Scott, National Park Service*)

Also of unique interest are the "rain forests" found at low elevations in a series of deep mountain valleys on the west side of Olympic National Park in the state of Washington. Here, where the annual precipitation is in excess of 140 inches per year [7,27,30,41], is an extraordinary plant association featured by huge evergreen trees, many of which are over 10 feet in diameter and more than 200 feet in height, and a vast array of other plants; of particular interest are many species of mosses which thickly clothe the trunks of fallen forest monarchs and festoon the branches of living trees [7,27,30,41]. These "rain forests," ethereal in their sombre, peaceful grandeur, offer an opportunity to observe and study a forest association found nowhere else in the country and provide as well an insight into the character of Pacific Northwest coast vegetation before the coming of civilized man to the region.

Similarly, the complex plant cover typical of Great Smoky Mountains National Park on the Tennessee–North Carolina border preserves a segment of the fabulously diverse vegetation of the southern Appalachian region [7,27,30], and Everglades National Park, Florida, embraces a subtropical area [7,30,41].

Many other units of the National Park System offer unique botanical interests. Included are the bizarre Joshua trees (*Yucca brevifolia*) in Joshua Tree National Monument in Southern California and a variety of unique desert plants, featuring the organ pipe and saguaro cacti, in Organ Pipe Cactus and Saguaro National Monuments, Arizona [7,30,41].

FIG. 5-8. General Sherman Tree, largest living thing, Sequoia National Park, California. (*Photo by Alcorn, National Park Service*)

The National Park System also provides a habitat for a wide variety of native animals. Yellowstone National Park, most famous of these wildlife sanctuaries, is well known for its bison, bighorn sheep, elk, moose, pronghorn antelope, grizzly and American black bear, many kinds of waterfowl, and numerous other less spectacular mammals and birds [7,27]. Carlsbad Caverns National Park has its fabulous bat cave; the regular evening flight of countless bats is a never-to-be-forgotten spectacle [7,27,30]. In Everglades National Park one finds a wide variety of birds including heron, egret, pelican, and pink roseatte spoonbill; also found here is the rare but interesting aquatic mammal known as the manatee or "sea cow" and such spectacular reptiles as the alligator and crocodile [7,30]. Mount McKinley National Park, Alaska, in addition to having the highest mountain in North America, is noted for its wildlife population, with emphasis on caribou, Dall sheep, moose, grizzly bear, and wolf [7,27,30,41]. Glacier National Park, although its animal interests are not limited to that species, is most famous for its numbers of mountain goat [7,30]. One also finds numerous bands of mountain goat in Mount Rainier National Park, but one of the most interesting animals of that region is the ptarmigan, an arctic grouse which

FIG. 5-9. Cliff Palace, Mesa Verde National Park, Colorado, is a significant reminder of the way of life of some of the early inhabitants of the American Southwest. (*Photo by Leland J. Abel, National Park Service*)

changes the color of its plumage with the season [29]. Grand Teton National Park and the adjacent Jackson Hole country have the largest herd of elk in the country [41]. Large bands of elk may also be observed in both Olympic [41] and Rocky Mountain National Parks [30]; in the latter area one may also find mountain sheep; and Isle Royal National Park, Michigan, is noteworthy for its great moose herd [7,41].

The foregoing are but a few examples; in most of the national parks and monuments animals form one of the principal attractions.

The great variety of plant and animal species typical of many National Park Service areas is due largely to the great differences in elevation within their borders. Changes in altitude are responsible for differences in climate which in turn sponsor "life zones," each supporting typical associations of plants and animals. For instance, Grand Canyon National Park includes four life zones ranging in climatic types, and consequently plant and animal forms, typical of latitudes ranging from Mexico to northern Canada [30], and Yosemite, Sequoia, and Kings Canyon National Parks, each with five life zones, embrace climates typical of areas from northern Mexico to the Arctic [26]. Similar striking climatic differences with altitude are found in numerous other national parks.

Some Archeological Interests of the National Park System. Among the units of the National Park System famous for their significant archeological interests are the cliff dwellings and mesa-top pueblos in the Southwest. The most noteworthy of these are included in Mesa Verde National Park, Colorado; Canyon de Chelly, Casa Grande, Montezuma Castle, Navajo, Wuputki, and Tonto National Monuments in Arizona; and Aztec Ruins, Bandelier, and Chaco Canyon National Monuments in New Mexico [7,8,30,41]. In addition, the Effigy Mounds National Monument in Iowa [8,36,41] and the unique remains of prehistoric towns in Ocmulgee National Monument, Georgia [8,36,41], give us additional glimpses of peoples who occupied various parts of our land in bygone years.

Some Historical Interests of the National Park System. The National Park System also preserves areas which are linked with significant events throughout the entire range of the history of our country. The colonial period is featured in certain early Spanish forts and missions in Florida, Puerto Rico, Arizona, and New Mexico, as well as at sites of early English settlements on the Atlantic seaboard. The site of the birthplace of the "father of our country" is preserved at George Washington Birthplace National Monument, Virginia [35], and Independence Hall in Philadelphia is also a part of the National Park System [35,41].

Important events of the American Revolution assume reality at such places as Fort McHenry National Monument, Maryland, Saratoga National Historical Park, New York, and King's Mountain National Military Park in South Carolina [35,36,41]. Chalmette National Historical Park commemorates the American victory at New Orleans in the War of 1812 [35,41]. Epic chapters in the War between the States come alive at such places as Fort Sumter National Monument in South Carolina, Manassas and Richmond National Battlefield Parks in Virginia, numerous national military parks, such as Fredericksburg in Virginia, Shiloh in Tennessee, and Gettysburg in Pennsylvania, and at Appomattox Courthouse National Historical Park in Virginia [35,36,41]. In addition, the soul-stirring story of American exploration and settlement of the West may be brought into sharp focus in such national monuments as Custer Battlefield in Montana, Pipe Spring in Arizona, Scotts Bluff in Nebraska, Fort Laramie in Wyoming, Whitman and Fort Vancouver in Washington, and Homestead in Nebraska [41].

FIG. 5-10. Gettysburg National Military Park, Pennsylvania, is one of many nationally significant historical areas under National Park Service administration. (*National Park Service*)

These and other historical areas of the National Park System serve to develop a better understanding of our American heritage, as well as greater pride in American hardihood, valor, and courage.

ORGANIZATION OF THE NATIONAL PARK SERVICE[5]

The National Park Service organization includes a headquarters staff in Washington, D.C., five regional offices, two branch offices of the Division of Design and Construction, and personnel in each of the various national parks, monuments, historic sites and related areas.

The principal administrative officer of the National Park Service is the Director, who is responsible to the Secretary of the Interior. Each of the five regional offices is in charge of a Regional Director who supervises National Park Service activities within a given region and reports to the Director of the National Park Service in Washington, D.C. Each of the national parks, monuments, historic sites, and related areas is administered by a Superintendent who reports to his Regional Director.

The headquarters staff in Washington, D.C., includes, in addition to the Director, the Associate Director, and two Assistant Directors, administrative and technical personnel concerned with varied broad aspects of National Park Service work and responsibility. The two Assistant

[5] Data relative to the organization of the National Park Service checked by Hillory A. Tolson, Assistant Director, National Park Service (personal correspondence of Feb. 7, 1958) and Preston P. Macy, Superintendent, Mount Rainier National Park (personal correspondence, Feb. 21, 1958).

Directors also serve as Division Chiefs. One is concerned primarily with administration and supervises the branches of Finance, Personnel, Property and Records Management, and Safety; the other deals primarily with operations and directs the work of the branches of Lands, Concessions Management, Maintenance, and Programs and Plans Control.

Also in the upper echelon of the headquarters organization are the Chiefs of four divisions. The Chief of the Division of Design and Construction supervises the work of the branches of Engineering, Landscape Architecture, and Architecture. Under the Chief of the Division of Interpretation are the branches of History, Information, Museums, and Natural History. The Chief of the Recreation Resource Planning Division has under him the branches of National Park System Planning, Recreation Surveys, and State Cooperation. The Chief of the most recently established division, that of Ranger Activities, supervises the branch of Park Forest and Wildlife Protection and the branch of Visitor Protection. At the same level with these are the Chief of the Mission 66 staff, who guides the ten-year conservation and development program for the National Park System, launched in 1956, and the Chief Auditor. An Assistant Solicitor, responsible for handling legal matters affecting the service of the National Park System, is a member of the staff of the Solicitor of the Department of the Interior but attends, or is represented at, meetings of the staff of the Director of the National Park Service.

Regional offices are somewhat similarly organized. The five Regional Directors represent the Director of the National Park Service in specific sections of the country and are responsible for proper administration of National Park Service affairs therein. Each Regional Director is aided by an Assistant Regional Director and a staff of administrative and professional employees concerned with specific National Park Service activities within the region.

Headquarters for Region I (Southeastern United States, Puerto Rico, and the Virgin Islands) are at Richmond, Virginia; for Region II (Northern Rocky Mountain and Great Plains area), Omaha, Nebraska; for Region III (Southern Rocky Mountain and the Southwest), Santa Fe, New Mexico; for Region IV (Pacific Coast states, Alaska, and Hawaii), San Francisco, California; for Region V (Lake states and Northeastern United States), Philadelphia, Pennsylvania.

The two branch offices of the Division of Design and Construction—one located at Philadelphia, Pennsylvania, and the other at San Francisco, California—are responsible to the Chief of the Division of Design and Construction in Washington, D.C.

Various national parks, monuments, historic sites, and related areas complete the National Park Service organization. In each case the Superintendent is responsible for all matters pertaining to proper management

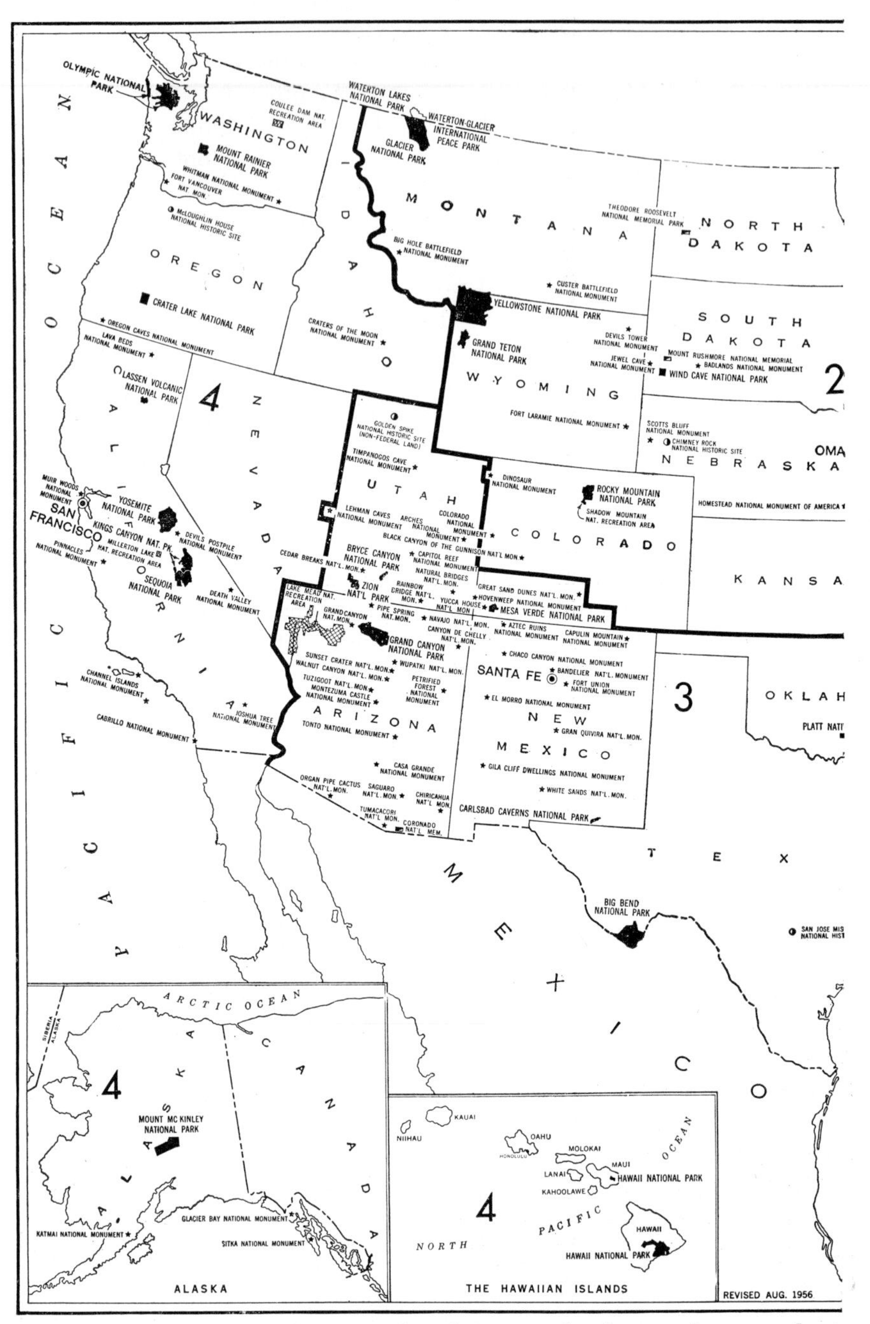

FIG 5-11. The National Park Service; distribution of areas under its

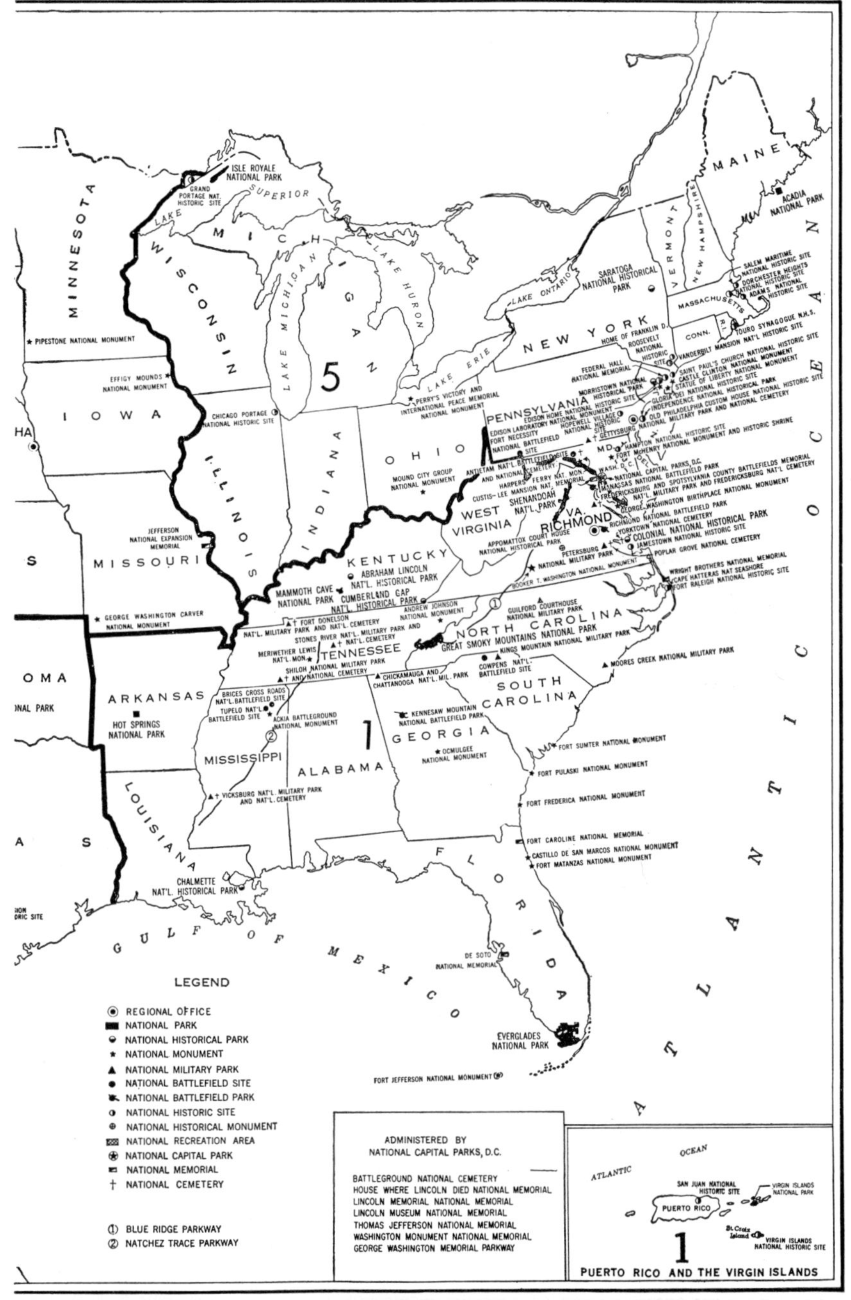

administration and its regional organization. (*National Park Service*)

and administration of his area, including general supervision of all planning and development therein. The size and complexity of the staff in each unit of the National Park System is dependent upon the character of the area. The more complex organizations are divided into several principal departments—protection under supervision of the Chief Park Ranger; fiscal, or varied business functions, in charge of the Administrative Officer (in large areas) or the Administrative Assistant (in small areas); research and interpretation supervised by the Park Naturalist; engineering and maintenance in charge of the Park Engineer. The organization of some areas also includes a sanitary department in charge of a Sanitary Engineer; in addition, many national parks also have a Park Landscape Architect who is advisory to the Superintendent in landscape matters.

ADMINISTRATIVE POLICY OF THE NATIONAL PARK SERVICE

The policy of the National Park Service was first defined approximately one and one-half years after its establishment in a letter, dated May 13, 1918, signed by Secretary of the Interior Lane and addressed to Director Stephen T. Mather. Preliminary to discussing details pertaining to national park operation, as well as to the establishment of additional national parks, the Secretary listed the following broad principles of national park management [9,36]:

> First, that the national parks must be maintained in absolutely unimpaired form for the use of future generations as well as those of our own time; second, that they are set apart for the use, observation, health, and pleasure of the people; and third, that the national interest must dictate all decisions affecting public or private enterprise in the parks.

An official statement of national park policy, prepared in conjunction with others interested in national park affairs, by Louis C. Crampton, special attorney for the Secretary of the Interior, was incorporated in the annual report of the Director of the National Park Service for the fiscal year ended June 30, 1932. It is the administrative formula upon which all later action has been based and reads as follows [33]:

> 1. A national park is an area maintained by the Federal Government and "dedicated and set apart for the benefit and enjoyment of the people." Such Federal maintenance should occur only where the preservation of the area in question is of national interest because of its outstanding value from a scenic, scientific, or historical point of view. Whether a certain area is to be so maintained by the Federal Government as a national park should not depend upon the financial capacity of the State within which it is located, or upon its nearness to centers of population which would insure a large attendance there-

from, or upon its remoteness from such centers which would insure its majority attendance from without its State. It should depend upon its own outstanding scenic, scientific, or historical quality and the resultant national interest in its preservation.

2. The national-park system should possess variety, accepting the supreme in each of the various types and subjects of scenic, scientific, and historical importance. The requisite national interest does not necessarily involve a universal interest, but should imply a wide-spread interest, appealing to many individuals, regardless of residence, because of its outstanding merit in its class.

3. The twin purposes of the establishment of such an area as a national park are its enjoyment and use by the present generation, with its preservation unspoiled for the future; to conserve the scenery, the natural and historic objects and the wildlife therein, by such means as will insure that their present use leaves them unimpaired. Proper administration will retain these areas in their natural condition, sparing them the vandalism of improvement. Exotic animal or plant life should not be introduced. There should be no capture of fish or game for purposes of merchandise or profit and no destruction of animals except such as are detrimental to use of the parks now and hereafter. Timber should never be considered from a commercial standpoint but may be cut when necessary in order to control the attacks of insects or diseases or otherwise conserve the scenery or the natural or historic objects, and dead or down timber may be removed for protection or improvement. Removal of antiquities or scientific specimens should be permitted only for reputable public museums or for universities, colleges, or other recognized scientific or educational institutions, and always under department supervision and careful restriction and never to an extent detrimental to the interest of the area or of the local museum.

4. Education is a major phase of the enjoyment and benefit to be derived by the people from these parks and an important service to individual development is that of inspiration. Containing the supreme in objects of scenic, historical, or scientific interest, the educational opportunities are preeminent, supplementing rather than duplicating those of schools and colleges, and are available to all. There should be no governmental attempt to dominate or to limit such education within definite lines. The effort should be to make available to each park visitor as fully and effectively as possible these opportunities, aiding each to truer interpretation and appreciation and to the working out of his own aspirations and desires, whether they be elementary or technical, casual or constant.

5. Recreation, in its broadest sense, includes much of education and inspiration. Even in its narrower sense, having a good time, it is a proper incidental use. In planning for recreational use of the parks, in this more restricted meaning, the development should be related to their inherent values and calculated to promote the beneficial use thereof by the people. It should not encourage exotic forms of amusement and should never permit that which conflicts with or weakens the enjoyment of these inherent values.

6. These areas are best administered by park-trained civilian authority.

7. Such administration must deal with important problems in forestry, road building and wild life conservation, which it must approach from the angles peculiar to its own responsibilities. It should define its objectives in harmony with the fundamental purposes of the parks. It should carry them into effect through its own personnel except when economy and efficiency can thereby best be served without sacrifice of such objectives, through cooperation with other bureaus of the Federal Government having to do with similar subjects. In forestry, it should consider scenic rather than commercial values and preservation rather than marketable products; in road building, the route, the type of construction and the treatment of related objects should all contribute to the fullest accomplishment of the intended use of the area; and, in wildlife conservation, the preservation of the primitive rather than the development of any artificial ideal should be sought.

8. National park administration should seek primarily the benefit and enjoyment of the people rather than financial gain and such enjoyment should be free to the people without vexatious admission charges and other fees.

9. Every effort is to be made to provide accommodations for all visitors, suitable to their respective tastes and pocketbooks. Safe travel is to be provided for over suitable roads and trails. Through proper sanitation the health of the individual and of the changing community is always to be protected.

10. Roads, buildings, and other structures necessary for park administration and for public use and comfort should intrude upon the landscape or conflict with it only to the absolute minimum.

11. The national parks are essentially non-commercial in character and no utilitarian activity should exist therein except as essential to the care and comfort of park visitors.

12. The welfare of the public and the best interests of park visitors will be conserved by protective permits for utilities created to serve them in transportation, lodging, food, and incidentals.

13. The national interest should be held supreme in the national-park areas and encroachments conflicting therewith for local or individual benefit should not be permitted.

14. Private ownership or lease of land within a national park constitutes an undesirable encroachment, setting up exclusive benefits for the individual as against the common enjoyment by all, and is contrary to the fundamental purposes of such parks.

15. National parks, established for the permanent preservation of areas and objects of national interest, are intended to exist forever. When, under the general circumstances such action is feasible, even though special considerations require the continuance of limited commercial activities or of limited encroachments for local or individual benefit, an area of national-park caliber should be accorded that status now, rather than to abandon it permanently to full commercial exploitation and probable destruction of its sources of national interest. Permanent objectives highly important may thus be accomplished and the compromises, undesired in principle but not greatly destructive in effect, may later be eliminated as occasion for their continuance passes.

16. In a small national park the national laws and regulations should be

enforced by a national tribunal. Therefore, exclusive jurisdiction of the Federal Government is important.

17. National monuments, under jurisdiction of the Department of the Interior, established to preserve historic landmarks, historic and prehistoric structures, and other objects of scientific or historical interest, do not relate primarily to scenery and differ in extent of interest and importance from national parks, but the principles herein set forth should, so far as applicable, govern them.

Since the foregoing policy was framed, acts of Congress and Executive orders have greatly expanded the duties and responsibilities of the National Park Service. Areas added, including those of the Reorganization Act of 1933 and the Historic Sites Act of 1935, were of a type that could be similarly administered. Thus, the foregoing policy indicates the basic procedure under which all National Park Service areas are administered.

As in any general statement, certain principles of National Park Service policy permit wide latitude in their interpretation. Application of these principles to detailed activities relating to the administration and management of National Park Service areas is dependent upon one's understanding of the concept of the national-park idea which fostered these tangible declarations of principle. Differences in points of view are responsible for different interpretations, not only by the general public but occasionally even by employees of the National Park Service. Such differences of opinion often lead to complications in the management, development, and use of these areas, complications which are often extremely difficult to resolve.

How, for instance, do National Park Service areas relate to the phrase in item 1, "for the benefit and enjoyment of the people"? Are there not many interests and activities which contribute to such laudable objectives which may not be appropriate in areas of the National Park System? Further, item 3 sets forth a dual principle, use of National Park Service areas by present generations coupled with unimpaired preservation of their values and interests for the future. Are not these two objectives at variance with one another? Can anything be used and at the same time preserved in a completely unimpaired state? An old adage states that one cannot eat his cake and have it too; in actual practice it is difficult, if not impossible, for even the best management procedures to refute the logic of that statement. This is attested to by abnormal wear and tear, due to overcrowded conditions, typical of many National Park Service areas. In large degree, at least, the Mission 66 program was inaugurated to alleviate overcrowded conditions in the national parks.

Further, what is a completely acceptable definition of the term "natural condition"? Does it refer to a static situation at some particular time or to the slow but inevitable changes that are constantly taking place in nature, and which may eventually modify the appearance of an area? If we accept the former definition, at what period is an area to be considered "natural"? Specifically, in the case of Yosemite National Park, should we relate that term to some former period in geological time when the valley was filled with glacial ice or when it was occupied by a large postglacial lake? And if such examples seem too facetious, can the term be applied to the period following the discovery of the valley by civilized man? It will require but a casual investigation to indicate that since that period the once extensive meadows of Yosemite Valley have been seriously encroached upon by the forest, thus greatly modifying many spectacular vistas. Should this change be accepted as a natural phenomenon or should these trees be cut to maintain the vistas?

If the word "natural" refers to the inevitable changes that take place, how far are we prepared to go in preserving conditions which sponsor such changes? Is not nature often destructive as well as constructive? Specifically, have not insects, lightning-caused fire, and similar influences often wrought havoc on the beauty of a forest? Have not landslides destroyed evidences of important geological events or interesting scenic features? Have not certain animal species suffered by competition with others, as well as through environmental changes? When viewed in that light, what determines the limits of management to the end of maintaining "natural conditions"? In particular, what is the relationship of potential destructive insect epidemics, fungus diseases, and fire—other than man-caused—to the management of National Park Service land?

True, item 3 provides for certain activities which may apply in some of these cases, yet while specifically stating that National Park Service areas should be "spared the vandalism of improvement," it provides for certain procedures that are intended to improve, with particular reference to removal of certain timber.[6] Obviously different meanings were read into the word "improvement" in each of these cases, but in such instances these meanings lack clarity. In reference to item 8 the charging of entrance fees has long been standard practice in many national parks. Can such entrance fees be classed as vexatious, or can they be reconciled as a logical means of distributing a portion of the management costs among those who have an opportunity to use these areas? Doubtless this statement did not mean to imply that all admission charges and other fees are vexatious but that, when necessary, such charges should be kept low enough to prevent their being considered vexations. It would, of

[6] See Anonymous, National Park Timber Policy, *The Living Wilderness*, vol. 21, no. 58, pp. 42–50, Fall and Winter, 1956–57; and Bruce M. Kilgore, More Salvage at Olympic, *National Parks Magazine*, vol. 31, no. 131, pp. 149–153, October–December, 1957.

course, be impossible to fulfill literally the requirement stated in the first sentence of item 9. The economics of park management alone would rule out the possibility of providing accommodations of such diverse type that any and all personal needs would be satisfied. In fact in many National Park Service areas overnight accommodations are undesirable, unnecessary, or impossible to supply; this is particularly true of some of the smaller historical sites. At any rate, the statement referred to is a rather broad generalization.

A detailed analysis of this kind is logically criticized as being pedantic, yet it is about apparently minor points such as these that many disagreements and administrative difficulties revolve.

It should be emphasized that these statements are not intended as a criticism of national park policy. On the contrary these statements have been made to show how difficult it is to set down rules and regulations of such complete clarity that they will relate to any situation that may arise at any time, in any section of the country, and in any type of National Park Service area. Such an analysis points up the basic need in national park administration and use—the development of a true understanding of the underlying concept of what a National Park Service area is and how these lands may contribute maximum value and service for the longest time to public recreational needs. Such understanding serves as a yardstick in the proper interpretation of the cold printed words of any statement of policy.

RELATIONSHIP OF NATIONAL PARK SERVICE AREAS TO OTHER OUTDOOR RECREATIONAL LANDS

As indicated in the foregoing policy statement, areas under the administration of the National Park Service have a specialized function in the field of outdoor recreation. Although the bill establishing Yellowstone National Park referred to that area as a "pleasuring ground," and in spite of the fact that the national parks were commonly called outdoor playgrounds during the days of the See America First boom, just after World War I, the basic concept upon which these areas were established and upon which they are administered differs considerably from that of an outdoor playground or resort. Basically, each area of the National Park System is an outdoor museum, although that definition does not rule out the possibility of fun and enjoyment in a visit to these areas. Administration of National Park Service areas in accordance with the outdoor-museum concept does, however, attempt to guide outdoor interests and activities into channels which are in keeping with the character of areas in the National Park System.

The term "outdoor museum," now widely recognized, was first voiced by Robert Sterling Yard of the National Parks Association. He made the following statement in an article published in the *Scientific Monthly* of April, 1923 [48].

> The primary use may be described sufficiently for present purposes by calling a national park a museum. Our national parks system is a national museum. Its purpose is to preserve forever, "for the use and enjoyment of the people," certain areas of extraordinary scenic magnificence in a condition of primitive nature. Its recreational value is also very great, but recreation is not distinctive of this system. Our national reservations are also recreational. Our national forest, set apart for scientific commercial utilization, is very highly recreational. The function which alone distinguishes the national parks system from the national forest is the museum function made possible only by the parks' complete conservation.

Earlier statements relative to the national parks, although they did not use the term "outdoor museum," were a reflection of that concept. In his "Diary of the Washburn Expedition to the Yellowstone and Firehole Rivers in the Year 1870," N. P. Langford states that [15]:

> . . . amid the canyon and the falls, the boiling springs and sulphur mountain, and, above all, the mud volcano and the geysers of the Yellowstone, your memory becomes filled and clogged with objects new in experience, wonderful in extent, and possessing unlimited grandeur and beauty. It is a new phase in the natural world; a fresh exhibition of the handiwork of the Great Architect; and, while you see and wonder, you seem to need an additional sense, fully to comprehend and believe.

The fiscal year ended June 30, 1916 marked the publication of the first annual report relative to the national parks, in which is the following statement [32]:

> Clearly they are not designated solely for the purpose of supplying recreation grounds. The fostering of recreation purely as such is more properly the function of the city, county, and State parks, and there should be a clear distinction between the character of such parks and national parks.

Thus, as outdoor museums, each area in the National Park System embodies features of such great significance and of such high national value that the greatest possible return from their use can be derived only through complete preservation and maximum public understanding of their significant characteristics. Like chapters in a book, various units of the National Park System portray, in dramatic, inspirational fashion, various segments of a complete story. The greatest and most lasting value of a visit to these areas is derived through understanding of their significant interests. The beauty of the waterfalls and the magnitude of the monumental granite cliffs typical of Yosemite Valley in Yosemite National Park are much more meaningful if one understands the reasons for their existence. Grand Canyon National Park is viewed in its true perspective when one knows something of the geological processes by which the great canyon of the Colorado River was formed. Mesa Verde National Park may be truly enjoyed if one views its numerous cliff dwellings from the perspective of the original inhabitants of that area. A knowledge of factors which contributed to the great age and size, even the very existence in modern times, of the huge giant sequoias adds zest to a visit to Sequoia National Park. The scenery, the plant and animal life, the remains of former civilizations found in these areas, or the events of history which transpired within their boundaries, are related to scientific and historical fact. So, to aid visitors in enjoying these areas by really *seeing* them, rather than merely looking at them, the National Park Service has developed a corps of trained naturalists and historians to interpret their significance in an accurate yet interesting and understandable fashion.

The outdoor-museum concept rules out commercial exploitation of the natural resources of National Park Service areas; it limits the development of facilities for public use to the minimum and makes mandatory the inclusion of an area of sufficient size to ensure the preservation of the features of significant interest.

As outdoor museums, areas of the National Park System are distinct from other types of outdoor recreational areas which, because of lesser significance, may be better adapted to multiple use of their natural resources or, if primarily recreational in character, permit a greater development of physical facilities and a greater variety of outdoor recreational activities. Because of this basic difference in philosophy of administration between areas of the National Park System and other recreational areas, standards for their establishment and administration are radically different. It follows that:

1. If an area is not of sufficient significance to warrant its preservation by the Federal government as an outdoor museum, it should not be in the National Park System, although it might conceivably be administered as a recreational area of a different type, or render recreational benefits in conjunction with other values.

2. Boundaries of areas of national significance considered for inclusion in the National Park System should be drawn so that their significant features may be properly protected, and so that they may provide a satisfactory year-round habitat for native wildlife.

3. If in determining the boundary of an area in the National Park System there are to be included, along with areas of significance, certain lands which do not possess such significance, their inclusion is justified only when they are necessary for proper administration and protection of the significant values.

MISSION 66

The term "Mission 66" was coined by the National Park Service in an effort to dramatize the acute need for rehabilitation and remodernization of varied physical facilities in various areas in its charge, as well as the need for development of adequate personnel, in keeping with the greatness of these significant American treasures. This program, initiated in 1956, was synchronized with a ten-year period scheduled to end in 1966, the fiftieth anniversary of the establishment of the National Park Service [36].

Rapidly growing public interest in outdoor recreation in response to increased leisure time, advanced technology and greater productive power, improved transportation, and the like has been reflected in greatly increased public use of all lands having recreational values. Although the problem is not limited to them by any means, it is particularly acute in areas administered by the National Park Service because of the fragile quality of their unique features. The difficulties involved in maintaining proper public use and adequate supervision of visitor movement, activities, health, and safety, not to mention that of employees who must of necessity reside in these areas, are problems that demand solutions if the national parks and related areas are to continue to provide the recreational services and values which render them of greatest importance.

It has been repeatedly stated in these pages that National Park Service areas are much more than outdoor playgrounds; the quality of their varied unique interests demands extreme care in various aspects of their management if the largest number of people are to share in those interests today, and if such interests are to be preserved for continued use and enjoyment by future generations. The outdoor-playground function is logically a prerequisite for other types of recreational lands which lack the significance and unique qualities typical of areas under National Park Service administration.

A glance at the tabulation of public use of the National Park System (Tables 5-2 and 5-3) will indicate that patronage of these areas has been characterized by a rapid upward trend. Within each decade it has more than doubled. This tremendous pressure is greater than the ability of these areas to withstand without serious damage. Such overcrowding not only increases the likelihood of vandalism, but when such unique areas cannot accommodate the large crowds that are attracted to them, the simple presence of great numbers causes excessive wear and tear that often cannot be repaired. Our present National Park System was designed and organized to accommodate a public patronage typical of that of about 1941 when they were visited by slightly more than 21 million people [36]. There were many manifestations of overuse in specific cases even under such conditions. In recent years, however, the total number of annual visits has increased to about 60 million. It is predicted that this number will increase to approximately 80 million by 1966 [36].

The simple fact is that the National Park System cannot withstand such heavy use. Visitors have often been understandably disturbed and disgruntled at the many difficulties and frustrations of what was expected to be a pleasant and rewarding experience. Difficulties resulting

Table 5-2. Summary of Total Annual Use of Areas Administered by the National Park Service

Year	Number	Year	Number	Year	Number	Year	Number
1904	120,690	1918	454,841	1932	3,754,596	1945	11,713,852
1905	140,954	1919	811,516	1933	3,481,590	1946	21,752,315
1906	30,569	1920	1,058,455	1934	6,337,206	1947	25,534,188
1907	61,335	1921	1,171,797	1935	7,676,490	1948	29,858,828
1908	69,018	1922	2,216,497	1936	11,989,793	1949	31,736,402
1909	86,089	1923	1,493,712	1937	15,133,432	1950	33,252,589
1910	198,606	1924	1,670,908	1938	16,331,467	1951	37,106,440
1911	224,407	1925	2,054,562	1939	15,530,636	1952	42,299,836
1912	229,534	1926	2,314,995	1940	16,755,251	1953	46,224,794
1913	252,153	1927	2,797,840	1941	21,236,947	1954	47,833,913
1914	240,193	1928	3,024,544	1942	9,370,969	1955	50,007,838
1915	335,299	1929	3,248,264	1943	6,828,420	1956	54,923,443
1916	258,006	1930	3,246,656	1944	8,339,775	1957	59,284,969
1917	490,705	1931	3,544,938				

SOURCE: Data for years 1904–1940, inclusive (based on "travel year" of Oct. 1–Sept. 30), derived from personal communication, Oct. 5, 1954, from National Park Service, Washington. Data for years 1941–1953 inclusive (based on calendar year), from "Public Use Tabulations of Visitors to Areas Administered by the National Park Service, 1941–1953," U.S. Department of the Interior, Washington, February, 1954. Data for years 1954–1957 inclusive (based on calendar year), from "Public Use Tabulations of Visitors to Areas Administered by the National Park Service," U.S. Department of the Interior, Washington, December, 1954, December, 1955, December, 1956, and December, 1957.

from heavy use of National Park Service areas have been further complicated by the fact that World War II necessarily froze all funds except those required for national survival, and the situation was not appreciably eased in the following years due to the Korean conflict and the unsettled nature of world affairs. Thus, in spite of rapidly mounting public use of national parks and related areas, sufficient public funds for development and maintenance were not available to keep abreast of the need. Even private concerns which operate under contract with the Federal government in the provision of hotel and meal service and related needs found it impossible to bring their facilities and services up to desired standards.

Table 5-3. Summary: Total Use of Various Types of Areas Administered by the National Park Service

Year	National parks	National monuments	National historical areas	National parkways	National recreation areas	National memorial park
1904	120,609					
1905	140,954					
1906	30,569					
1907	61,335					
1908	69,018					
1909	86,089					
1910	198,606					
1911	223,957	450				
1912	229,084	450				
1913	251,703	450				
1914	239,693	500				
1915	334,799	500				
1916	356,097	1,909				
1917	488,268	2,437				
1918	451,691	3,150				
1919	757,139	54,377				
1920	919,504	138,951				
1921	1,007,336	164,461				
1922	1,044,509	171,988				
1923	1,280,886	212,826				
1924	1,423,633	247,275				
1925	1,762,306	292,256				
1926	1,941,859	373,136				
1927	2,381,079	416,761				
1928	2,568,523	456,021				
1929	2,757,419	490,845				
1930	2,774,561	472,095				
1931	3,152,845	392,093				
1932	2,948,507	406,089	400,000			
1933	2,867,474	522,698	91,418			
1934	3,516,720	1,386,115	1,434,371			
1935	4,056,362	1,332,221	2,287,907			
1936	5,790,506	1,681,062	4,218,225			
1937	6,705,324	1,966,125	6,072,689	....	289,294	
1938	6,619,109	2,363,630	6,783,928	....	564,800	
1939	6,854,485	2,592,452	5,471,804	....	611,895	

Table 5-3. Summary: Total Use of Various Types of Areas Administered by the National Park Service (*Continued*)

Year	National parks	National monuments	National historical areas	National parkways	National recreation areas	National memorial park
1940	7,358,080	2,816,922	5,924,339	....	655,910	
1941	8,458,847	3,745,023	7,292,430	895,874	844,773	
1942	3,815,103	1,831,603	3,130,134	255,809	338,320	
1943	2,054,406	1,577,949	2,851,273	130,603	214,190	
1944	2,646,291	1,851,481	3,310,146	286,324	263,533	
1945	4,538,103	2,511,506	3,693,864	382,943	587,436	
1946	8,991,468	3,602,774	6,734,267	1,261,769	1,162,037	
1947	10,673,774	4,027,010	7,574,715	1,246,564	2,012,125	
1948	11,292,500	4,438,180	7,822,495	1,509,808	4,769,070	26,773
1949	12,967,517	4,923,059	8,694,995	1,422,316	3,645,705	82,810
1950	13,918,872	5,309,976	9,404,802	1,996,435	2,551,057	71,447
1951	15,079,165	6,187,105	10,508,687	2,448,745	2,801,148	81,590
1952	17,142,658	6,806,528	11,846,991	3,558,139	2,813,747	131,773
1953	17,372,080	7,540,498	12,472,337	5,692,604	3,026,471	120,804
1954	17,968,596	7,804,870	12,452,991	6,066,633	3,407,253	133,570
1955	18,829,541	7,953,397	12,480,262	6,699,541	3,919,985	125,112
1956	20,054,701	8,769,180	13,388,498	7,437,658	5,118,712	154,694
1957	20,903,136	9,350,703	15,452,881	7,889,702	5,559,472	129,075

SOURCE: Data for years 1904–1940, inclusive (based on "travel year" of Oct. 1–Sept. 30), derived from personal communication, Oct. 5, 1954, from National Park Service, Washington. Data for years 1941–1953, inclusive (based on calendar year), from "Public Use Tabulations of Visitors to Areas Administered by the National Park Service, 1941–1953," U.S. Department of the Interior, Washington, February, 1954. Data for years 1954–1957, inclusive (based on calendar year), from "Public Use Tabulations of Visitors to Areas Administered by the National Park Service," U.S. Department of the Interior, Washington, December, 1954, December, 1955, December, 1956, and December, 1957.

In short, the physical facilities and staff of the National Park System have become worn and outmoded. If this priceless heritage is to be preserved, immediate corrective action is necessary. To this end the National Park Service has set forth upon the Mission 66 program, founded upon the following basic principles [36]:

1. Provide additional accommodations and related services of types adapted to modern recreational needs within and near the parks, through greater participation of private enterprise.
2. Provide the government-operated facilities needed to serve the public, to protect the park resources, and to maintain the physical plant.

3. Provide the services which will make the parks more usable, more enjoyable, and more meaningful, and thereby improve the protection of the parks through visitor cooperation.

4. Provide operating funds and field staff to manage the areas, protect the resources, and provide a high standard of maintenance for all developments.

5. Provide adequate living quarters for the field employees of the Service.

6. Acquire lands within the parks and such other lands as necessary for protection or use, acquire the water rights needed to insure adequate water supplies, and extinguish grazing rights and other competing uses.

7. Institute a coordinated nation-wide recreation plan to produce a system of recreational developments by each level of government; Federal, State and local, each bearing its proper share of the expanding recreational load.

8. Provide for the protection and preservation of wilderness areas within the National Park System and encourage their appreciation and enjoyment in ways that will leave them unimpaired.

PUBLIC USE OF AREAS ADMINISTERED BY THE NATIONAL PARK SERVICE

Interest of the American people in the National Park System is reflected in the phenomenal use of these areas. With the exception of a relatively few periods, the number of visitors has mounted constantly. Detailed data are given in Tables 5-2 and 5-3.

SUMMARY

Lands administered by the National Park Service, aggregating a total of about 23 million acres, include numerous types af areas varying in size from small historical sites to extensive land units embracing many thousands of acres. Designations of various categories of lands within the National Park System, largely indicative of their particular interests, are often incorrectly interpreted as being indicative of a degree of importance, significance, or size. Basic differences between the various types of areas, however, relate largely to the nature of their legal status, for they were all established according to different procedures founded upon particular Federal laws. Each unit of the National Park System, regardless of its size or primary feature of interest, is managed in accordance with certain basic principles, first outlined in 1916, upon the establishment of the National Park Service, and later reiterated in subsequent policy statements. The basic aim of the management of these areas is to protect and preserve their varied unique features of interest in such manner that they may be maintained for the proper use and enjoyment of both present and future generations.

Within the National Park System are outstanding examples of the geological, biological, archeological, and historical interests of our country. Selection of these areas for inclusion in this system is predicated upon their significance in a particular field of interest, and the dramatic, inspirational manner by which that interest is portrayed. Thus, in essence, they are outdoor museums, important as recreational areas because of their vital contribution to American culture and education. In no sense are they resorts or outdoor playgrounds; those aspects of outdoor recreation can be more adequately provided for on lands of lesser significance.

The National Park Service is a bureau in the U.S. Department of the Interior. The basic administrative structure of this organization is composed of the headquarters and office of the Director in Washington, D.C., five regional offices strategically located with reference to National Park Service lands of somewhat similar characteristics, and between 175 and 180 field offices in specific units of the Service.

The popularity of the National Park System has resulted in a phenomenal growth in public use over the years which gives every indication of continued expansion. This expanding use has not only greatly overtaxed existing facilities but in many instances has resulted in deterioration of many significant interests typical of these areas. As a result, a program of rehabilitation and public education has been undertaken. It is hoped that this program, known as Mission 66, will correct such abuses, provide for better visitor accommodations, and develop better public understanding of the particular recreational services for which these areas were established.

SELECTED REFERENCES*

1. American Planning and Civic Association: National Park Supplement, *Planning and Civic Comment*, vol. 2, no. 4, pp. 1–36, October–December, 1936.
2. Anonymous: The Park Service and Wilderness, *National Parks Magazine*, vol. 31, no. 130, pp. 104ff, July–September, 1957.
3. Anonymous: Preservation of Natural Wilderness Values in the National Parks, *National Parks Magazine*, vol. 31, no. 130, pp. 105–106, July–September, 1957.

* Publications relative to specific interests of various National Park Service areas (e.g., geology, flora, fauna, Indians, archeology, history) may be obtained from natural history or museum associations which operate in many of these areas, or from the Superintendent of Documents, or the National Park Service, in Washington.

Among periodicals which feature various aspects of national park management and use are *American Forests*, published by the American Forestry Association; *The Living Wilderness*, published by the Wilderness Society; *National Parks Magazine*, published by the National Parks Association; *Nature Magazine*, published by the American Nature Association; and *Planning and Civic Comment*, published by the American Planning and Civic Association. Each of the foregoing organizations has headquarters in Washington.

4. Anonymous: Winter Use of National Parks, *National Parks Magazine*, vol. 31, no. 131, pp. 164–165, October–December, 1957.
5. Bailey, Vernon, and Florence M. Bailey: "Wild Animals of Glacier National Park," U.S. Government Printing Office, Washington, 1918.
6. Bryant, H. C., and W. W. Atwood: "Research and Education in the National Parks," U.S. Government Printing Office, Washington, 1936.
7. Butcher, Devereux: "Exploring Our National Parks and Monuments," Oxford University Press, New York, 1947.
8. Butcher, Devereux: "Exploring Our Prehistoric Indian Ruins," National Parks Association, Washington, 1952.
9. Cameron, Jenks: The National Park Service: Its History, Activities, and Organization, *Service Monographs of the U.S. Government*, no. 11, Institute for Government Research, Appleton-Century-Crofts, Inc., New York, 1922.
10. Campbell, M. R.: "The Glacier National Park: A Popular Guide to Its Geology and Scenery," U.S. Government Printing Office, Washington, 1914.
11. Chilson, Hatfield: The Department of the Interior and Its National Park Service, *Planning and Civic Comment*, vol. 23, no. 2, pp. 3–7, June, 1957.
12. Crampton, L. C.: "Early History of Yellowstone National Park and Its Relation to National Park Policies," U.S. Government Printing Office, Washington, 1932.
13. Drury, Newton B.: The Dilemma of Our Parks, *American Forests*, vol. 55, no. 6, pp. 6–11, June, 1949.
14. Hussey, John A.: "The History of Fort Vancouver and Its Physical Structure," Washington State Historical Society, Tacoma, Wash., 1957.
15. Langford, N. P.: "The Discovery of Yellowstone National Park, 1870," J. E. Haynes, St. Paul, Minn., 1923.
16. Lee, Willis T.: "The Geologic Story of Rocky Mountain National Park," U.S. Government Printing Office, Washington, 1917.
17. MacDonald, Gordon A., and Douglas H. Hubbard: Volcanoes of Hawaii National Park, *Hawaii Nature Notes*, special issue, vol. 4, no. 2, May, 1951.
18. Matthes, Francois E.: "Mount Rainier and Its Glaciers," U.S. Government Printing Office, Washington, 1922.
19. Matthes, Francois E.: Geologic History of Yosemite Valley, *Professional Paper* 160, U.S. Government Printing Office, Washington, 1930.
20. Merriam, John C.: The Meaning of National Parks, *National Parks Bulletin*, vol. 57, no. 10, pp. 1–2, November, 1929.
21. National Park Service and U.S. Forest Service: "National Parks and National Forests," Washington, 1956.
22. Newhall, Nancy: "A Contribution to the Heritage of Every American: The Conservation Activities of John D. Rockefeller, Jr.," Alfred A. Knopf, Inc., New York, 1957.
23. Shankland, Robert: "Steve Mather of the National Parks," Alfred A. Knopf, Inc., New York, 1951.
24. Shirley, J. C.: "The Redwoods of Coast and Sierra," University of California Press, Berkeley, Calif., 1940.
25. Stagner, Howard: "Behind the Scenery of Mount Rainier National Park," Mount Rainier National Park Natural History Association, Longmire, Wash., 1947.

26. Storer, Tracy: "Animal Life in Yosemite," University of California Press, Berkeley, Calif., 1924.
27. Storey, Isabelle: "Glimpses of Our National Parks," U.S. Government Printing Office, Washington, 1941.
28. Swift, Ernest: Parks–or Resorts? *National Parks Magazine*, vol. 31, no. 131, pp. 147–148, October–December, 1951.
29. Taylor, Walter P., and William T. Shaw: "Mammals and Birds of Mount Rainier National Park," U.S. Government Printing Office, Washington, 1927.
30. Tilden, Freeman: "The National Parks: What They Mean to You and Me," Alfred A. Knopf, Inc., New York, 1954.
31. Tolson, Hillory: "Laws Relating to the National Park Service, the National Parks and Monuments," U.S. Government Printing Office, Washington, 1935.
32. U.S. Department of the Interior, National Park Service: "Annual Report of the Superintendent of National Parks to the Secretary of the Interior, for the Fiscal Year Ended June 30, 1916," Washington, 1916.
33. U.S. Department of the Interior, National Park Service: "Annual Report of the Director of the National Park Service to the Secretary of the Interior for the Fiscal Year Ended June 30, 1932," Washington, 1932.
34. U.S. Department of the Interior, National Park Service: "Circulars of General Information," containing information on various National Park Service Areas, Washington, v.d.
35. U.S. Department of the Interior, National Park Service: "Glimpses of Historical Areas East of the Mississippi River," Washington, 1937.
36. U.S. Department of the Interior, National Park Service: "Our Heritage, a Plan for Its Protection and Use: Mission 66," Washington, n.d.
37. U.S. Department of the Interior, National Park Service: "The National Park Wilderness," Washington, n.d.
38. U.S. Department of the Interior, National Park Service: "Bryce Canyon National Park, Utah," Washington, 1947.
39. U.S. Department of the Interior, National Park Service: "Lava Beds National Monument," Washington, 1949.
40. U.S. Department of the Interior, National Park Service: "Grand Canyon National Park, Arizona," Washington, 1949.
41. U.S. Department of the Interior, National Park Service: "Areas Administered by the National Park Service, December 31, 1957," Washington, 1958.
42. U.S. Department of the Interior, National Park Service: "Preservation of Natural and Wilderness Values in the National Parks," Washington, March, 1957. (Mimeographed.)
43. Weed, W. H.: "Geysers of Yellowstone National Park," U.S. Government Printing Office, Washington, 1929.
44. Williams, Howel: "Geology of Lassen Volcanic National Park," University of California Press, Berkeley, Calif., 1932.
45. Williams, Howel: "Crater Lake: The Story of Its Origin," University of California Press, Berkeley, Calif., 1941.
46. Wirth, Conrad L.: Mission 66: The National Park System in 1966, *Proceedings of the Society of American Foresters Meeting*, Memphis, Tenn., Oct. 15–17, 1956, pp. 22–24, Washington, 1957.

47. Yard, Robert S.: "The Book of the National Parks," Charles Scribner's Sons, New York, 1920.
48. Yard, Robert S.: Economic Aspects of Our National Parks Policy, *Scientific Monthly,* vol. 16, no. 4, pp. 380–388, April, 1923.
49. Yard, Robert S.: Historical Basis of National Park Standards, *National Parks Bulletin,* vol. 10, no. 57, pp. 3–6, November, 1929.
50. Zahniser, Howard: The Wilderness Bill and the National Parks, *National Parks Magazine,* vol. 31, no. 129, pp. 70–76, April–June, 1957.

CHAPTER 6 *The National Forests as Outdoor Recreational Areas*

At the present time there are 149 national forests located in forty-four states (including Alaska) and Puerto Rico, with an aggregate area of more than 180 million acres [39].

Although originally established to provide for continued production of a wide variety of products and services other than recreation, national forests, today, are among the most popular and important of our recreational lands. In addition to over 150 million visits by casual motorists, who merely drove through these areas (see Table 6-2), public recreational use of the national forests in 1957 exceeded 60 million visits. It is predicted that this figure will be increased to 66 million by 1962 [38].

In common with other types of public outdoor recreational areas, use of the national forests for recreation has developed phenomenally in recent years; between 1950 and 1957 a 92 per cent increase was recorded [39]. This heavy use, coupled with lack of funds and the effects of World War II, has resulted in severe deterioration of recreational facilities on the national forests to a point where they have become inadequate, not only for the future, but also for present needs. To remedy this situation the U.S. Forest Service has initiated Operation Outdoors, a five-year program of rehabilitation and development scheduled for completion in 1962; total cost of this five-year program will be 85 million dollars [38]. Further, plans for the period from 1963 to 1967 call for additional expenditures for recreational facilities of about 12.5 million dollars annually [38].

NATIONAL FORESTS IN RELATION TO FOREST REGIONS OF THE UNITED STATES

National forest lands, although located largely in the West, are found in each of the principal forest regions of the United States. They embody

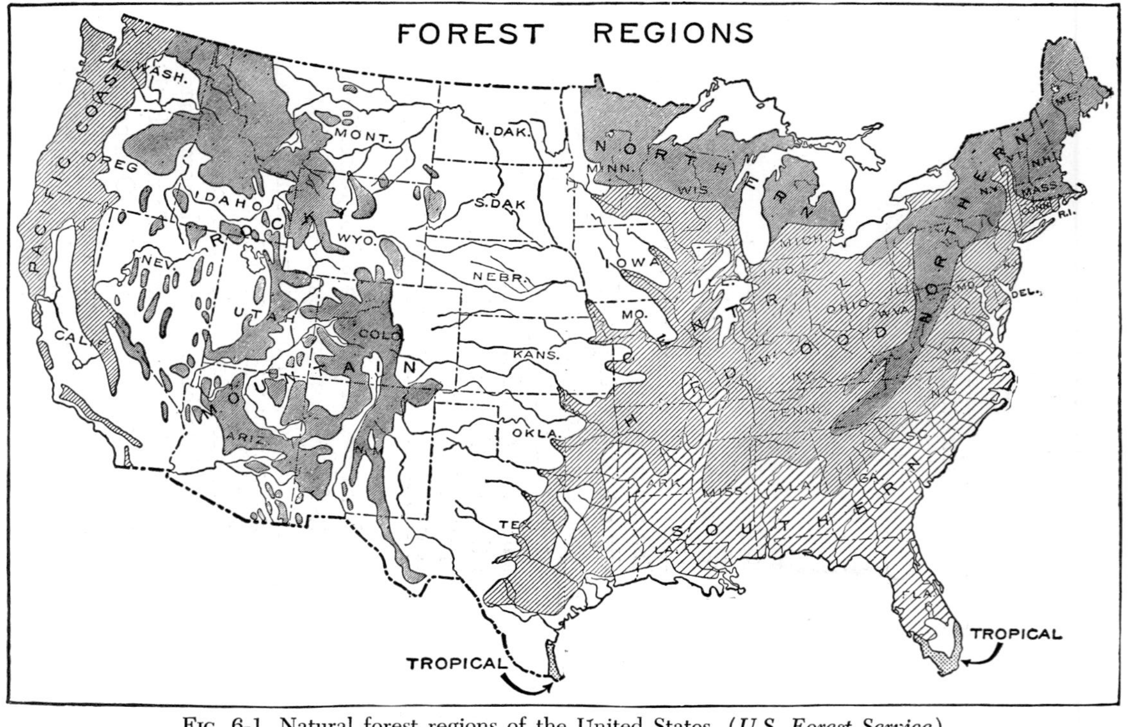

FIG. 6-1. Natural forest regions of the United States. (*U.S. Forest Service*)

forest types typical of every section of the country, their climate and scenery are equally diverse, and a majority of wild-animal species native to the United States spend at least part of the year in these areas.

The *Northern forest region,* including the Lake states, New England and the Appalachian highlands as far south as northern Georgia, is noteworthy for its mixed forests of cone-bearing and deciduous broad-leaved trees [26]. Among the more important trees typical of various parts of this area are several species of pine, spruce, birch, aspen, oak, elm, and hickory; in addition, there are larch or tamarack, balsam fir, northern white cedar, eastern hemlock, tulip poplar, and cucumber magnolia. Included in this forest region are the famous lake country of northern Minnesota, the White and Green Mountains of New England, and the

FIG. 6-2. Hikers on trail to summit of Mount Washington (6,288 feet), White Mountain National Forest, New Hampshire. (*Photo by Leland J. Prater, U.S. Forest Service*)

Piedmont and Blue Ridge Mountains of the southern Appalachians. Recreational interests of national forest lands in the northern portion of this forest region are highlighted by varied winter sports activities and opportunities for wilderness canoe travel; in addition, the Appalachian Trail, which extends from Mount Katahdin in Maine to Mount Oglethorpe in Georgia, passes through eight national forests. Opportunities for hunting and fishing are also varied in the national forests of the Northern forest region, and the proximity of these areas to large centers of population has favored the development of many picnic and camping facilities.

The many recreational advantages offered by various sections of the Northern forest region throughout the year are highly favored by many people. Among its primary attractions are the vivid colors assumed by the foliage of its deciduous trees in the fall.

The *Southern forest region* embraces the South Atlantic and Gulf Coast area from Chesapeake Bay to East Texas. National forests of this area embrace swamps wherein such species as tupelo and the weird bald cypress are found; alluvial bottoms with such trees as evergreen magnolia, holly, bay, a number of evergreen and deciduous oaks, and pecan and several other species of hickory; and drier, sandy soils which are particularly noteworthy for shortleaf, longleaf, loblolly, and slash pines [26]. Although recreational facilities have not been developed as extensively as on national forest lands in some sections of the country, campgrounds and picnic areas are available in national forests of the Southern forest region and hunting and fishing are popular activities.

Fig. 6-3. Horseback riding, Blanchard Springs Recreation Area, Ozark National Forest, Arkansas. (*Photo by Daniel O. Todd, U.S. Forest Service*)

The *Central hardwood forest region* is well known for its wide variety of deciduous broad-leaved trees. Among these are numerous species of oak, hickory, maple, elm, and ash, as well as sycamore, black walnut, American beech, red gum, hackberry, persimmon, and Osage-orange [26]. This region, in addition to a portion of the eastern slope of the Appalachians as far north as southern New England, embraces the Ohio and Mississippi Valleys westward to the Great Plains. National forest acreage in the Central hardwood region, while not extensive, includes portions of the recreationally interesting Ouachita and Ozark Mountains of Arkansas and southern Missouri which embody a variety of noteworthy recreational developments. Elsewhere in the Central hardwood region recreational facilities of national forest lands are largely limited to picnic areas and campgrounds.

The *Rocky Mountain forest region* occupies the higher elevations along the Continental Divide, the "backbone" of our country. Although differing somewhat from north to south, the forests of this region are largely composed of cone-bearing evergreen trees. Most important of these are ponderosa, lodgepole, limber, western white, and pinon pine, Engelmann and blue spruce, alpine and white fir, Douglas-fir, western larch and juniper [26]. Most abundant and colorful of the deciduous broad-leaved trees of this region is the quaking aspen which enlivens the scene each fall when its foliage turns to brilliant yellow or gold.

The Rocky Mountain forest region, a land of scenic magnificence and varied climate, is richly endowed with national forests offering a wide range of recreational interests. Rugged mountains are interspersed with beautiful parklike valleys, and high alpine meadows are contrasted with expansive plateaus and mesas. Many species of interesting animals inhabit the Rocky Mountain forest region, including deer, elk, antelope, mountain sheep, mountain goat, American black and (in the north) grizzly bear, and a variety of waterfowl and upland game birds. In consequence the national forests of the Rocky Mountain forest region are favorites of naturalists, photographers, hikers, mountain climbers, horseback riders, hunters, fishermen, skiers, and campers.

The *Pacific Coast forest region,* which includes most of California and the western parts of the states of Oregon and Washington, is preeminent in our country for the magnificence of its forests and the size of individual trees. Composed primarily of cone-bearing, evergreen species, the forests of this region vary greatly in appearance, largely owing to differences in the amount of available moisture. The more humid northern and coastal sections, amply watered by reason of the prevailing winds that sweep inland from the Pacific, are noteworthy for Douglas-fir, Sitka spruce, western hemlock, western redcedar and Port-Orford-cedar, coast redwood, and grand and Pacific silver fir. Drier inland sections, as well as more southerly portions of the Pacific Coast forest region, are typified by stands of such species as giant sequoia, ponderosa, Jeffrey, sugar, Coulter, knobcone, Digger, and pinon pine, white fir, and incense-cedar. Higher elevations are characterized by western white, lodgepole and whitebark pine, alpine, noble, and California red fir, mountain hemlock, Engelmann spruce, and Alaska-cedar. Most noteworthy broad-leaved trees of the Pacific Coast forest region include Pacific dogwood, Pacific madrone, bigleaf maple, red and white alder, California-laurel or Oregon-myrtle, black cottonwood, California buckeye, and several species of oak [26].

The many national forests found in the Pacific Coast forest region are outstanding in their scenic magnificence, their varied climate, and their opportunities for a wide variety of outdoor recreational pursuits. They include large segments of the rugged Olympics, Cascades, Siskiyous, and Sierra Nevada and such great glacier-clad volcanic peaks as Mount Baker, Mount Adams, Mount St. Helens, and Glacier Peak in Washington, Mount Hood and Mount Jefferson in Oregon, and Mount Shasta in California. Densely forested lower elevations are sharply contrasted with colorful subalpine meadows and expanses of barren rocky terrain at and above the timber line. There are myriads of lakes, tempestuous mountain streams, deep valleys, and sharply incised canyons. Deep snows which blanket the higher elevations in winter give way to a profusion of wild flowers of many species during the summer, and the native animal life is equally varied. As a result hunters and fishermen, hikers, mountain climbers, skiers, photographers, naturalists, and campers find ample opportunity to pursue their particular recreational interests on these lands. Further, the proximity of the national forests of this region to such large centers of population as Los Angeles, San Francisco, Portland, and Seattle make possible extensive use of these areas by people who have limited time and money.

DISTINCTION BETWEEN NATIONAL FORESTS AND NATIONAL PARKS

Since national forests and many national parks are often characterized by interesting forest cover, the purposes served by these two types of public lands often seem similar to many people. Yet the distinction between national forests and national parks is clear-cut [18].

The national forests are administered by the U.S. Forest Service of the U.S. Department of Agriculture for multiple use of their varied natural resources. These resources include timber, forage for livestock, water for domestic, agricultural, and industrial uses, native animal life, and a variety of outdoor recreational values.

National forests are basically utilitarian. With few exceptions (e.g., minerals) their natural resources are renewable and may, by proper management, be repeatedly harvested and reestablished on the same land. Except on those portions of the national forests specifically designated for recreation, timber is treated as a crop. As in the case of products of agricultural land, the national forest is managed for periodic harvest, except that the interval between timber harvests is much longer. In a similar manner, forage on national forests is managed to permit grazing at the proper time by controlled numbers of cattle and sheep. These periodic harvests of timber and forage are handled so that the amount and purity of water derived from watersheds in the national forests will not be materially affected. Further, the population of native animals is regulated in accordance with their natural food supply; surplus animals are cropped by hunting, trapping, or fishing. Recreation, also considered an important natural resource on the national forests, is likewise managed. Provision is made for different types of outdoor recreational activity on portions of the national forests best adapted to specific recreational interests, and considerable effort is expended in guarding against destructive recreational overuse of such areas. A wide variety of facilities are provided, varying from readily accessible picnic areas and campgrounds along main highways to remote wilderness areas.

FIG. 6-4. Administration by the U.S. Forest Service ensures the sustained utilization of renewable natural resources of the national forests, including timber, forage for livestock, water supply, native animal life, and a wide variety of recreational values; a logging operation in the Willamette National Forest, Oregon. (*Photo by Leland J. Prater, U.S. Forest Service*)

By contrast, National Park Service areas are administered by the National Park Service of the U.S. Department of the Interior. As noted in Chapter 5, they are managed on a single-use basis with emphasis on recreation in an outdoor museum sense. The significance of these areas is such that it transcends any utilitarian values which they embody; thus they are of greatest value to the nation if retained in a natural state. Since their significant interests are fragile, any modification of National Park Service areas through periodic harvest of natural resources, however well managed, destroys their primary value and their reason for existence.

Both these basic philosophies of wild-land management are concerned with different aspects of natural resource conservation and fulfill vital and specific needs. Properly coordinated they supplement one another in the provision of the widest variety of highly necessary public benefits and services.

The difference between these two types of land areas is analogous to the difference between an illustrated calendar that one uses constantly, but replaces periodically, and a prized painting that one hangs permanently in the home.

Most national forests are recreationally interesting; often they are exceptionally beautiful, but either their features are not of such outstanding significance that the public interest dictates the preservation of absolutely natural conditions, or they are duplicated in more dramatic fashion in one or more National Park Service areas. Thus, management of recreational values of the national forests is integrated with properly managed use of other natural resources. Since recreational management of national forests is guided by more liberal policies than those of National Park System areas, there is greater freedom in the choice of recreational activities and in the provision of necessary physical facilities.[1]

LEGAL STATUS OF NATIONAL FORESTS

National forests are based fundamentally upon the act of March 3, 1891, which authorized the President to reserve, by proclamation, certain lands from the public domain and to designate such lands as forest reserves. The act provided [27]:

> That the President of the United States may, from time to time, set apart and reserve, in any State or Territory having public land bearing forests, in any part of the public lands wholly or in part covered with timber or undergrowth, whether of commercial value or not, as public reservations, and the President shall, by public proclamation, declare the establishment of such reservations and the limits thereof.

This act was prepared primarily for the purpose of effecting a general revision of various laws concerned with the disposition of public lands which had sometimes been characterized by irregular practices. The act contained twenty-four sections, the twenty-fourth providing for the establishment of forest reserves. The first of these areas to be established was the Yellowstone Park Timberland Reserve [9], now the Shoshone National Forest, Wyoming [32]; it was proclaimed a forest reserve by

[1] Certain areas (e.g., wilderness and wild areas), although coordinated within the framework of multiple use management of the national forests, have been designated by the U.S. Forest Service as most valuable in the perpetuation of primitive conditions. Fundamentally, such lands are administered with a single use objective of a particular type in mind, with all but rudimentary developments prohibited (see pp. 166–167).

President Benjamin Harrison on March 30, 1891. Before his term expired President Harrison established forest reservations aggregating an area of 13 million acres [3] and additional millions of acres of forest reserves were later established in the West by Presidents Cleveland, McKinley, and Theodore Roosevelt. President Theodore Roosevelt gave particular support to the cause of forest conservation; between 1901 and 1909 he placed 148 million acres of public land under Federal supervision [9].

ORGANIZATION AND ADMINISTRATION OF THE NATIONAL FORESTS

The U.S. Forest Service, a Bureau of the Department of Agriculture, has its headquarters in Washington, D.C.

The headquarters organization consists of the Chief Forester and his staff, various units of which are concerned with the administration of specific activities relative to these areas on a national level. Among these units is the Division of Recreation and Land Uses which provides over-all leadership relative to the management of recreational resources of the national forests throughout the country [13].

Table 6-1. Regions of the U.S. Forest Service

Number	Name	Headquarters
1	Northern	Missoula, Mont.
2	Rocky Mountain	Denver, Colo.
3	Southwestern	Albuquerque, N. Mex.
4	Intermountain	Ogden, Utah
5	California	San Francisco, Calif.
6	North Pacific	Portland, Ore.
7	Eastern	Philadelphia, Pa.
8	Southern	Atlanta, Ga.
9	Lake States	Milwaukee, Wis.
10	Alaska	Juneau, Alas.

To promote administrative efficiency the field organization of the U.S. Forest Service is divided into ten regions (see Table 6-1), each of which is characterized by similar broad problems relative to varied uses of wild lands. Administration of the national forests within each region is in charge of a Regional Forester, subject to general administrative direction of the Chief Forester. Various units of each regional staff supervise specific activities in the national forests within their jurisdiction; management of recreational resources is in charge of each region's Division of Recreation and Lands.

Each of the ten regions is further divided into national forests, which,

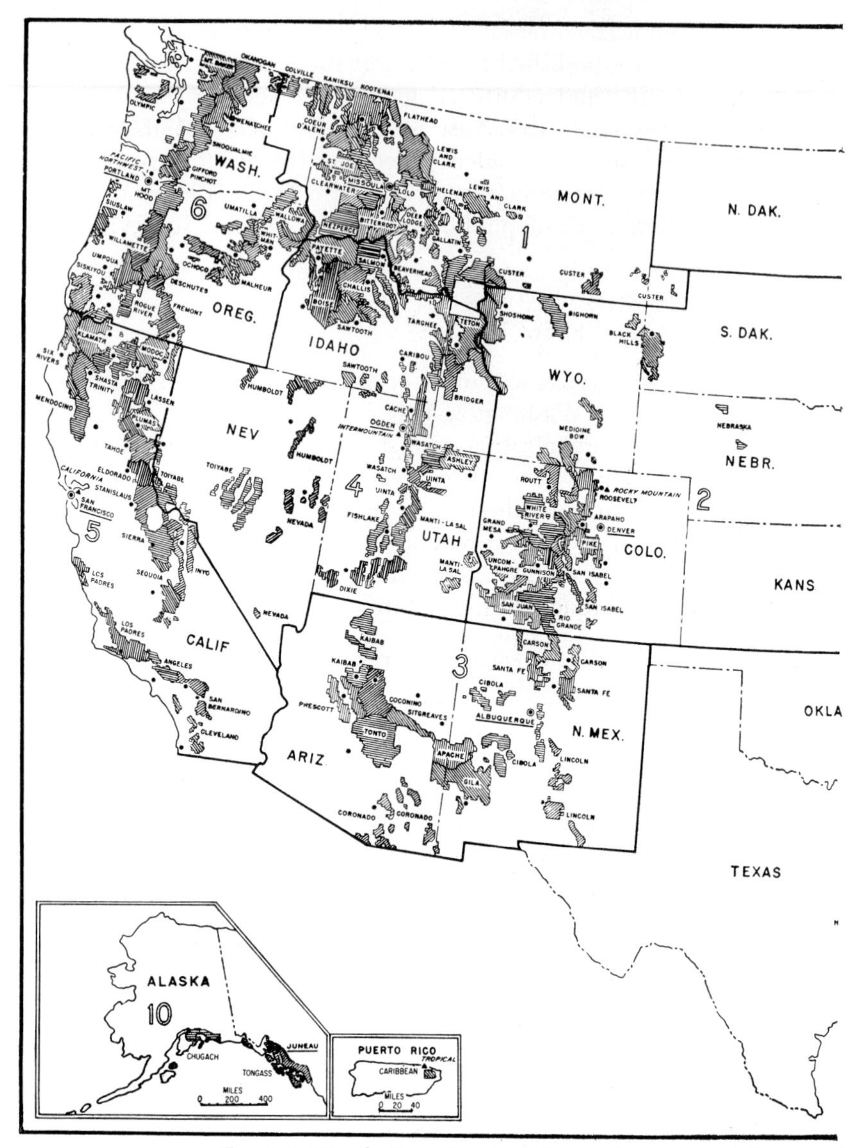

FIG. 6-5. Distribution of national forests in the United States and

in turn, are composed of one or more ranger districts, the basic administrative unit of the U.S. Forest Service. Each national forest is in charge of a Forest Supervisor who is aided by a number of staff assistants responsible for various specific activities on the forest; each ranger district is in charge of a District Ranger who, with his assistants, directs and supervises all activities on his particular area.

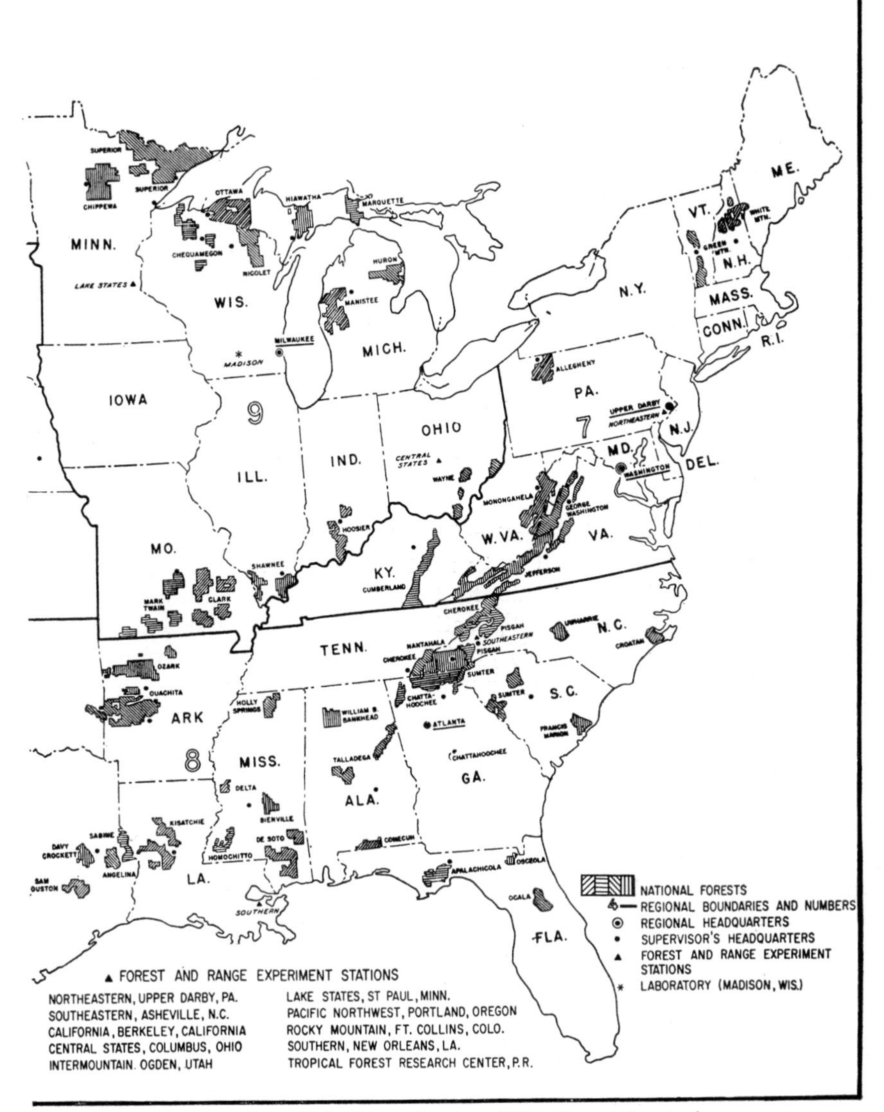

regional organization of the U.S. Forest Service. (*U.S. Forest Service*)

As noted in greater detail in Chapter 3, the present organization of the U.S. Forest Service was consummated in 1905. At that time the forest reserves, established by Presidential proclamation by authority of the act of Congress passed in 1891, were transferred from the jurisdiction of the General Land Office of the Department of the Interior to the Bureau of Forestry of the Department of Agriculture. At the same time the name Bureau of Forestry was changed to U.S. Forest Service, and Gifford Pinchot, who headed a small group of technical foresters then comprising that organization, was named Chief Forester. Two years later the name "forest reserve" was changed to "national forest" [3].

Although Congress made provision for the establishment of Federal forests in 1891, it failed to give consideration to the proper protection and management of such areas for several years; the original forest reserves were merely areas closed to legal use of timber and other natural resources. Not until the act of June 4, 1897, did Congress outline broad policies of operation for these areas, making possible the managed use of all their resources. National forests are still administered under provisions of this act, together with its later amendments [3].

The policy of national forest administration is most aptly outlined in Secretary of Agriculture James Wilson's letter of February 1, 1905, to Chief Forester Gifford Pinchot. The following statement was included in that document [33]:

> In the administration of the national forests it must be clearly borne in mind that all land is to be devoted to its most productive use for the permanent good of the whole people, and not for the temporary benefit of individuals or companies. All the resources of the national forests are for use, and this must be brought about in a thoroughly prompt and businesslike manner under such restrictions only as will insure the permanence of these resources. You will see to it that the water, wood, and the forage of the forest are conserved and wisely used for the benefit of the home builder first of all, upon whom depends the best permanent use of the lands and resources alike. In the management of each forest local questions will be decided upon first, but with as little restriction to minor industries as possible. Sudden changes in industrial conditions will be avoided by gradual adjustment after due notice, and where conflicting interests must be reconciled the question will always be decided from the standpoint of the greatest good for the greatest number in the long run.

In response to growing public recreational use of the national forests, the U.S. Forest Service eventually recognized recreation as one of the important resources of areas under its control and gave it official status in its program of multiple-use management. As noted in Chapter 3, broad policies relative to recreational use of the national forests were first formulated by E. A. Sherman, Associate Forester, in 1925.

PRESENT RECREATIONAL POLICY OF THE U.S. FOREST SERVICE

The relative importance of recreation in national forest administration varies in accordance with conditions which differ in various sections of the country, and from one national forest to another. All national forest lands have some recreational value, but this aspect of their management assumes a greater degree of importance on some areas than on others; on a number of national forests recreation is paramount.

Of necessity, the original recreational policy of the U.S. Forest Service has had to be greatly expanded as public interest in the recreational values of the national forests increased. Present objectives and policies, as stated in the *Administrative Manual* of the U.S. Forest Service, are as follows [29]:

Coordination

1. The recreation resources of the national forests will be managed in conjunction with all the other forest resources under the principles of multiple use. This does not mean that limited areas may not be devoted exclusively to recreation. In general, however, over any area large enough to be classified as an administrative unit, such as a ranger district, recreation use will take its place with other uses such as timber production, grazing, mining, and water storage.

2. The recreation developments on the national forests will not duplicate those available on other public lands or on private lands in the same locality, provided the latter are adequate for the public needs under conditions comparable to those which might be provided on the national forests.

National Forest recreation developments in the vicinity of National Parks and along park approach roads will be planned in consultation with the National Park Service in relation to developments in National Parks—the objective being to obtain coordination between the two Services as far as practicable so that developments on the two types of area may complement each other.

3. In planning the development of the recreation resource and the necessary adjustments with other uses, the viewpoints of interested groups will be considered. The organization of associations of those concerned with recreation to act in an advisory capacity in national forest recreation planning, development, and administration will be encouraged.

Preservation of the Natural and the Primitive

4. One of the distinctive characteristics of forest recreation is that it is enjoyed in a natural environment. Every effort will be made to preserve this quality and the atmosphere of spaciousness in the planning and development of recreation opportunities.

Further than this, suitable provision will be made for the establishment of areas which will preserve primitive conditions of transportation or vegetation, and where possible, a combination of the two.

Developments

5. The Forest Service will develop or permit the development of such facilities as will aid in the enjoyment of those types of recreation appropriate to the forest. It will especially discourage developments which tend to introduce urbanization into the forest.

6. The Forest Service will install or permit the installation of facilities only to the extent required to serve public needs so as to keep to a minimum the introduction of artificial developments in the forest environment.

7. The basic objective in designing national forest developments is to have them perform their intended function and at the same time harmonize as much as possible with the natural environment.

8. Preference will be given to recreation developments which emphasize opportunities for participant rather than spectator enjoyment of forest recreation activities.

9. When Federal funds are expended on recreation developments the objective should be to provide recreation opportunities for relatively large numbers of people and not for the exclusive use of individuals or small groups. The determination of priorities in the expenditure of funds under this policy requires consideration both of the quantity and quality of recreation enjoyment made possible by a development. It also requires that any development should be considered in relation to other developments so that a well-balanced system of recreation facilities will be provided.

Use

10. The recreation use of the national forests will be handled with the fewest possible restrictions on users, consistent with the protection of the forest against damage, the observance of essential sanitary and safety measures, and the prevention of actions by individuals or groups which unduly interfere with the enjoyment of others.

11. Uses which require exclusive private occupancy, such as summer homes and limited membership clubs, have a proper place in the national forests, but will be granted only where it appears certain that the desired areas will not be needed for more general public uses. In determining the public need, future as well as present requirements must be considered and the estimates of future needs should be liberal.

12. Charges will be made at public recreation areas for special services such as (1) charcoal, (2) electricity, (3) checking clothes, renting suits and towels, (4) boat rental, (5) use of ski tows and lifts, (6) hot showers (if artificially heated), and (7) any special services of similar character.

13. Permit fees for resorts, services, and summer homes will be based on the fair value of the land, as determined by the rental charged for comparable privately-owned land, with due allowance for all differences between the conditions associated with the use of public and private land.

14. Particular attention will be given to facilities for the use of the majority of American citizens who can enjoy forest recreation only if its cost is small. This means emphasis on camping and picnicking facilities, and on organization camps owned by the Government and made available either to individuals or organizations whose members are in the low-income groups.

15. The Forest Service will cooperate with public, semi-public, and private welfare organizations endeavoring to sponsor or further forest vacations for underprivileged groups.

RECREATIONAL PLANNING AND ADMINISTRATION ON THE NATIONAL FORESTS

Recreational values of the national forests receive the same consideration as do other major functions of these areas; their use, planning, development, and maintenance are handled, in varying detail and degrees of responsibility, at all levels of the Forest Service organization from the office of the Chief Forester to that of the District Ranger.

Detailed planning of recreational facilities and services on each national forest is, in consultation with the Supervisor, directed by a staff assistant in the Supervisor's office delegated to this task; he works with recreational specialists from the regional headquarters, as well as with various district rangers on the forest. District rangers may also make recommendations as to recreational features, policies, and needs to the Forest Supervisor. Such recommendations, after proper consideration, may be included in the recreational plan for the forest as prepared in the office of the Supervisor. Thus, any proposed recreational development acceptable on the national forests, as provided by the broad policy determined in the office of the Chief Forester, may be initiated at any level of the organization.

BASIS FOR RECREATIONAL PLANS

The recreational plan of a national forest usually consists of a base map of the forest upon which are indicated all existing and proposed recreational areas; a minimum of necessary descriptive material and factual data supporting various aspects of this program is also included on the base map. The preparation of such a plan, which may be revised periodically as conditions warrant, is guided by the following factors [29]:

1. *Current recreational resources of the forest.* These are listed in an inventory of varied recreational values of the forest and include a determination of specific areas best suited to different types of recreational use. In addition, the human capacity for each type of recreational use, as well as for each type of recreational area, is estimated and an outline of recreational developments in the vicinity, other than those on the forest, is prepared.

2. *Limitations of recreational use on the forest.* This considers other needs capable of being supplied by the forest which may be of equal or greater importance than recreation (e.g., timber, forage, water supply).

3. *The potential recreational demand of the forest.* Future public recreational needs and their relationship to national forest management

are important in planning. Factors such as present and probable population trends, technological developments affecting recreation, and probable trends in public recreational interests must be carefully weighed in arriving at the most logical decisions.

In consideration of the foregoing factors various areas selected for recreational development are allocated on the basis of their particular value or combination of values to specific types of recreational activity. The current status of such areas is indicated on the recreational base map as "developed and in use" or "reserved for future development." In the latter case areas scheduled for immediate future development are separated from lands to be held in reserve.

Actual development of each recreational area, as provided for in the general recreational plan for the forest, is preceded by the preparation of detailed tract plans showing the location and design of all improvements, together with necessary specifications. Such plans are prepared by specialists in the Regional Forester's office or the Supervisor's office, upon the advice of the Forest Supervisor or District Ranger.

CLASSIFICATION OF RECREATIONAL LANDS

To effect proper coordination of the most logical uses of the national forests, lands having present or potential recreational values are classified in the administrative manual of the U.S. Forest Service as [29]:

1. Dominant—land on which recreation is so important that all other uses are barred.
2. Codominant—land on which recreation is of approximately equal importance with one or more other uses.
3. Subordinate—land where recreation use is of low priority, either because the area is not inherently desirable for recreation or because other uses warrant first consideration.

Classification of national forest land in the above manner necessitates wise judgment; a great many factors must be considered. In particular, public recreational benefits inherent on a national forest must be balanced with more tangible economic values (e.g., timber, forage, and the like). The objective is to designate various units of the national forest for that use which will result in continuous maximum public benefits.

VARIETY OF RECREATIONAL OPPORTUNITY ON THE NATIONAL FORESTS

Diversity of recreational opportunity is one of the principal characteristics of the national forests; they serve practically every kind of outdoor interest.

In addition to many Federal, state, and county highways which bisect the national forests, there are many miles of secondary forest roads[2] that are open to the public. Roads in the national forests invariably afford striking views and scenic panoramas of interest not only to the casual motorist but also to those who utilize such roads in reaching specific vantage points from which journeys into more remote areas may be initiated on foot or on horseback. Numerous picnic areas and campgrounds are strategically located in attractive surroundings along these roads, not only along well-traveled arterial highways but along more remote byways. This affords a wide choice in the desired picnicking or camping experience. One of the more readily accessible, better developed, and consequently more heavily patronized picnic areas or campgrounds may be selected, or a more remote location, typified by more primitive facilities but greater seclusion, may be favored. Hotel accommodations are equally diverse; they include "rustic" cabins or lodges, dude ranches, and modern hotels. Recreational administration of the national forests also makes provision for the establishment of organized camps by various types of youth and church groups, and by municipalities, while opportunity for development of more personalized accommodations is available in summer-home site areas. Nor are those who wish to "rough it" neglected; ample opportunity to enjoy activities of that nature is found in the many wilderness, wild, and roadless areas in the national forests [1].

Since hunting and fishing are permitted on the national forests, these areas play a vital role in such forms of outdoor recreation. The U.S. Forest Service, through its Division of Wildlife Management, works closely with various state fish and game departments and gives careful consideration to the welfare of native animal populations on areas under its jurisdiction. It should be pointed out, however, that the U.S. Forest Service does not establish, administer, or enforce hunting and fishing regulations on national forest lands; such activities are the prerogative of various state fish and game departments, and state hunting and fishing laws apply on the national forests.

To foster proper and safe use of national forest lands for recreation, and to guard against the destruction of varied interests of such areas, the U.S. Forest Service issues maps and related material for public distribution. These aids may be obtained from the offices of various forest supervisors.

Obviously, public use of the national forests for recreation should be accompanied by care and consideration. One should be properly equipped for the type of recreational activity which is planned; the hazards of

[2] Under certain conditions, such as periods of extreme fire hazard, closures may be invoked.

what is often an unfamiliar environment must be recognized and avoided; proper respect should be shown the facilities that are provided; and natural beauty or interests should not be despoiled. Further, the popularity of the national forests for recreation often results in overcrowded conditions on more readily accessible areas; it is therefore paramount that everyone show proper consideration for the rights and privileges of others. Of course, good outdoor manners are not only applicable to the national forests; they should typify the use of all types of recreational

FIG. 6-6. Hunting, in season, is permitted on national forest lands, subject to state game laws. (*Photo by K. D. Swan, U.S. Forest Service*)

lands. Rules and regulations, with specific penalties which may be imposed for certain infractions, are only part of the answer to improper use of recreational lands; public responsibilities will be discharged only if proper respect and appreciation for such rights and privileges are demonstrated. Machinery for enforcing good behavior in the outdoors is unnecessary when basic principles of unselfishness, decency, and integrity are exercised.

In the management of the recreational resources of the national forests attention is given to the preservation of scenic beauty and specific interests (e.g., important forest types and biological communities, and geological, archeological, and historical values). A great variety of recreational areas are listed by the U.S. Forest Service. These may be segregated into two major groups; the first includes lands which are retained in essentially their natural condition, while the second is composed of areas having a recreational potential which can be most advantageously realized by means of certain types of physical development. Owing to the great variety of recreational interest and value embodied in national forest lands in widely different sections of the country, no official priorities are listed by the U.S. Forest Service as a guide for recreational planning, except that types of use which serve the general

FIG. 6-7. Mount Adams, principal topographic feature of the Mount Adams Wild Area, Gifford Pinchot National Forest, Washington. (*Photo by Leland J. Prater, U.S. Forest Service*)

public have priority over those of a private nature (e.g., summer homes). Initiation of decisions as to the type of recreational use best adapted to specific areas of national forest lands is left largely to local forest officers who are acquainted with local needs and conditions. However, final approval of such decisions, constituting a formal closing of such areas to any use or occupancy inconsistent with the classification, rests with higher authority. In certain cases final approval is given by the Regional Forester, in others by the Chief of the U.S. Forest Service, and in a few classifications by the Secretary of Agriculture.

Brief comments on each type of recreational area recognized by the U.S. Forest Service follow:[3]

Wilderness and Wild Areas. The wilderness and wild areas of the national forests, over seventy-five in number and aggregating an area in excess of 14 million acres [1], represent one of the most noteworthy achievements in national forest recreational policy. They are especially appealing to those who enjoy recreational experiences which are removed as completely as possible from the influences of "civilization."

The difference between a wilderness and a wild area in the national forests is primarily one of size. Wilderness areas[4] must contain more than 100,000 acres and are designated, modified, or eliminated by the Secretary of Agriculture upon the recommendation of the Chief Forester. Wild areas[5] are subject to the same general administrative restrictions as wilderness areas except that they are between 5,000 and 100,000 acres in area and are designated, modified, or eliminated by the Chief of the U.S. Forest Service. Neither wilderness nor wild areas are modified or eliminated unless it has been clearly demonstrated that such action is in the public interest.

By comparison with the multitudes who seek less rigorous outdoor recreational activities the number who use the national forest wilderness and wild areas is relatively small, a factor which occasionally serves as one rallying point for those who contend that the size of these areas is out of proportion to their patronage. It must be remembered, however, that the principal recreational values of these areas are intimately linked with their untrammeled nature, values which would be destroyed if they were used by large numbers of people. Further, everyone has a vital stake in the preservation of such primitive lands, even those who do not possess wilderness interests, those who are characterized by physical frailties, or those who lack sufficient time or proper experience to make wilderness recreation safe and pleasurable. These wilderness and wild areas are part of our legacy to our children and grandchildren. They

[3] Basic data concerning various types of forest lands designated for different forms of recreational use derived largely from bibliographical references 29 and 29-*a*.

[4] There are twenty-nine wilderness areas aggregating over 11 million acres in area. Among the larger and more important are High Sierra in California, 393,945 acres; Idaho, 1,232,744 acres, in Idaho, and Selway-Bitterroot, 1,581,210 acres, in Idaho and Montana; Bob Marshall in Montana, 950,000 acres; North Cascade in Washington, 801,000 acres; and Bridger, 383,000 acres, North Absaroka, 379,460 acres, South Absaroka, 614,216 acres, and Teton, 565,291 acres, in Wyoming [1].

[5] There are fifty-four wild areas aggregating more than 2 million acres in area. Among the larger and more important are Emigrant Basin, 98,043 acres, and San Rafael, 74,990 acres, in California; Maroon-Snowmass, 64,600 acres, and Uncompahgre, 69,253 acres, in Colorado; Cabinet Mountains, 90,000 acres, and Mission Mountains, 75,500 acres, in Montana; Kalmiopsis, 78,850 acres, and Mount Jefferson, 86,700 acres, in Oregon; Goat Rocks in Washington, 82,680 acres; and Cloud Peak in Wyoming, 94,000 acres [1].

will increase in value with time and with the inevitable development of our country, for once destroyed or seriously modified, wilderness values can never be completely restored.

Wilderness and wild areas of the national forests are practically free of artificial influences and are accessible only by trail; modern improvements are almost totally lacking and commercial utilization of natural resources is largely eliminated. Stores, hotels, lodges, organization camps, summer-home sites, and similar accommodations are nonexistent. Except where necessary, mechanized transportation and related necessary facilities are prohibited. These exceptions are determined by the Chief Forester; for instance, minor roads and truck trails are permitted for fire-control purposes and airplanes may be permitted to land on remote lakes in emergency situations. Boundaries of wilderness and wild areas embrace lands at higher elevations where timber, by reason of species or inaccessibility, is largely of noncommercial character and where other tangible forest-land resources are limited. However, hunting and fishing are permitted, subject to state game laws, and in certain instances grazing of livestock may be sanctioned.

Those who use these areas must do so "on their own," exploring on foot and carrying necessary food and equipment, by utilizing horses as pack and riding stock, or, in some regions, by use of a burro to carry the camp gear. Many of the difficulties inherent in wilderness travel are alleviated by various outdoor clubs and related groups who sponsor different types of annual outings to these and similar remote lands. In such instances the individuals of each party share the cost of food and packing. In addition, such organizations as the Trail Riders, sponsored by the American Forestry Association, provide food, and riding and pack stock at slightly higher cost [2].

Although incorporated within the broad framework of the multiple-use program of the U.S. Forest Service, wilderness and wild areas of the national forests are operated largely on a single-use basis with emphasis on outdoor recreation of a self-sufficient type. As such their management is closely akin to that typical of those national parks which also include extensive wilderness terrain.

Primitive Areas and Limited Areas. In a number of U.S. Forest Service regions an original classification of primitive area still applies to certain lands although the authority by which such areas were designated (Regulation L-20) has been rescinded by the Secretary of Agriculture and replaced by the more recent classifications of wilderness area (Regulation U-1) and wild area (Regulation U-2). Primitive areas established and still in existence under the old regulation retain their status until revoked by the Chief Forester. The basic difference between the former classification of primitive area and the more recent categories of wilderness or wild area is that the latter are more restrictive, prohibiting development of roads and commercial timber cutting; further, ninety days' notice is required for their establishment, modification, or elimination [30].

In addition, within Region 6 of the U.S. Forest Service there are also a number of areas which have been given the special classification of limited area. This classification was devised to protect the recreational values of large areas of land until studies could be made to identify specific recreational values, and to determine the boundaries necessary to the protection of such values. In effect, the classification of limited area represents a recreational option which prohibits road development, provision for motorized transportation, commercial cutting of timber, and occupancy under special-use permit, except by special approval of the Regional Forester [30].

For example, the recreational interests of the area surrounding Glacier Peak in the northern Cascades are protected by the special limited-area classification. The eventual status of the Glacier Peak area is currently under discussion between the U.S. Forest Service and various interested groups favoring different forms of land use [5,10,17,20,40].

In addition to the foregoing other areas are established and managed by the U.S. Forest Service so that they will remain in essentially a natural condition. If less than 100,000 acres in size these areas (roadless, virgin, scenic, geological, archeological, historical) are approved and classified by the Chief of the U.S. Forest Service or such forest officers as he may designate. Larger areas of this type are approved and classified by the Secretary of Agriculture.

Roadless Areas. Extensive units of land generally qualifying as wilderness but embodying important codominant economic assets are classified as roadless areas. In such cases, although utilization of economic resources is permitted, much of the wilderness values may be saved by prohibiting other than temporary roads. Such roads, although suitable for harvesting certain resources, are not open for general motor travel. Three roadless areas, aggregating an area of more than one million acres, have been established by the U.S. Forest Service; all are in the Superior National Forest, Minnesota, and are mainly accessible by canoe.[6]

Virgin Areas. Units of land not less than 5,000 acres in size in which there has been virtually no disturbance of natural vegetation are referred to as virgin areas. This classification is usually applied to low-altitude forest types where the value of the timber does not warrant establishment of larger wilderness areas.

On virgin areas commercial timber cutting, grazing, reservoirs, and any

[6] Caribou (45,750 acres), Little Indian Sioux (103,018 acres), and Superior (889,975 acres) [1].

development for public concentration is excluded, but minor road development, sufficient to facilitate public enjoyment of the area, may be permitted.

Scenic Areas. Specifically designated lands of this type are characterized by unique or outstanding beauty. Although their size varies, they are always smaller than 5,000 acres. They are maintained, as nearly as possible, in an undisturbed condition; hence, development of roads, trials, and other facilities is permitted only to the minimum required to make the area accessible.

Fig. 6-8. The Superior National Forest, Minnesota, offers opportunity for wilderness travel by canoe. (*Photo by Leland J. Prater, U.S. Forest Service*)

Geological, Archeological, or Historical Areas. These are of varying size but of sufficient extent to protect and preserve specific interests of these types found on the national forests.

Recreation Zones. The U.S. Forest Service further safeguards the recreational interests of the national forests by limiting or excluding commercial development, use, and occupancy from areas designated as recreation zones. Such areas usually border routes of travel or bodies of water, or surround established recreational developments. The size and conformation of recreation zones varies with individual requirements.

Principal areas of this type include roadside zones, trail zones, waterfront zones, buffer zones, and observation sites. Roadside zones embrace strips of land of varying width along highways and roads which have high scenic value. Trail zones, established along heavily used foot and horse trails, are similar in general concept and management to roadside zones. Similarly, water-front zones apply to areas bordering lakes, ponds, streams, ocean frontage, and the like. Buffer zones of varying size and shape may be established adjacent to different types of recreational lands; they are generally located about heavily used recreational areas (e.g., camp and picnic areas, organization camps, resort areas) where public enjoyment of such areas is enhanced by preservation of related environment and background. Observation sites are reserved for special development to facilitate the enjoyment of a view of outstanding beauty or interest; in such cases the view, foreground, and adjacent lands are preserved in a natural state and only simple developments required for public access, safety, and sanitation are permitted.

Recreation zones along interstate highways are designated by the Chief Forester and any modification of such areas, which must be amply justified, can be accomplished only by his authority. Designation of other types of recreation zones, as well as authority for fully justified modification, is the responsibility of Regional Foresters.

National forest lands considered to be primarily valuable as developed recreational areas include campgrounds and picnic areas, summer and winter sports areas, organization campsites, commercial public-service sites, and recreation residence (summer-home) sites. Such areas are designated on the recreational plans of various ranger districts, national forests, and regions of the U.S. Forest Service. The establishment, development, and coordination of such necessary public recreational facilities, carried out with due regard for the maintenance of varied recreational interests, public health, and safety, is determined, respectively, by district rangers, forest supervisors, and regional foresters under broad authority granted by the Chief Forester.

Campgrounds and Picnic Areas. Facilities required for the safe, sanitary, and convenient use of the national forests by the public are supplied on campground and picnic areas. Since overnight camping and transient picnicking are rarely compatible, an effort is made to keep picnic and camping areas separate from one another whenever possible.

Campgrounds and picnic areas in the national forests exceed 4,000 in number and are planned to accommodate as many as 280,000 people at one time [37]; some are readily accessible and very popular, catering to more than 100,000 visitors annually, while others are used only infrequently. Such areas include tables and benches, stoves or masonry fireplaces, sanitary facilities, garbage receptacles, and approved drinking water; some offer community shelters and facilities for swimming, including diving boards and bathhouses, and a few campgrounds make provision for use by trailers (except for special water and electrical connections). Because of the heavy patronage typical of readily accessible campgrounds, it is often necessary to limit the length of use by individual parties in order to provide similar opportunity for others.

Sports Areas. Summer outdoor sports and related interests which are in keeping with the forest environment are encouraged on sports areas.

Many lakes and streams in the national forests are suited for a variety of water sports, including swimming. In some cases such activities have been encouraged by the development or enlargement of existing lakes through the construction of dams, beach improvement, and bottom grading to remove obstructions and hazards, as well as the construction of facilities such as diving boards, rafts, docks, and bathhouses.

Where justified sports areas may also provide for the enjoyment of impromptu outdoor activities (e.g., baseball, volleyball) on playfields and playgrounds; provision is also made for the inclusion of informal informational displays relative to the region.

Winter Sports Areas. Recreational use of the national forests is not limited to the summer season. Over 200 winter sports areas with necessary facilities and services are found in the national forests of New England, the Lake states, the Rocky Mountain region, the Cascade area, and the Sierra Nevada region [37]. Although emphasis is placed upon skiing, other winter sports activities such as skating, tobogganing, and snowshoeing are also provided for, consistent with the demand. In 1956 more than 3 million skiers and other winter recreationalists used these areas [39]; their total capacity at any one time is nearly 300,000.

In order to administer this extensive winter sports program the U.S. Forest Service has formulated certain well-defined policies and has established procedures necessary to the provision of adequate facilities and the protection of visitors from inherent hazards.

Special facilities for the highly proficient are of secondary importance on national forest winter sports areas; instead they are planned for the enjoyment and use of the average participant with specific portions of each area designated for skiers of varying abilities. Facilities such as warming shelters, lunch counters, rope tows, and ski lifts are generally available and some of the larger and more isolated developments offer regular hotel and meal services. In most cases essential needs are provided by the U.S. Forest Service while facilities for which charges are required, such as tows and ski lifts, lunch or meal services, hotel accommodations, and the like, are installed and operated by private parties, subject to full administrative control of the U.S. Forest Service. Since national forests generally lack the unique characteristics typical of such areas as national parks, national forest winter sports developments need not be subject to the severe restrictions applicable in national parks; hence permanent ski lifts of varying types can usually be provided. Yet, as an indication that the U.S. Forest Service is mindful of the need for preserving the scenic beauty of areas in their charge, permanent ski lifts cannot be erected without permission of the Chief Forester. Further, hotels for overnight accommodation are not viewed with favor unless an area lacks such facilities in the immediate vicinity and unless the ski area is located at a distance from population centers.

Qualified Forest Service personnel known as snow rangers are stationed at individual winter sports areas to supervise varied aspects of these operations. Research in such matters as avalanche hazard removal

FIG. 6-9. Boy scout camp operated under special use permit with the U.S. Forest Service, Eldorado National Forest, California. (*Photo by Leland J. Prater, U.S. Forest Service*)

has also been conducted [35], and on areas located along main highways the U.S. Forest Service has enlisted the cooperation of state highway departments relative to snow removal from roads and parking areas, as well as the cooperation of state highway patrols relative to traffic control. Further, the National Ski Patrol cooperates with the snow rangers in supervising winter sports activities; this is of particular importance in the rescue of lost or injured skiers and in the provision of competent first aid. In addition, at many winter sports areas on the national forests competent ski instruction is provided for beginners and those not yet thoroughly proficient in this outdoor sport by instructors certified by the National Ski Association.

Organization Camp Areas. Facilities (e.g., lodging, meal service) necessary for the accommodation of organized groups are developed on organization camp areas. Such areas are specifically designated for development by nonprofit organizations and public agencies, or by the U.S. Forest Service, and are generally used by those who cannot afford expensive accommodations or costly camping equipment. Opportunities of this nature are often favored by such groups as Boy Scouts, Girl Scouts, Campfire Girls, the YMCA, 4-H clubs, churches, and welfare agencies. Administrative control of these areas, allotted on the basis of need, remains within the U.S. Forest Service.

Approximately four hundred organization camps, most of which are privately owned, operate within the national forests [33]. These units are capable of serving a maximum of about 40,000 people at one time.

Commercial Public-service Sites. Specifically designated areas of this type on national forest land include various public accommodations (hotels, motels, resorts, trailer sites) that are more elaborate than campgrounds and organization camps and are incidental to the enjoyment of the national forests. They also provide for the establishment of related necessary public services (e.g., restaurants, stores, gasoline stations, horse and boat liveries).

Facilities of this type must be in keeping with the forest environment and are constructed with private funds, except where essential services cannot otherwise be obtained.[7] Full administrative authority over resort areas is retained by the U.S. Forest Service.

Recreation Residence (Summer-home) Sites. Units of national forest land which are not needed or suitable for uses of higher priority are so designated on some national forests. On such areas individuals may be permitted to lease lots for summer residences at an annual rate determined by appraisal. Any buildings erected must conform to U.S. Forest Service architectural and construction standards. Over 16,000 summer homes are found in the national forests [37]. Establishment of new recreation residence sites requires the approval of the Chief Forester.

PUBLIC RECREATIONAL USE OF THE NATIONAL FORESTS

The rapid development of public interest in the diversified recreational advantages offered by the national forests is reflected in Table 6-2. Such interest had its inception many years ago, even before the U.S. Forest Service gave formal official recognition to recreation as a valid resource of these areas. In 1925 when an official recreational policy was first formulated by the U.S. Forest Service, more than 5 million people used the national forests for various forms of recreation. Since that time growth in this form of use of the national forests has paralleled that typical of other types of public lands; except for the depression years of the 1930's and World War II, recreational patronage of the national

[7] Two hotels within the national forests, Timberline Lodge in the Mount Hood National Forest, Oregon, and Magazine Mountain Lodge, in the Ouachita National Forest of Arkansas, were built with Federal funds and are owned by the Federal government. They are operated by private concessioners under U.S. Forest Service supervision.

forests has shown a constant and rapid acceleration which gives no indication of abating.

The popularity of certain forms of outdoor recreation on national forest lands has not been greatly modified by the phenomenal growth in recreational use of the national forests. In recent years the most popular activities have been picnicking, fishing, hunting, camping, and winter sports [39].

SUMMARY

It was inevitable that the national forests should become of major importance in outdoor recreation. Aggregating an area of over 180 million acres, the national forests include major portions of our principal mountain ranges, extensive sections of noteworthy lake country, and large areas of all principal forest regions in the United States; in addition, they provide a habitat for numerous species of native animal life, are characterized by wide variety in climate and, although located largely in the West, are also represented in many of the Eastern states. Many miles of highways, varying from main, cross-country thoroughfares to minor forest roads, render large parts of these areas accessible to the motorist, yet there are thousands of acres of rugged back country accessible only by trail. As a result the national forests offer a wide variety of recreational interests, ranging from a simple picnic of a few hours' duration to extensive wilderness travel.

The national forests are administered by the U.S. Forest Service, a bureau in the Department of Agriculture. Although established primarily for the sustained-yield management of such tangible renewable natural resources as timber, forage, and water, the recreational values of the forests are also recognized as one of their primary benefits and are managed accordingly.

The principles upon which the national forests were established, and upon which they are managed, are basically different from those of the National Park Service, a bureau in the U.S. Department of the Interior. Both types of areas embody important recreational values, but of different types. National forests are fundamentally utilitarian and are managed on a multiple-use basis. National Park Service areas are unique examples of their type and are managed on a single-use basis as outdoor museums.

Although many national forests are scenically beautiful, their features of interest are not so unique that the public interest dictates their complete preservation; or, where such unique features do exist within the national forests, they are duplicated on a more impressive scale in the National Park System. Thus, recreational use of the national forests can be guided by more liberal policies, affording opportunity for hunting

Table 6-2. Recreational Use of the National Forests

Year	Campgrounds	Picnic areas	Winter sports areas	Organization camps	Hotels and resorts	Recreation residences	Wilderness areas	Other forest areas	Total	Miscellaneous casual motorists
Cal.										
1924	1,588,489	1,871,534	....	....	1,018,541	181,825	....	....	4,660,389	1,450,000[a]
1925	2,129,968	2,086,717	....	....	1,161,660	243,861	....	....	5,622,206	2,110,000[a]
1926	2,056,742	2,403,411	....	....	1,318,965	265,149	....	....	6,044,267	2,400,000[a]
1927	1,845,709	2,623,608	....	....	1,350,123	317,373	....	....	6,136,813	2,690,000[a]
1928	1,845,693	2,937,511	....	....	1,381,595	385,518	....	....	6,550,317	3,590,000[a]
1929	1,902,961	3,056,456	....	....	1,795,861	376,780	....	....	7,132,058	5,380,000[a]
1930	1,980,736	3,272,682	....	....	1,330,610	326,896	....	....	6,910,924	5,450,000[a]
1931	2,193,866	3,765,025	....	....	1,618,460	496,566	....	....	8,073,917	5,250,000[a]
1932	2,178,231	4,048,796	....	....	1,138,634	530,182	....	....	7,895,843	6,382,628[a]
Fiscal										
1933	2,219,804	4,355,936	....	....	1,037,096	552,685	....	....	8,165,521	5,197,622[a]
1934	2,343,132	4,610,171	....	....	1,014,008	613,495	....	....	8,580,806	4,646,086
1935	2,395,658	5,326,037	....	....	1,268,998	727,637	....	....	9,718,330	7,104,686
1936	2,421,275	5,811,720	....	....	1,712,134	835,965	....	....	10,781,094	11,166,405
1937	2,836,040	5,973,930	....	....	2,165,329	857,359	....	....	11,832,658	18,969,780
1938	3,181,817	7,627,914	....	....	2,758,224	927,319	....	....	14,495,274	18,259,961
1939	3,157,490	7,019,180	1,289,211	....	1,987,812	878,168	....	....	14,331,861	20,470,855
Cal.										
1940	3,583,091	7,931,485	1,538,432	....	2,257,548	852,411	....	....	16,162,967	22,270,119
1941	3,349,898	5,818,963	1,519,054	244,111	1,917,766	601,288	87,078	4,466,627	18,004,785	28,079,191
1942	1,771,340	3,300,632	993,920	159,911	1,136,271	379,599	55,614	2,609,833	10,407,120[b]	16,851,811
1943	1,095,212	2,050,384	266,765	115,222	679,863	244,385	43,194	1,779,634	6,274,659[b]	10,915,582
1944	1,246,768	2,051,077	287,426	176,918	715,369	370,173	50,018	2,254,204	7,151,953[b]	10,967,270
1945	1,814,928	2,729,376	527,291	276,225	1,271,369	505,963	74,477	2,874,460	10,074,089[b]	14,529,515
1946	3,055,114	4,458,748	1,249,200	385,290	2,286,107	713,380	144,433	5,948,405	18,240,677	36,969,220
1947	3,518,147	5,262,600	1,725,675	322,529	2,110,406	535,978	194,141	7,661,275	21,330,751	56,494,738
1948	3,424,088	7,682,158	2,284,943	325,226	1,928,756	572,499	213,450	8,579,844	24,010,964	53,148,372
1949	3,837,010	7,659,234	1,712,607	386,306	1,929,597	615,242	243,599	9,696,660	26,080,255	54,536,616
1950	3,858,845	7,577,575	1,504,575	453,613	1,902,140	627,481	245,806	11,197,762	27,367,797	56,796,773
1951	4,140,866	8,669,341	1,929,270	478,460	2,133,674	636,173	312,385	11,650,083	29,950,252	65,454,119
1952	4,527,979	9,515,926	1,758,073	561,058	2,500,196	670,632	386,724	13,086,297	33,006,885	84,493,052
1953	4,810,341	10,335,910	1,944,193	587,468	2,564,219	758,493	408,305	13,994,121	35,403,050	89,842,564
1954	5,806,130	11,467,849	2,362,420	636,026	2,990,264	864,568	395,784	15,780,996	40,304,037	104,259,058
1955	6,796,706	12,418,342	2,977,220	655,455	3,230,860	863,332	462,094	18,308,859	45,712,868	119,585,516
1956	7,204,986	14,667,226	3,040,513	707,981	4,128,912	851,474	448,340	21,506,652	52,556,084	131,301,245
1957[c]	8,352,360	16,138,508	3,158,675	....	4,211,682	828,550	....	28,267,498	60,957,273	154,245,631

[a] Adjusted from figure representing "passers through" and "primarily to enjoy scenery."
[b] Does not include visits by armed forces personnel (1942—345,526; 1943—283,084; 1944—310,142; 1945—121,235).
[c] Figure for "Other forest areas" includes users of wilderness areas and organization camps.
SOURCE: Data 1924–1940 from summary provided by the U.S. Forest Service, Washington; 1941–1952 from Statistical Supplements to Report of the Chief of the Forest Service, U.S. Government Printing Office, Washington; 1953–1954 from Annual Statistical Report, "Recreation Visits," Forest Service, Washington; 1955–1956 from Report of the Chief of the Forest Service, U.S. Government Printing Office, Washington, 1957 from summary provided by U.S. Forest Service, Washington.

(within season) and, in certain instances, a greater degree of physical development. Briefly, the recreational values of both national forests and areas under National Park Service administration are important; properly coordinated they supplement one another in providing for a wide variety of highly necessary public recreational services.

Recreational use of the national forests has increased phenomenally since its inception many years ago; today over 60 million people use these areas annually for various forms of outdoor activities. As a result, many areas in the national forests especially designated for recreation have become overcrowded and their facilities show evidences of severe deterioration. To rehabilitate existing recreational facilities and to provide for anticipated increases in recreational use of the national forests in the future, the U.S. Forest Service has embarked upon an 85 million dollar program of improvement and development, known as Operation Outdoors, scheduled for completion in 1962.

SELECTED REFERENCES

1. Anonymous: A Vacation Guide, National Forests, "Trees: The Yearbook of Agriculture, 1949," U.S. Government Printing Office, Washington, 1949, pp. 855–889.
2. Allen, Shirley W.: Trail Riding in the Wilderness, "Trees: The Yearbook of Agriculture, 1949," U.S. Government Printing Office, Washington, 1949, pp. 537–544.
3. Allen, Shirley W.: "An Introduction to American Forestry," McGraw-Hill Book Company, Inc., New York, 1950.
4. Anonymous: Operation Outdoors in the National Forests, *Planning and Civic Comment*, vol. 23, no. 1, pp. 17–18, March, 1957.
5. Anonymous: "What Is Your Stake in the Northern Cascades—and what can you do to help?" Sierra Club, San Francisco, March, 1958.
6. Bassett, Ray E.: Recreational Forest Management as a Part of the Forestry Profession, *Proceedings of the Society of American Foresters Meeting*, Minneapolis, Minn., Dec. 17–20, 1947, pp. 152–159, Washington, 1948.
7. Buck, C. J.: The Place of Recreation in the Forest Program, *Journal of Forestry*, vol. 31, no. 2, pp. 191–202, February, 1933.
8. Granger, C. M.: "Recreational Development in the National Forests," American Planning and Civic Annual, American Planning and Civic Association, Washington, 1938.
9. Illick, Joseph S.: "An Outline of General Forestry," Barnes & Noble, Inc., New York, 1939.
10. Johnson, Rev. R. Riley: "Do You Know the Facts on the Proposed Glacier Peak Wilderness Area?" National Forest Multiple Use Association, Washington State Chapter, Bellingham, Wash., Nov. 1, 1957. (Mimeographed.)
11. Kneipp, L. F.: New Values in the Minds of Men, "Trees: The Yearbook of Agriculture, 1949," U.S. Government Printing Office, Washington, 1949, pp. 533–537.
12. Lord, Russell: "Forest Outings," U.S. Government Printing Office, Washington, 1940.

13. Loveridge, E. W.: The Administration of the National Forests, "Trees: The Yearbook of Agriculture, 1949," U.S. Government Printing Office, Washington, 1948, pp. 372–380.
14. Marshall, Robert: Priorities in Forest Recreation, *American Forests,* vol. 41, no. 1, pp. 11–13, January, 1935.
15. Maughan, Kenneth O.: Recreational Development in the National Forests, *Technical Publication,* no. 45, New York State College of Forestry, Syracuse University, Syracuse, N.Y., 1934.
16. Morse, C. B.: The Place of Recreation in the Forest Program, *Journal of Forestry,* vol. 31, no. 2, pp. 203–207, February, 1933.
17. Mountaineers, The: "Glacier Peak Area: Today a Wilderness Intact," Seattle, Wash., 1957. (Folder.)
18. National Park Service and U.S. Forest Service: "National Parks and National Forests," Washington, 1956.
19. Parke, William N.: Recent Experiments in Administering and Charging for Camping and Picnicking Privileges on the National Forests, *Journal of Forestry,* vol. 48, no. 4, pp. 275–277, April, 1950.
20. Pomeroy, Kenneth B.: Glacier Peak Wilderness, *American Forests,* vol. 63, no. 7, pp. 26–27, July, 1957.
21. Rutledge, R. H.: Principles of Conservation in the Use of Wild Lands, *Journal of Forestry,* vol. 31, no. 2, pp. 159–166, February, 1933.
22. Saunderson, M. H.: The National Forest Officer Looks at Resource Values, *Journal of Forestry,* vol. 45, no. 4, pp. 244–248, April, 1947.
23. Sieker, John: Everyone Is Welcome, "Trees: The Yearbook of Agriculture, 1949," U.S. Government Printing Office, Washington, 1949, pp. 551–556.
24. Spencer, John W.: The Place of Recreation in the Multiple Use Management of the National Forests, *Proceedings of the Society of American Foresters Meeting,* Minneapolis, Minn., Dec. 17–20, 1947, pp. 178–182, Washington, 1948.
25. Tremain, R. L.: Legal Aspects and Owner Responsibilities in Forest Recreation, *Proceedings of the Society of American Foresters Meeting,* Memphis, Tenn., Oct. 15–19, 1956, pp. 38–41, Washington, 1957.
26. U.S. Department of Agriculture, Forest Service: "Forest Regions of the United States Listing the Principal Trees of Each Region," Washington, 1937. (Map.)
27. U.S. Department of Agriculture: The Principal Laws Relating to the Establishment and Administration of the National Forests and to Other Forest Service Activities, *Miscellaneous Publication,* no. 135, Washington, 1939.
28. U.S. Department of Agriculture: "Trees: The Yearbook of Agriculture, 1949," Washington, 1949, pp. 372–380, 533–537, 551–556, 855–889.
29. U.S. Department of Agriculture, Forest Service: National Forest Protection and Management, Recreation, vol. III of "Forest Service Manual," Washington, v.d. (Multilithed.)
29-*a*. U.S. Department of Agriculture, Forest Service: Title 2300, Recreation Management, "Forest Service Manual," Washington, 1958.
30. U.S. Department of Agriculture, Forest Service, North Pacific Region: "Recreation Handbook," current revision, Portland, Ore., n.d. (Mimeographed.)
31. U.S. Department of Agriculture, Forest Service: "Recreation Handbooks,"

current revision, containing information on various regions other than Region 6, n.d. (Mimeographed.)

32. U.S. Department of Agriculture, Forest Service: "Shoshone National Forest, Wyoming: 1940," Washington, 1941.
33. U.S. Department of Agriculture, Forest Service: Our National Forests, *Agriculture Information Bulletin,* no. 49, Washington, 1951.
34. U.S. Department of Agriculture, Forest Service: The Work of the U.S. Forest Service, *Agriculture Bulletin,* no. 91, Washington, 1952.
35. U.S. Department of Agriculture, Forest Service: "Avalanche Handbook," Washington, 1953.
36. U.S. Department of Agriculture, Forest Service: Our Forest Resources: What They Are and What They Mean to Us, *Agriculture Information Bulletin,* no. 131, Washington, 1954.
37. U.S. Department of Agriculture, Forest Service: "National Forest Vacations," Washington, 1955.
38. U.S. Department of Agriculture, Forest Service: "Operation Outdoors: Part 1, National Forest Recreation," Washington, 1957.
39. U.S. Department of Agriculture, Forest Service: "Report of the Chief of the Forest Service, 1956," Washington, 1957.
40. U.S. Department of Agriculture, Forest Service, Pacific Northwest Region: "Glacier Peak Land Management Study, Mount Baker and Wenatchee National Forests, Washington," Portland, Ore., Feb. 7, 1957. (Mimeographed.)
41. U.S. Department of Agriculture, Forest Service: "Statistical Supplement to Report of the Chief of the Forest Service, 1942–1953," Washington, v.d.
42. Wagar, J. V. K.: Services and Facilities for Forest Recreationalists, *Journal of Forestry,* vol. 44, no. 11, pp. 883–887, November, 1946.
43. Wolff, M. H.: Some Aspects of Legal and Economic Provisions Governing Forest Recreation, *Journal of Forestry,* vol. 44, no. 11, pp. 892–896, November, 1946.

CHAPTER 7 *Economic Value of Recreational Lands*

Outdoor recreation is big business. One needs to exert little effort to become aware of this fact. Numerous advertisements in newspapers and magazines extol the recreational advantages of different sections of the country which compete with one another for the "tourist dollar," and a simple request will command a colorful array of maps, booklets, and brochures about these areas. Many states have well-organized travel bureaus which, in addition to similar efforts on the part of private concerns, assist the prospective traveler in obtaining a wealth of information relative to his vacation needs. Highways are dotted with numerous establishments catering to those in a holiday mood, and the provision of services related to outdoor recreation is a means of livelihood for thousands; consequently such activities are a primary basis for the economic stability of many areas. In addition, certain industries, almost wholly dependent upon outdoor recreational pursuits (e.g., hunting, fishing, boating, camping, skiing), have shown a startling development in recent years. Finally, as outlined in previous chapters, a wide variety of public outdoor recreational areas, administered by all units of government and aggregating an area of millions of acres, are characterized by a phenomenal and constantly growing patronage; even many owners of certain types of private lands who formerly frowned upon recreational use of areas under their control are now viewing such activities in a more favorable light.

Some idea of the tremendous economic impact of various kinds of recreational expenditures can be obtained from a number of surveys that have been conducted in recent years. In 1955, according to a study made under the auspices of the U.S. Fish and Wildlife Service, nearly 25 million hunters and fishermen spent approximately 3 billion dollars [40]. Further, Table 7-1, which lists certain conclusions from a number of economic recreational surveys, gives some idea of the value that various sections of the country place upon recreation as an income producer.

A few additional facts related to the economics of recreation might also be of interest. In Minnesota, in addition to the $67,300,000 spent in 1948 by out-of-state visitors, recreational activities of local residents

Table 7-1. Estimates of Total Recreational Expenditures in Various Parts of the United States

Area	Expenditures	Area	Expenditures
Arkansas, 1949–1950 [11]	$100,000,000	Oregon, Southwestern,	
Arizona, 1948 [34]	140,000,000	1950 [38]	$ 3,945,000
1949 [34]	135,000,000	Pennsylvania, 1948 [31]	600,000,000
1950 [34]	145,000,000	Tennessee:	
1951 [34]	160,000,000	Great Smoky Mountains National Park,	
1952 [34]	175,000,000	1947 [35]	10,965,551
1953 [34]	170,000,000	Knoxville, 1951 [17]	26,000,000
Grand Canyon National Park, 1954 [3]	10,663,000	1952 [18]	28,000,000
California:		1953 [19]	32,033,703
Southern, 1948 [1]	457,838,000	Virginia, 1950 [32]	270,879,238
1952 [2]	512,506,625	1952 [30]	600,000,000
1953 [2]	609,518,783	Shenandoah National	
Yosemite National		Park, 1952 [41]	12,000,000
Park, 1952–1953 [39]	10,841,100	Washington, 1939 [33]	89,000,000
Colorado, 1953 [6]	265,341,000	1940 [33]	90,000,000
Florida, Southeastern,		1948 [9]	116,000,000
Winter, 1952–1953 [44]	367,421,770	1949 [10]	123,200,000
Minnesota, 1948 [26]	67,300,000	1950 [21]	122,700,000
Missouri, 1949–1950 [27]	83,096,327[a]	1951 [22]	118,900,000
Montana, Glacier National Park, 1951 [28]	12,287,773	1952 [23]	134,500,000
New Hampshire, 1946 [13]	75,000,000[b]	Wisconsin, 1949 [20]	76,716,000
		Wyoming, Yellowstone National Park, 1949–1950 [45]	18,994,301

[a] For pleasure trips only; total money spent by out-of-state tourists on combined pleasure and business trips was $42,642,097 additional.

[b] Report stated between 75 and 80 million dollars.

SOURCE: Compiled from results noted in a variety of economic recreational surveys, as listed in the bibliography; figures represent only expenditures by visitors from outside the areas involved.

accounted for an added expenditure of $36,000,000 [26]. In the state of Washington a total of $26,000,000 was expended by local residents in 1952, approximately one-fifth the amount spent by nonresidents during that year [23]. In 1948 the tourist industry of Southern California supported a capital investment of $761,548,000, more than half of which consisted of investments in land, buildings, and equipment for hotels, motels, and related establishments. During the same year recreational expenditures in Southern California were also the basis for $7,615,000 in real and personal property taxes, $6,016,000 in retail tax payments, and $5,632,000 in gasoline taxes. It is not difficult to see why "tourism" is rated as Southern California's second largest industry [1].

BASIC VALUES OF OUTDOOR RECREATION

Before one can attempt to evaluate the financial returns from outdoor recreational areas, it is necessary to understand the nature of the public benefits resulting from the use of such lands. Basically, these may be grouped broadly into two principal categories: primary or direct benefits, and those values which are secondary, indirect, or otherwise incidental to the purpose for which such areas were established.

Primary or Direct Benefits. Public outdoor recreational areas are not established or operated for the purpose of returning a profit. Their primary values, the basic, underlying reasons for their existence, transcend any return which may be readily measured by the standards of the market place. These primary values, although they cannot be gauged accurately by known economic rules, are reflected in our economy in a positive though intangible manner. Some of the intangible benefits derived from the recreational use of wild lands are:

1. Improved efficiency of the individual in his daily tasks, through provision of opportunities for periodic release from daily routine, resulting in increased national productivity and wealth.
2. Increased national productivity resulting from the development in individuals of new or latent skills, broader interests, greater knowledge, and deeper perceptions, through educational and inspirational values of outdoor recreation.
3. Stimulated use of public recreational facilities and maximum dispersion of benefits noted above by provision of a wide variety of recreational opportunities at the lowest possible per capita cost. This is of particular importance to low-income groups.
4. Reduced need or lower expenditures for extensive law-enforcement programs, correctional institutions of various kinds, mental hospitals, and the like.

Thus, the primary purpose of public recreational lands is the provision of the widest possible variety of proper recreational outlets to all classes of society at the lowest possible cost. Such recreational lands offer people the opportunity to release physical and mental energy, foster broader interests and knowledge, develop better citizenship and individual responsibility, and relieve themselves of the stress and strain of modern life. Ideally, as a result of a more contented, energetic and forward-looking outlook developed in our citizens, the benefits of such lands are reflected in the national economy through increased production. The degree of this effect, however, in dollars and cents, is impossible to evaluate.

Secondary or Indirect Benefits. Although public recreational areas themselves are not established with a profit motive in mind, it is obvious that they induce certain expenditures. These expenditures, the secondary or indirect benefits of recreation, are reflected in the economy of the nation, the states, and individual communities. More tangible in character, many of these secondary values can be measured by customary economic rules, and their effect on the economy of a given region can be more readily determined. Some of these indirect or secondary benefits are:

FIG. 7-1. Primary benefits of recreational areas are almost impossible to evaluate economically.

a. Visitors relaxing on a sandy beach, Virgin Islands National Park. (*National Park Service*)

1. Stimulation of vacation travel. As a result of our higher standard of living many Americans have found that recreational values are worth their cost. Travelers look for these values much as they examine the merits of more tangible merchandise, spending their time, and dollars, in areas with the greatest personal appeal. Vacationers also compare the values gained from recreational travel with those of tangible needs (e.g., a new car, refrigerator, increased life insurance) and make purchases in accordance with the results of that comparison.

2. Development of business activity in areas within, adjacent to, or en route to recreational areas. Supplies and services in great variety are required by visitors attracted to recreational areas (e.g., hotel accommodations, meal services, supplies and equipment, gas and oil), thereby resulting in an inflow of money which might not otherwise have been spent in a given area.

3. Stimulation of business activities relative to the manufacture of recreational equipment, clothing, and supplies. The specialized needs of

b. A photographer records his visit to White Sands National Monument, New Mexico. (*National Park Service*)

c. Man is dwarfed by huge sequoias (*Sequoia gigantea*) in the Mariposa Grove, Yosemite National Park, California. (*Photo by Ralph H. Anderson, National Park Service*)

FIG. 7-1 (*Continued*)

recreationalists (e.g., campers, hunters and fishermen, mountain climbers, skiers, boating enthusiasts) promote and develop manufacturing enterprises whose activities are reflected in the national economy.

4. Increased property valuations. Vacation travel and other recreational activities, in stimulating business activity in and adjacent to

a

b

FIG. 7-2. Secondary benefits of recreational areas are more readily adapted to economic evaluation.

a. Substantial capital investment is required in various forms of accommodations: Many Glacier Hotel, Glacier National Park, Montana. (*Photo by Hedrich-Blessing, Great Northern Railway*)

b. Recreation often necessitates a wide variety of services and equipment; horseback party, Mt. Rainier National Park, Washington. (*National Park Service*)

recreational areas, bring about increased property valuations which are reflected in increased property-tax revenue to cities, counties, states, and the nation.

5. Increased miscellaneous-tax revenue. With particular reference to out-of-state visitors, recreational expenditures of all types include taxes of various kinds (e.g., gasoline tax, sales taxes, amusement taxes) which

are reflected in a direct monetary return to the nation and to various municipalities and states.

Other Benefits Related to Secondary or Indirect Recreational Returns. Careful consideration of all the obvious values derived from public use of recreational lands will reveal a number of other important benefits. First, recreational activities favor the development of individual initiative on the part of the small businessman, for recreational services and products are widely diversified and dependent upon personal interests. Thus, the pattern of the recreational industry is characterized by numerous small independent units, each providing a largely personalized version of a particular service or product. Only in very rare cases does the management of any recreational business approach monopoly form; in no case does it achieve a control characteristic of many other important industries. As yet, the recreational business is characterized by a pattern similar to that of the grocery business of a generation ago, before the advent of the chain store. Highly personalized recreational interests seem likely to maintain that pattern.

Further, since recreational lands are often located in relatively remote areas, the business activity which they stimulate is a vital factor in the stability and economic development of such regions. Even backward or retarded areas may be improved economically, and certain localities characterized by decline or past mismanagement of natural resources may, through development of recreational interests, be given a new lease on life.

Finally, recreational expenditures are an important factor in the dissemination of money within the nation, or within a given region. A large share of our national wealth results from activities in major industrial and business centers; it is derived largely from the processing and refinement of natural resources which are often obtained from relatively distant areas. Many of those who are supported by activities connected with such refinement and processing return a portion of that wealth to its point of origin through travel and recreational activities of various kinds.

DIFFICULTY OF DETERMINING ECONOMIC VALUE OF RECREATIONAL LANDS

In spite of the fact that recreational lands make a sizable contribution to the economic wealth of the nation, a complete monetary evaluation of that contribution is impossible. In particular, primary benefits do not lend themselves to customary methods of economic analysis. What monetary value, for instance, could be placed upon a spectacular sunset, a magnificent mountain, the thunder of the boiling sea along a rugged coast, or the hushed, cathedral-like quality of a virgin, coniferous forest?

The reactions of a hundred people viewing these identical scenes would be reflected in as many different ways; some would be refreshed in mind and spirit and thus able to attack their daily tasks with renewed vigor and greater efficiency, while others would be wholly unmoved. Yet such factors do have a monetary value. For instance, a location for a homesite which affords a spectacular view commands a higher price than a property of comparable size which lacks such an outlook. However, it would be difficult if not impossible to develop a mathematical formula that could be used in measuring such values, since they are so greatly varied, and since they appeal to different people in different ways.

Secondary benefits, since they are reflected in more easily recognizable monetary terms, are somewhat easier to estimate. Yet even in these instances the returns are so interrelated with other personal activities and so diffused through such a great variety of business channels that only the most careful and exhaustive studies can be expected to pinpoint them. At best, then, any survey attempting to evaluate the economic benefits derived from a given region as a result of public interest in that region as a recreational area presents only one aspect of the picture. It is indicative of only the secondary benefits, the expenditures induced by public interest in the recreational opportunities which the area offers.

It is thus difficult to determine the true economic value of recreational areas to a given region in a manner similar to that used for more prosaic industries. The following points must be considered:

1. Recreational benefits are intangible; they differ with each individual and even with different moods of the same individual.

2. Recreational values are not standardized as are those of automobiles, radios, TV sets, clothing, or refrigerators, which can be listed, catalogued, displayed, and compared, with some expectation of general understanding of the relative merits involved.

3. Significant data from which to draw conclusions for a complete economic evaluation of recreational benefits are limited; only in relatively recent years have efforts been made to measure adequately certain economic aspects of recreation. On the other hand, for some industries significant economic data are a matter of record, having evolved over a long period of time.

4. Recreational values, since they are obtained largely from public lands, are partially subsidized; instead of being sold under commercial market rules, they are made available to the public at or even below cost.

5. Financial support of recreational activities on public lands is usually derived from general funds; consequently such support is not identified with any specific tax source or other revenue.

In short, the economics of recreation has no ready, easily applied yardstick, no accepted unit of value, such as the board foot or kilowatt, by which one may readily compute the dollar value of timber or hydroelectric power. Recreation must have such an accepted unit of value before reliable estimates of the dollar potential of recreational areas can be determined in the most practical and universal manner. Adequate recreational surveys are obviously the source of such an accepted unit of value, but such surveys are expensive and time-consuming. To minimize our dependence upon these time-consuming, expensive processes and to foster the maintenance of reliable current estimates of the economic value of recreational areas, any recreational unit of value that may be devised should be of such character that it can be applied quickly, easily, and economically to any given situation. This need is particularly vital if one intends to compare the monetary value of recreational returns with returns from other forms of land use on the same area.

DANGER INVOLVED IN ECONOMIC EVALUATION OF RECREATIONAL LANDS

Many people feel that any attempt to justify recreation or recreational lands or facilities on the basis of economics is not only unnecessary and undesirable but even dangerous. Those who hold this view maintain that such an effort impairs the public concept of the purpose of many outdoor recreational areas and leads, through overcommercialization, to the ultimate destruction of the primary interests in these areas. Such objections are based upon solid ground; the interests of many important recreational areas have deteriorated as a result of operation on a dollar-producing basis.

It is natural, however, for many people to apply a dollar valuation to different needs and activities and, thus, to varied types of wild-land use. In controversies over reservation of lands for recreational purposes, it is often difficult to impress large numbers of people with the recreational value of such lands unless a monetary comparison is made between the returns from recreation as contrasted to returns from other forms of use. In such cases an economic evaluation of monetary benefits often serves a useful purpose. However, it should be clearly recognized that the benefits of such areas transcend a dollar value, for when people seek the recreational opportunities in any given area, they desire more than food, lodging, transportation, and the like, even though these are vitally important and the only things which are actually paid for. In effect, any economic recreational survey will indicate only the monetary return derived from minimum secondary values; primary values cannot be evaluated economically.

ECONOMIC RECREATIONAL SURVEYS

Economic evaluation of recreational lands is not new. In 1918 Waugh estimated the value of outdoor recreation in the national forests at 10 cents per person per hour [42]. In more recent years, however, since it has become obvious that recreational activities of various kinds were an important economic force, efforts at such evaluation were greatly intensified and systematized. As a result a wide variety of economic recreational surveys have been developed in different parts of the country. But these intensive surveys, although they present a wide variety of highly useful, significant facts, are not the final answer to many problems which are often faced by those concerned with the recreational use of wild lands.

In the first place many of these surveys deal with aspects of recreation which do not relate primarily to wild lands; wild-land recreational values are either completely ignored or, if considered, are so buried in the conclusions that their economic impact cannot be independently recognized. Although Table 7-1 lists some of the broad conclusions of a number of important recreational surveys, some of these do not bear specific relation to recreation on wild lands. Expenditures from other forms of recreation are also included and in some cases receive the greatest attention. Such is particularly the case in surveys concerned with Southern California and southeastern Florida, where major recreational expenditures are induced largely by night clubs, horse racing, and similar activities. Further, although the conclusions which these surveys present are useful in developing more generally acceptable data, they apply only to specific areas at a particular time; in addition, as already noted, they are expensive and time-consuming and require a relatively large staff of workers for assembling and digesting various kinds of information. Such elaborate programs are not often at the command of those faced with the need of quickly and easily evaluating the economic impact of specific recreational lands.

Such exhaustive surveys usually approach the problem of collecting significant data by requesting travelers to give written answers on printed forms to such pertinent questions as place of residence, number in the party, total length of the trip (in days and miles), purpose of the trip (vacation, personal visit, business), length of time spent in the area, type of accommodations used, total expenditure in the area, percentage of expenditure on various needs (food, lodging, gas and oil, and the like), and the economic status of the traveler. Questionnaires of this type are distributed in a variety of ways; by highway patrol officers, by hotel and motel employees, by the administrative staff of recreational areas (e.g., rangers in national parks), by employees of service stations, by operators of ferries or toll bridges, by Chambers of Commerce, and by automobile associations. The questionnaires are generally completed at the visitor's leisure and mailed to a central point for processing by experienced evaluators. As a result, a representative sample of visitor interests and preferences and their impact on the economy of the region is obtained which can be applied to the total tourist population.

It follows that the authenticity of such data is dependent upon the manner in which the survey was developed. Surveys which are based upon an inadequate sample, or which are slanted to obtain desired results, are of little value. If approached from an unbiased viewpoint, however, and carried out in a thorough, painstaking manner, such surveys provide valuable indicators of the appeal of given areas and the recreational expenditures which result.

APPLICATION OF DATA DERIVED FROM ECONOMIC RECREATIONAL SURVEYS

It has been pointed out that while we are dependent upon periodic surveys of an exhaustive character to supply basic information indicative of trends in recreational interests and expenditures, some more simple, less expensive, and more readily adaptable yardstick is also required. Average per capita expenditure per hour is suggested as such a yardstick (see Table 7-2). Within certain limitations, and considering each day as twenty-four hours, such a unit of value can be applied quickly to proper known data, thus providing an adequate estimate of the economic impact resulting from a given recreational situation.

The number of people attracted to a given area because of its recreational resources, or the number using a particular recreational facility (e.g., museum, ski tow, scenic highway), is largely dependent upon its inherent recreational interests; the greater those interests, the greater the number of visitors. Likewise, inherent interests will determine the length of time spent by each visitor in the area, or in the use of a particular facility. Both these factors are related to total recreational expenditures.

Although the number of visitors and the time spent will vary in relation to recreational interests, the average per capita expenditure per hour remains fairly constant in regions of similar recreational interests. Thus, if the number of visitors and the time which they spend is known, and this information can usually be obtained without setting up expensive, elaborate surveys, a fair estimate of the measurable economic value of any recreational area or facility in a given region may be quickly obtained (e.g., number of visitors times the average time spent by each visitor times the average per capita recreational expenditure for the region).

Similarly, estimates of the economic value of proposed recreational development may be derived by applying the unit of value to expected patronage and time spent, obtained by comparison with developments of similar type and location in the same region.

Table 7-2. Estimates of Average Daily and Hourly Recreational Expenditures per Person in Various Parts of the United States

Area	Day	Hour	Area	Day	Hour
Arkansas, State, 1949–1950 [11]	$4.99[a]	$0.21	Virginia: State, 1953 [30]	$4.79	$0.20
Colorado, State, 1953 [6]	7.64	0.32	Shenandoah National Park, 1952 [41]	5.80	0.24
Minnesota, State, 1953 [26]	6.26[b]	0.26	Washington: State, 1939 [33]	6.18	0.26
Missouri, State, 1949–1950 [27]	4.15[c]	0.17	1940 [33]	6.18	0.26
Montana: Glacier National Park, 1949 [14]	6.42	0.27	1948 [9]	6.03[d]	0.25
Glacier National Park, 1951 [28]	5.52	0.23	1949 [10]	6.38[e]	0.26
New Jersey, State, 1952 [29]	6.85	0.28	1950 [21]	5.60	0.23
Oregon, Rogue River area [38]	5.43	0.23	1951 [22]	5.00	0.21
Tennessee, Knoxville area, 1953 [19]	6.65	0.28	1952 [23]	5.25	0.22
			Wisconsin, State, 1949 [20]	4.32[f]	0.18
			Wyoming, Yellowstone National Park, 1950 [45]	5.73	0.24

[a] An average party of three people stayed 3.8 days in Arkansas, and spent $56.95 during that time.

[b] An average party of 3.5 people remained in Minnesota an average of 12.5 days, during which time they spent $274.15.

[c] Includes pleasure trips only; daily per person expenditures on combined pleasure and business trips were $5.77 or 24 cents per hour.

[d] An average party of 2.92 people remained in the state of Washington an average of 11.37 days, during which time they spent nearly $200.

[e] An average party of 2.9 people spent $18.50 per day while in the state.

[f] An average party of 4.1 people remained in Wisconsin for 16 days, during which time they spent $283.49.

SOURCE: Compiled from results noted in a variety of economic recreational surveys, as listed in the bibliography; figures given represent only those expenditures by visitors from outside the areas involved. Unless otherwise noted, daily expenditures are directly indicated in the survey; hourly rates computed.

Assuming that one is cognizant of its limitations, evaluation of the economic impact of recreational areas serves a variety of useful purposes.

1. It provides a picture of the importance of such areas in the economic structure of a given area, such as a community, a specific region, or a state.

2. It aids in the solution of land-use problems. On areas where recrea-

tional interests are in conflict with other uses, even though differences of opinion cannot be completely resolved wholly on economic grounds, an understanding of the comparative economic benefits derived from recreational development, as compared to other uses, may clarify such problems. Specifically, would the value of a given area be greater if utilized for recreational activities of a particular kind, or would a proposed hydroelectric power development return greater long-term benefits? On the basis of the needs of the foreseeable future, which type of management would be best for a given timbered area, one that proposes the utilization of wood products on a sustained-yield basis or one that involves retention of the original forest cover as a recreational asset? Where outdoor recreational needs of large centers of population are being considered, which values are paramount on a particular unit of land: those that may be derived from the establishment of a park, those that may result from the development of a residential site, or those that might accrue from industrial development?

3. It aids in determining the desired size of recreational areas. Average per capita expenditures per hour may be applied to expected use of proposed recreational areas to give a fair estimate of its total annual dollar value to the community. On the basis of current land values this figure can be used in determining necessary acreage to be purchased from available funds. If sufficient funds are not available, such an approach to the problem aids in presenting a clear picture of the financial requirements necessary for adequate recreational development.

4. By reasoning similar to that noted in the preceding paragraph, economic surveys justify existing recreational facilities or services and aid in evaluating proposed developments. For instance, the cost of a museum designed to interpret the significant interests of an area can be compared with its monetary value to a region by multiplying hourly per capita recreational expenditures by increased patronage and time spent in the region, as a result of public interest in the museum. In a similar manner the relative dollar return to a region from a modern highway planned for construction in a primitive area can be compared with the existing value of the area. Although a modern highway would certainly induce greater public use and increased financial return, this return may or may not be sufficient to justify the cost of highway construction and maintenance. Such a comparison might indicate that a higher percentage of return would be derived from the smaller investment necessary to the maintenance of its wilderness status.

5. Economic evaluations aid administrators of public recreational areas in obtaining adequate financial support for their operations. Although public recreational areas attract travel and new money to those regions in which they are located, only a small part of the revenue de-

rived from recreational expenditures accrues to agencies administering such lands; their financial support is derived from official appropriation which must be adequately justified to receive favorable action. Justification of necessary funds will be most forceful if based upon the importance of such lands in the economic welfare of a given region. If the principal administrative officer of a recreational area can present a clear picture of his needs and support his request for necessary funds with a firm estimate of the dollar value of such developments to the economy of the region in which his area is located, his request is more likely to develop an adequate response.

The more elaborate recreational economic surveys go much farther than the mere determination of dollar values involved. They also provide an understanding of the complex aspects of the recreation business in a given region by listing the total recreational expenditures of visitors, together with the percentage of expenditure for different items (e.g., food, lodging, transportation), the point of origin of visitors and the varied income groups represented, travel patterns, and other pertinent data useful to the vendor of recreational services. Such data are also useful to the administrator of public recreational lands in planning or conducting his particular operation. The more complex surveys are also valuable as a means of sponsoring most efficient public service on the part of employees by developing an understanding of the habits, interests, and characteristics of their customers. Further, since the recreation industry is a large one, an economic comparison with other important industries often develops pride on the part of those engaged in various aspects of it, thus raising the standards of service.

WEAKNESSES OF THIS THEORY

Anyone concerned with the administration of recreational lands, or anyone who has found it desirable to meet the challenge of those who insist upon gauging values of land use wholly on economic grounds, will quickly recognize certain weaknesses in the suggested plan. However, it is felt that these weaknesses are largely due to the lack of basic information collected by various recreational administrators rather than to the theory. Various media of communication have long based their charges for advertising space or time on the number of their subscribers, listeners, or viewers. Could not somewhat similar reasoning be applied to the numbers of visitors who are attracted to a given area because of its recreational advantages?

Yet for adequate application of per capita–per hour expenditures, changes and refinements in our customary system of collecting basic information in the field are required. Mere listing of total numbers of visitors is not sufficient. We must first utilize a self-contained area, one that is delineated by recognized political or topographical boundaries. Second, it is necessary that travel data be segregated. We must know how many people come from outside that area, since only their expenditures can be logically considered as contributing to improved localized economics. Travel from within the region, although it does have an effect upon certain specific businesses, does not reflect upon improved local economics, since such expenditures would accrue to the advantage of the area in some way in any case; such expenditures are merely transferred from one form to another (e.g., from one local recreation area to another or from the purchase of various tangible commodities to recreation). Finally, the average length of time that people from outside a given region remain in the area must be known.

For instance, it is impossible to develop a quick evaluation of the recreational value of the Snoqualmie National Forest in the state of Washington from available data. Although official statistics of recreational use of the Snoqualmie National Forest[1] indicated that 649,000 people used various recreational facilities of that area during 1957, and the average length of each visit was 1.5 days, no "breakdown" as to the origin of those visitors is given. If our formula is applied irrespective of where these recreationalists came from, and if we use the latest estimate of hourly recreational expenditures in Washington as noted in Table 7-2, a total dollar value of over 5 million dollars would be indicated.[2] This figure, if not wholly incorrect, would be extremely difficult to defend. Many of those who found recreational interests to their liking on the Snoqualmie National Forest were local people whose expenditures did not contribute to "new money" attracted to the region by the recreational advantages of this national forest. On extensive areas of this kind it would also be advisable to record "foreign" recreational visitors by ranger district; this would not only indicate relative recreational importance of each of these areas but would also aid in allocating funds for recreational development and improvement on the basis of greatest dollar return to specific areas within the national forest.

Finally, to get the most realistic figure we must also know how many people of a given region were induced to seek recreation beyond its borders. This figure should logically be subtracted from that which reflects "foreign" recreational expenditures.

However, with the exception of the last item mentioned these weak-

[1] "Recreation Visits, Annual Statistical Report, January 1, 1957–December 31, 1957," U.S. Forest Service, Snoqualmie National Forest. Data noted exclude 3,950,000 casual motorists who also visited the Snoqualmie National Forest during 1957.

[2] 649,000 visitors × 36 hours average visit × 22 cents estimated average hourly recreational expenditure in state of Washington (1952) indicates that recreational value of Snoqualmie National Forest in 1957 was $5,140,080.

nesses offer no insurmountable barriers. They can be remedied, if not overcome, by slight modification of current methods of collecting data on the ground, a modification which demands only a little more effort and which is within the limits of available employee time and administrative funds. The results that would certainly accrue from an ability to substantiate a firm figure of economic values would readily justify necessary changes in procedure.

SUMMARY

The recreational "industry" is a major factor in the economic stability of many sections of the country. Although the expenditures by those who use various forms of recreational lands contribute little to the direct support of these areas, such expenditures serve to attract travel and thus are responsible for the introduction of considerable "new" money in the surrounding region. In effect, recreational areas serve as a form of subsidy to the recreation business.

In spite of their economic importance recreational areas are not established or operated simply to make money. Their primary objectives are to provide opportunities for a variety of constructive spare-time interests which are necessary to the health and welfare of the people and to make those benefits available to everyone at a minimum cost. Such primary values of recreational areas are reflected in the national economy through improved individual productivity, but complete measurement of such benefits in dollars and cents is impossible. Thus, only *indirect* returns are reflected in any estimate of the economic value of recreation.

Indirect returns from recreation are indicated in a number of economic recreational surveys which have been made for different sections of the country; some of these have a very close relationship to the recreational values of wild land. From these surveys one may derive a unit of value (average per capita expenditures per hour) which can be used in quickly developing firm estimates of the measurable financial return from recreational areas or facilities within well-defined regions if information gathered in the field is adequately detailed. Properly used, such estimates are valuable in the development of public understanding of the magnitude of returns engendered by recreational areas and in justifying necessary financial support for their maintenance, development, or improvement.

The values of outdoor recreational lands are fragile, but they can be marketed indefinitely, provided that those values are known and understood and provided that they are administered in a manner that will ensure their preservation and proper maintenance. Like the fabled goose and the golden egg recreational values can be destroyed by overuse or improper development in an effort to make them function purely as profit-producing enterprises. The economic value of recreational lands is not only reflected in the dollars which a region derives as a result of the existence of such areas but also in what costs we are willing to bear in order to have and to preserve their varied interests.

SELECTED REFERENCES

1. All-year Club of Southern California, Ltd.: "Selling Climate at a Profit," Los Angeles, 1949.
2. All-year Club of California, Ltd.: "Report to Executives," Los Angeles, 1953.
3. Arizona Highway Department, Division of Economics and Statistics; the U.S. Department of Commerce, Bureau of Public Roads; and the U.S. Department of the Interior, National Park Service: "Grand Canyon Travel Study," n.p., n.d.
4. Bennett, Victor W., and Charles W. Wurst: "Characteristics of the Tourists in Greater Miami, 1951–52," University of Miami, Coral Gables, Fla., 1953.
5. Booth, A. W.: "The Lakes of the Northeastern Inland Empire: A Study of Recreational Sites," Bulletin, no. 5, State College of Washington, School of Economics and Business, Bureau of Economics and Research, Pullman, Wash., April, 1948.
6. Crampton, L. J., and F. W. Ellinghaus: "1953 Colorado Statewide Summer Tourist Survey," University of Colorado, School of Business, Bureau of Business Research, Boulder, Colo., December, 1953.
7. Friedman, Robert S.: "How States Find Out about Their Tourist Trade," University of Maryland, College of Business and Public Administration, Bureau of Governmental Research, College Park, Md., 1954.
8. Gibson, Weldon B.: "Pacific Northwest Tourism: A Billion Dollar Industry," Address before the Pacific Northwest Trade Association Conference, Vancouver, B.C., May 9, 1955.
9. Greenway, Don, and M. W. Lee: "The Washington Tourist Survey, 1948," Bulletin, no. 8, State College of Washington, School of Economics and Business, Bureau of Economic and Business Research, Pullman, Wash., January, 1949.
10. Greenway, Don, and R. R. Lanzillotti: "The Washington Tourist Survey, 1949," Bulletin, no. 15, State College of Washington, School of Economics and Business, Bureau of Economic and Business Research, Pullman, Wash., April, 1950.
11. Harvey, E. C.: The Contribution of Automobile Travelers to the Arkansas Tourist Industry, *Research Series,* no. 22, University of Arkansas, Institute of Science and Technology, Fayetteville, Ark., December, 1951.
12. Hines, L. G.: Wilderness Areas: An Extra-market Problem in Resource Allocation, *Land Economics,* vol. 27, no. 4, pp. 306–313, November, 1951.
13. Hodges, Sydnor: "The Vacation Business in New Hampshire, 1946," New Hampshire State Planning and Development Commission, Concord, N.H., 1949.
14. Hoflich, H. J., and M. E. Beatty: Glacier National Park Visitors in Montana, 1949, *Regional Study,* no. 1, Montana State University, Bureau of Business and Economic Research, Missoula, Mont., May, 1950.
15. Johnston, Fred T.: "An Analysis of the Economic Value of Yellowstone

National Park to Surrounding Communities and States," U.S. National Park Service, May 18, 1944. (Mimeographed.)

16. Keahey, James H.: Tourism in Texas, *Texas Business Review,* vol. 31, no. 3, pp. 6–8, March, 1957.
17. Knoxville Tourist Bureau: "$26,000,000 Tourist Cake," Knoxville, Tenn., 1951.
18. Knoxville Tourist Bureau: "$28,000,000 Tourist Melon: 1952 Survey Findings," Knoxville, Tenn., 1952.
19. Knoxville Tourist Bureau: "The Merriest Time of All Was Rung Up on the 1953 Cash Register," Knoxville, Tenn., 1953.
20. Lanning, V. H.: "The Wisconsin Tourist: A Study of the Resort and Recreation Business of Wisconsin, 1949," University of Wisconsin, University Extension Division, Bureau of Business Research and Service, School of Commerce and Bureau of Community Development, Madison, Wis., 1950.
21. Lanzillotti, R. F.: "The Washington Tourist Survey, 1950," Bulletin, no. 17, State College of Washington, School of Economics and Business, Bureau of Economic and Business Research, Pullman, Wash., January, 1951.
22. Lanzillotti, R. F.: "The Washington Tourist Survey, 1951," Bulletin, no. 20, State College of Washington, School of Economics and Business, Bureau of Economic and Business Research, Pullman, Wash., March, 1952.
23. Lanzillotti, R. F.: "The Washington Tourist Survey, 1952," Bulletin, no. 23, State College of Washington, School of Economics and Business, Bureau of Economic and Business Research, Pullman, Wash., March, 1953.
24. Maryland State Planning Commission: "Probable Economic Effects of the Chesapeake Bay Bridge on the Eastern Shore Counties of Maryland," Publication, no. 62, Baltimore, April, 1950. (Mimeographed.)
25. Maryland State Planning Commission: "Recreation in Western Maryland: A Major Economic Asset," Publication, no. 73, Baltimore, December, 1951. (Mimeographed.)
26. Minnesota Department of Business Research and Development: "A Survey of Minnesota's Vacation Industry: Steps to Better Vacations in Minnesota," St. Paul, Minn., n.d.
27. Missouri State Highway Department, Department of Highway Planning; and U.S. Bureau of Public Roads: "Survey Report of Out-of-state Passenger Car Traffic," Jefferson City, Mo., 1950.
28. Montana State Highway Commission Planning Survey, U.S. Bureau of Public Roads, and U.S. National Park Service: "Glacier National Park Tourist Survey, Summer, 1951," Helena, Mont., 1951.
29. New Jersey Department of Conservation and Economic Development, State Research and Promotion Sections: "Report on New Jersey's Vacation Guests in 1952," Trenton, N.J., n.d.
30. Pate, James E.: "Recreation as a Function of Government in Virginia," Preliminary report submitted to Inter-agency Committee on Recreation, Virginia Inter-agency Committee on Recreation, Richmond, Va., Jan. 20, 1953. (Mimeographed.)
31. Pennsylvania Bureau of Employment and Unemployment Compensation: The Resort Industry in Pennsylvania, *Statistical Information Bulletin,* no. 77, Harrisburg, Pa., Jan. 10, 1950. (Mimeographed.)
32. Quittmeyer, Charles L.: "The Virginia Travel Trade," Abstract prepared for the Subcommittee on Travel Trade, The Advisory Council on the Virginia Economy, Committee on Recreation, Richmond, Va., July, 1951.

33. Seymour, R. G.: "Washington State Tourist Industry Survey," University of Washington, College of Economics and Business, Bureau of Business Research, Seattle, Wash., 1947.
34. Shirer, John: Arizona's Tourist Trade in 1953, University of Arizona Bureau of Business Research, *Arizona Business and Economic Review,* vol. 3, no. 1, pp. 1–6, January, 1954.
35. Tennessee Department of Highways and Public Works, Division of Traffic and Finance Studies; U.S. Bureau of Public Roads; and U.S. National Park Service: "Great Smokies Mountains National Park Tourist Study, 1947," n.p., 1949.
36. U.S. Department of Commerce, Office of Area Development: "Your Community Can Profit from the Tourist Business," Washington, 1957.
37. U.S. Department of the Interior, National Park Service, Land and Recreational Planning Division: "The Economics of Public Recreation: An Economic Study of the Monetary Evaluation of Recreation in the National Parks," Washington, 1949.
38. U.S. Department of the Interior, National Park Service: "Vacation Survey: Rogue River Basin, 1950," n.p., 1950.
39. U.S. Department of the Interior, California Division of Highways; and U.S. Bureau of Public Roads: "Yosemite National Park Travel Survey, December 16, 1952–December 15, 1953," n.p., n.d.
40. U.S. Department of the Interior, Fish and Wildlife Service: "National Survey of Fishing and Hunting: A Report on the First Nationwide Economic Survey of Sport Fishing and Hunting in the United States during the Calendar Year 1955," Circular, no. 44, Washington, 1956.
41. Virginia Department of Highways, Division of Traffic and Planning; U.S. National Park Service; and U.S. Bureau of Public Roads: "Shenandoah National Park Tourist Study," Richmond, Va., 1952.
42. Waugh, Frank A.: "Recreation Uses on the National Forests," U.S. Government Printing Office, Washington, 1918.
43. Weinberger, Julius: Economic Aspects of Recreation, *Harvard Business Review,* vol. 15, no. 4. pp. 448–463, Summer, 1937.
44. Wolff, R. P.: "Tourist Days and Tourist Spending: Fall–Winter and Spring Season 1952–1953 in Southeastern Florida," University of Miami, Bureau of Business and Economic Research, Coral Gables, Fla., n.d. (Mimeographed.)
45. Wyoming Highway Department, Planning Division; U.S. Bureau of Public Roads; and U.S. National Park Service: "Yellowstone National Park Tourist Study, 1950," n.p., 1950.

CHAPTER 8 *Administration and Management of Recreational Lands*

The primary objectives of recreational land management are the provision of the maximum variety of outdoor recreational opportunities for the greatest number of people at the lowest possible cost and, at the same time, the perpetuation of the inherent recreational values of such lands for the future. Attainment of this goal is beset by many perplexing problems. It cannot be achieved without adequate planning which considers not only public recreational needs and the nature of different types of recreational benefits, but also the fact that the national economy requires proper, optimum commercial utilization of other natural resources.

Most wild lands have recreational values of some kind. These values, in view of their importance to public health and welfare, should be considered in any over-all program of land use. But recreation represents only one phase of land use. On certain areas tangible natural resources (e.g., timber, forage, minerals, hydroelectric power) are of such great economic importance that the public welfare can be served best by a management program which gives first consideration to the sustained utilization of commercial products. In such cases recreation may be minimized or, in certain instances, even eliminated from consideration. Conversely, on other wild lands recreational benefits are dominant; under such conditions commercial use of natural resources, however well managed, should be materially reduced or totally excluded. Between these two extremes lie areas with natural resources of such character that, by careful management, both utilitarian and recreational needs may be satisfied without serious consequences in either case [10,16,20,23,26,31,56].

In order to determine the best function of wild lands and to ensure policies of administration which will properly use and sustain their basic values, it is necessary to study carefully all possible uses of the wild lands on the basis of present and future needs. Good planning fosters the development of an administrative policy for specific areas which serves as a guide in details of management, emphasizes the proper functions of these lands, and coupled with enlightened techniques, promotes uses which will return maximum sustained benefits, both socially and economically, to the community and the nation.

On lands which are obviously of paramount utilitarian merit severe objections cannot logically be raised to *proper* utilization of natural resources required as raw materials for industry, nor can *appropriate* methods necessary to the manufacture or marketing of resultant products be condemned. Although many activities concerned with the production, harvesting, and processing of essential raw materials unnecessarily depreciate many recreational interests, these difficulties can often be eliminated, or at least alleviated, by the application of modern techniques or enlightened procedures. For instance, on lands where commercial forest utilization is recognized as desirable, it is not necessary to forfeit certain recreational values if timber is harvested in accordance with sound silvicultural principles and in areas removed from general travel. Commercial utilization of natural resources need not be accompanied by fire, overgrazing, soil erosion, and similar effects of bad land management, nor should pollution of waters necessarily be synonymous with manufacturing enterprises or the growth of metropolitan centers. Further, careful study relative to indiscriminate drainage of marshes and swamps, which provide food, shelter, or nesting sites for large numbers of waterfowl, may reveal the likelihood of a poor trade of that important wildlife resource for agricultural land of dubious value. Structures necessary to public use of the outdoors need not be designed in poor taste or in a manner out of keeping with their environment. Business must advertise its wares, but an unsightly conglomeration of signs along our highways is not necessarily the answer to that problem.

RECREATIONAL PLANNING

Since recreation involves many diverse interests and activities, lands which are recognized as predominantly desirable for such uses vary widely in character. No one area can provide opportunities for all types of outdoor recreation. Many outdoor recreational interests are incompatible; some lands are best adapted to certain activities, others to radically different types of diversion. Thus, a variety of areas serving different basic recreational purposes is required; the number, distribution, and size of such areas are dependent upon public needs. The fact that many recreational areas once considered ample for any possible degree of use are now seriously overrun indicates that the complaint of "excessive size" is not always valid.

Proper recreational planning involves careful evaluation of all recreational benefits which may be derived from different types of terrain. By this means various recreational lands may be brought into proper relationship with each other. Such planning:

1. Defines the purpose and scope of various areas in the over-all recreational program of a given region.
2. Ensures proper integration of these areas with each other, as well as with important utilitarian land values.
3. Facilitates proper distribution of recreational opportunities of different types, provides adequate outlets for a variety of leisure-time activities, and develops broader and more diversified recreational advantages for all classes of society.
4. Promotes maximum interest in maintaining intrinsic, nonrenewable qualities of recreational areas.
5. Fosters economy in providing for outdoor recreational opportunities.

Ideally, recreational lands serving specific purposes should supplement one another so that unnecessary duplication of services and facilities can be eliminated. Although certain types of recreational areas may be more numerous or of greater size than others, each, like the component parts of an orchestra, has its particular job in the over-all plan.

Although their functions may appear to overlap in certain cases, recreational lands may be grouped broadly in two classes. One category embraces areas which serve public recreational needs best by being maintained in essentially a natural condition. The other includes lands having recreational potentials which can be enhanced by judicious modification of their original character.

Recreational Lands of Essentially Natural Character. Certain outdoor recreational activities are valuable because of the feeling of physical and mental self-reliance or accomplishment which they develop in individuals. Such benefits are derived largely from areas typified by a truly natural landscape. These benefits may be derived from such divergent activities as the ascent of a mountain or the identification of wild flowers, but the primary value is a feeling of personal accomplishment that is derived from overcoming unusual physical difficulties not typical of modern living.

Recreational rewards of this type are derived largely from primitive and significant areas. Primitive areas are extensive tracts unmarred by any type of modern development. Figuratively, they are "islands in the sea of civilization," and those who use them must be as nearly self-sufficient as possible under today's conditions. Outstanding among lands of this type are specifically designated wilderness and wild areas in our national forests. Extensive wilderness terrain is also characteristic of many national parks, national monuments, wildlife refuges, and Indian reservations [47,49].

The true wilderness, characterized by solitude and unmodified natural conditions, is a priceless recreational heritage. Any relaxation of the standards which have been established to guard the characteristics of such lands, or any improvements which modify the necessity for individual self-sufficiency in their use, destroys their value. Further, as our way of life develops, it will become increasingly important to guard our remaining wilderness areas from mounting pressures which, although often presented as logical and harmless, would destroy them [15,17,21,23, 27,31,38,44,47,49,59].

True, the lack of modern facilities and comforts and the greater degree of experience and time required in the enjoyment of wilderness conditions restrict the use of such lands to a small segment of our population. But this is a case for, not against, the retention of adequate wilderness country; it is a necessary adjunct of an over-all outdoor recreational program. Were wilderness areas made easily accessible, the very presence of large numbers of people, irrespective of the facilities that would certainly be required, would destroy the basic qualities of these areas. Other types of recreational lands are better adapted to the needs of individuals whose recreational interests do not require primitive conditions or who have insufficient time, experience, physical ability, or resourcefulness to ensure safe and proper use of primitive lands.

Significant areas, characterized by unique geological, biological, archeological, or historical interests in a natural setting, are of primary value as a means of promoting public understanding of the inspirational qualities of the world in which we live. In effect, they are outdoor museums of national, regional, or local interest. Their size varies, being dependent upon the nature of their characteristics; their development should be restricted to the minimum required for bringing visitors in contact with representative examples of their particular qualities.

Most units under National Park Service administration, many state parks, and to a great degree, varied types of lands designated for wilderness use fall in this category. They owe their existence to public interest in the educational and inspirational qualities embodied in the dramatic nature of their setting or in their primitive, unspoiled beauty. Their values would be seriously impaired by the introduction of facilities or activities which divert public attention from the primary reasons for their existence or which promote public uses that are not in accord with their cardinal purpose. On occasion, such difficulties are far reaching and almost impossible to correct. For instance, a number of the disagreements that developed over the boundaries of some national parks were not due entirely to a lack of appreciation of the need for recreation but to a misunderstanding of the particular recreational service that national parks provide. The roots of these misunderstandings are embedded in a concept of the national parks which achieved maximum development during the See America First boom. During that period, contrary to the original conception of national parks as outdoor museums, public interest in the national parks favored an outdoor playground aspect. As outdoor recreation gradually came of age, and as its pattern assumed a more logical course, the National Park Service intensified its efforts to shelve this viewpoint. The public, however, conditioned by the playground notion, has been loath to alter that point of view. As a result too few people understand the basic difference between national parks and other types of extensive, interesting outdoor recreational lands.

Areas established because of significant features of interest should be large enough to ensure adequate protection of their values, the necessary size being dependent upon the type of interest involved. An area of less than a city block may be satisfactory for the preservation of an important historical structure in a metropolitan center. On the other hand, the preservation of a biological community will require much more expansive terrain; in addition to land embracing the biological community itself, adjacent territory which contributes to its existence should also be included.

Modified Recreational Lands. Public recreational needs embrace numerous interests other than those provided for by natural areas. Further, many people lack the time, energy, ability, interest, or background to gain maximum value from the use of truly natural areas. Provision for many types of outdoor recreational activity can be made on lands where prudent modification of natural conditions does not materially depreciate their recreational benefits. Such areas, although characterized by pleasant, attractive surroundings, are usually designed for use by large crowds. Campgrounds and picnic areas, resort developments, lands providing for active enjoyment of physical sports, parkways, roadside attractions or waysides, and buffer zones may be so classified.

Camping and picnicking are so closely interwoven with many broader outdoor objectives that sites which are for such uses are usually a part of more extensive recreational areas. However, since camping and picnicking are important leisure-time activities in their own right, areas suited to such uses are often independently established. Although resort areas emphasize outdoor playground aspects, in so far as possible the natural features of the areas should be maintained to preserve the qualities which serve to attract their patronage. Sports areas vary from small, specifically designed municipal playgrounds to extensive regions of rugged terrain. Since these areas are concerned primarily with the provision of accouterments necessary to such activities as hunting, fishing, swimming, boating, skiing, and organized games, natural conditions may occasionally be sacrificed. Maintenance of natural conditions is not obligatory in the provision of good hunting and fishing; in fact good forest management often enhances the development of game populations by improving the food and habitat of certain species. Even on many wildlife refuges, although often of extensive size and of essentially natural character, certain modifications favoring the development of conditions required by particular animal associations may be permissible. Roadside attractions and waysides are usually of small size; parking space for a few cars, water, limited picnic facilities (occasionally camp and trailer space), and attractive explanatory signs may be provided where desirable. They are useful as rest stops for motorists, as scenic vantage points, or as locations where varied roadside interests may be emphasized. Buffer zones serve as "cushions" against the encroachments of civilization by limiting or prohibiting commercial use or development of adjacent lands of greater intrinsic merit.

DEVELOPMENT OF AN ADMINISTRATIVE POLICY FOR RECREATIONAL LANDS

Each area of land having recreational value, as determined by the broad land-use program, should be managed in accordance with a concise but comprehensive administrative policy developed through consideration of the following factors:

1. The nature of the land area in question—the topography, soil, climate, water resources, special significance (e.g., plant and animal life, geological, historical, archeological interests), and related characteristics. Particular attention should be given to whether or not the area possesses unique irreplaceable features, the preservation of which is vital to long-term public benefit.
2. Population and character of use—the density, dispersal, and trend of population in the region from which an area draws the major share of its visitors and the present and probable character of use (whether constant, intermittent, or seasonal).
3. The means of access—the nature of both present and probable transportation facilities to and within the area.
4. The character of local, regional, and national recreational needs and the trends of such needs.

As noted earlier in this chapter, the administrative policy serves as a guide in specific details of management. It recognizes the type or types of recreational benefits which an area can provide best and indicates the nature of recreational activities which are compatible with its primary purpose. It defines the recreational objective or objectives of each area in relation to other lands considered in the over-all recreational program for the region, ensuring maximum economy of operation through elimination of expensive duplication of services and facilities. Further, while allowing for possible future changes as a result of unforeseen developments or public needs, the administrative policy provides for the continuity of a well-balanced program and the preservation of intrinsic recreational values.

Nature of the Land Area. Climate, topography, soils, water resources, and the like not only affect the quality of recreational areas but also the type of recreational service they can render best. The nature of the land is also important in determining the physical development that is possible and the interests and the activities of visitors.

FIG. 8-1. Scenery, as well as many other recreational interests of land, are greatly affected by climate; sand dunes near Stovepipe Wells, Death Valley National Monument, California-Nevada. (*Photo by George A. Grant, National Park Service*)

Climate, as a major factor in the distribution of plant and animal life, bears strongly upon the characteristics of various recreational areas. Climate also affects the cultural patterns of people; consequently, ethnological and archeological interests vary widely in different sections of the country. Climate also modifies scenery; it is responsible for such features as deserts and glaciers, and structural land patterns as well as fossilized remains are indicative of conditions in past geological time.

Climate is also important in matters pertaining to the destruction of many recreational values. For example, fire reacts differently under varying meteorological influences, and in certain areas alternate freezing and thawing contribute to the deterioration of exposed fossilized wood.

Climate also determines and regulates public recreational interests and, thus, is responsible for differences in facilities required for similar activities in various regions. For example, trail shelters for the comfort and convenience of hikers are necessary where weather is uncertain; by contrast such facilities are not required where dependable weather is the rule.

Indirectly, climate may also materially affect recreational values by causing excessive seasonal concentrations of people, and such concentrations, if not properly guarded against, result in abnormal wear and tear and eventual modification of recreational lands.

Large concentrations of people invariably cause deterioration of many recreational interests in the outdoors. In addition to the likelihood of

FIG. 8-2. An undisturbed environment fosters the maintenance of many biological interests in the outdoors. (*Photo by Bob Haugen, National Park Service*)

increased vandalism, the mere presence of large crowds has a wearing effect upon recreational lands. Hazard from fire is increased. Horses distribute seeds of undesirable plants. Shrubs and vegetation may be literally tramped out. Certain soil types place definite limitations on the degree and type of public use. In particular, interesting plant associations characteristic of loose, friable soils may be quickly destroyed by unregulated visitor traffic, and packing of soil about the roots of trees may damage campgrounds and other heavily used forest areas, for reduced soil aeration adversely affects tree vigor, thus prompting epidemics of destructive insects and fungi [25,29,30]. The disappearance of interesting animal species is often a reflection of the modification of a natural environment; other animals, like the American black bear in many national parks, may be pauperized through public overattention, thus causing a depreciation in the interest value of the animals and an increase in the possibility of property damage and physical harm resulting from misdirected intimacy. In addition, historical, archeological, and paleontological treasures may be seriously impaired by pressure of constant attention; even massive geological features may be marred through improper interest or by damage caused by unregulated human activity.

Where recreational benefits are dependent upon the maintenance of natural conditions, management of recreational areas must give particular attention to maintenance of the biological balance. For instance, although the values to be maintained must be balanced against the degree of public hazard, extensive snag removal in a forest eliminates the nesting sites of many birds; indiscriminate clearing of brush and debris from the forest floor destroys many elements of food, cover, and related factors necessary to the survival of certain animals; the flooding of lands and, conversely, the draining of swamps or bogs cause even greater damage to natural conditions and dependent plants and animals. To the uninitiated it may seem ridiculous to give profound consideration to such details as homeless woodpeckers, unhappy winter wrens, frustrated cottontails, or hungry raccoons, but if natural values are basic to the quality of a recreational area, the maintenance of conditions upon which those natural values are dependent is vital.

Administrators of recreational lands must also wrestle with problems inherent in the topography of areas under their jurisdiction. Boating, skiing, mountain climbing, riding, and numerous other activities are dependent upon the character of the terrain. In addition to their importance in determining the nature and location of roads, trails, campgrounds, hotels, and similar developments, topographical characteristics are responsible for numerous public dangers which must be recognized, understood, and guarded against. Physical barriers erected to protect the public from certain hazards are not always desirable, for they are costly and often destroy the esthetic qualities of the surroundings. The necessity for such barriers can often be avoided by proper planning; roads and trails may be located to eliminate hazards and yet to provide attractive views, or caution may be developed in individuals by means of an interpretive program which fosters public understanding of the nature of such dangers.

Water resources are obviously important. The presence of interesting waterfalls, lakes, streams, or expanses of salt water bear strongly upon the interests and hazards of recreational areas. Further, water resources are a determining factor in the nature of specific developments, for campgrounds, hotels, sanitary facilities, and similar needs are dependent upon an adequate water supply.

Population and Character of Use. Since population and leisure time give evidence of a continuing upward trend, we cannot expect the problem of providing adequate public outdoor recreational opportunities to resolve itself. Proper land-use planning, coupled with the development of a satisfactory administrative policy for specific areas of recreational value, and the subsequent efficient management of these areas, is the most logical answer.

The population pattern of a region, that is to say its density, dispersal, and increasing or decreasing trends, obviously bears strongly upon all aspects of land-use planning, including that concerned with recreation. The greater the number of potential users of recreational lands, the greater the need for recreational areas of adequate size, proper dispersion, and suitable diversity of interests, and the greater the difficulties of recreational land management. In particular, problems related to congestion and overuse are intensified. Each region has singular land-use questions which must be answered upon their own merits by good planning if all vital public needs, both social as well as economic, are to be most advantageously served. In sections of the country having a highly concentrated population, such as in parts of the Eastern United States, the solution of land-use problems is particularly difficult; not only are there a great number of competing interests for available lands but inappropriate uses are often so firmly established that it is impossible or economically unfeasible to dislodge them. A rapidly expanding population presents different but equally difficult questions. Many Western areas exhibit evidences of "growing pains"; their complicated or controversial land-use problems can be minimized only by timely, proper planning.

Severe fluctuations in the use of recreational areas often complicate their management. Sudden week-end expansions in visitor population, which as quickly subside, can be very troublesome. All types of recreational lands accessible to large centers of population are characterized by a use pattern of this nature, yet owing to prohibitive costs, it is unsound and uneconomic to gear the operation of such areas to their maximum patronage. As a result they are plagued by overtaxed facilities and inadequate personnel during peak periods and by a lack of complete utilization at other times. Further, the physical character of most areas places a definite limit on physical development. Excessive periodic concentration of people invariably results in damage to basic recreational values; they may be either worn out by simple public pressure or destroyed through modification of the area as a result of attempts to provide sufficient facilities for the accommodation of large crowds. On areas typified by excessive use for long periods, damage to basic characteristics is even more likely.

Since the coordination of many outdoor recreational activities with commercial utilization of other wild-land resources is feasible, a multiple-use program should be instituted whenever practical. A single-use administration serves recreational needs and activities which are not compatible with such a plan; in such cases current or potential recreational patronage may either be so great that any use other than recreation must necessarily be barred, or, as on significant areas, the nature of recreational benefits precludes commercial utilization of other natural resources.

FIG. 8-3. Significant recreational interests, like this cliff dwelling in Mesa Verde National Park, are especially vulnerable to damage if subjected to continued heavy use by large crowds. (*National Park Service*)

Significant recreational lands are often augmented by other nearby sites that are better adapted to use by large crowds. In a sense such areas serve as buffer zones, dissipating many damaging pressures which militate against recreational benefits of greater intrinsic merit. There can be no objection to any form of constructive, healthful outdoor recreation as such, in its proper place, but in the interest of preserving diverse intrinsic values, as well as economy of operation, no activity, however popular, should usurp the basic reason for the existence of significant lands.

Different types of recreational lands, if established on the basis of careful evaluation of long-term public needs and if managed for the purpose for which they are best adapted, will attract people of kindred interests to the exclusion of others. Thus congestion will be alleviated, controversy over competing interests will be largely avoided, and necessary duplication of costly services and facilities will be minimized.

On recreational areas of extensive size specific sections can often be designated for different uses, thus isolating basically incompatible public activities.

Means of Access. The development of an administrative policy for different types of recreational lands both affects and is affected by the nature of related transportation facilities. In some cases established or impending future transportation patterns predispose certain areas to specific kinds of recreational uses. For instance, existing or definitely planned roads or well-entrenched use of lakes as landing sites for aircraft will nullify wilderness conditions; or if several areas are being considered for winter sports development, lower operational costs of a location adjacent to a highway regularly maintained for winter travel may outweigh certain minor deficiencies in terrain. Conversely, decisions as to specific recreational functions may affect the character of necessary transportation. If an area is designated for wilderness use, only trail travel is allowed within its boundaries. By the same token, the transportation system of recreational areas established primarily because of their unique, irreplaceable characteristics will have to be planned and developed with due regard to the resultant effect of such facilities on those interests [6]. On the other hand, a more liberal interpretation of transportation needs may be necessary for recreational areas designed for certain activities, or for large crowds.

The nature of transportation facilities also affects the character and the degree of patronage typical of different recreational lands. Where visitors come from, their background, economic status and interests, the distance they travel, the length of their stay, and the type of accommodations and services required are all related to the type of available transportation.

Character and Trends of Recreational Needs. Within the last several decades public interest in the recreational benefits of wild lands has developed to such an extent that careful evaluation of its trends is becoming increasingly important. Public outdoor recreational interests change and new forms develop, often necessitating revisions in the administrative program of affected areas. For instance, compact and convenient hotel developments have largely replaced the monstrous structures typical of many recreational areas a generation ago, and the greater mobility of our people has minimized the need for permanent summer-home sites in favor of a variety of transient overnight accommodations. Even the nature of campgrounds is subject to change; modern campers insist on certain refinements and many campgrounds must also be designed for use by trailers. Skiing is another case in point. The phenomenal development of this sport has extended the use of many recreational areas, but skiing has also presented a number of perplexing problems such as the safety of visitors, the solution of avalanche hazards, and the difficulties and expense of winter road maintenance. The organization of the National Ski Patrol alleviated the first of these difficulties, and studies by the U.S. Forest Service have provided a better knowledge of how to

FIG. 8-4. The maintenance of highways in winter is expensive and often dangerous. (*National Park Service*)

combat avalanche dangers [50]; but in spite of improved equipment, the maintenance of winter highways continues to be precarious and expensive.

In particular the phenomenal development of interest in skiing has complicated the administration of certain national parks [2,3]. There can be no objection to skiing in national parks if this activity follows a pattern adapted to primary national park purposes, which require that varied winter interests be enjoyed in a truly natural manner. It has been stated repeatedly that the national parks are essentially outdoor museums, not resorts or playgrounds. To maintain this fundamental concept it is necessary to prevent introduction of resort or playground activities; the significant inspirational quality of national park scenery must be guarded, winter and summer, from development of both physical modifications and public attitudes which might undermine the basic national park idea. Thus large permanent physical facilities such as chair lifts and development of competitive winter sports shows which attract large numbers of spectators are not in keeping with the purpose of national parks.

Although extensive development of skiing areas is not suitable on the national parks, skiing is a desirable and important form of outdoor recreation for which adequate provision should be made. This can be readily accomplished on areas which do not possess the intrinsic qualities typical of the national parks but which have equal or often superior terrain and snow conditions. Such developments, available in many national forests, are usually located along major highways maintained for general travel. In such instances road-maintenance costs need not be charged exclusively to winter recreation; further, the presence of necessary permanent facilities does not materially damage related recreational interests.

The growing use of aircraft as a means of reaching remote areas poses an even greater problem [12,41,42]. Unless this trend is properly guided, the ultimate effect upon wilderness values is not difficult to visualize. Although it is useless, sometimes even undesirable, to resist completely the development of modern transportation, proper planning can foster a program which provides adequate access without destroying wilderness values. Each situation will have to be judged upon its own merits, but, in general, a zoning system restricting landing facilities and other developments required of aircraft to locations outside such areas, but readily accessible to them, is worth consideration. Such a plan is followed by the National Park Service and U.S. Forest Service. Although often located nearby, facilities for direct air access within the national parks are lacking, and except in emergencies, aircraft are prohibited from landing in wilderness and wild areas in the national forests.

PERTINENT DETAILS OF RECREATIONAL LAND MANAGEMENT

Being concerned primarily with people, the management and operation of recreational lands are a rewarding and at the same time often an exasperating experience. The successful accomplishment of one's allotted tasks, whatever they may be, is a test of one's patience, diplomacy, initiative, resourcefulness, and technical skills. Basically, details of recreational land management are concerned with the following broad factors:

1. Protection and preservation of inherent recreational interests.
2. Planning, design, construction, and maintenance of necessary struc-

tures and related facilities which are in keeping with the character of the area, and the provision and operation of services necessary to the area's public use.

3. Protection of the health, safety, and property of visitors and employees, and the protection of park facilities.

4. Relationship between the administration of the area and operators of necessary commercial services.

5. Organization of adequate personnel and the proper coordination of their various activities.

Protection and Preservation of Inherent Recreational Interests. Unregulated, unwise, or unenlightened management of recreational lands invariably modifies the basic reasons for public interest in such areas and greatly depreciates their recreational values. Protection and preservation of basic values, then, are axiomatic; they underlie all activities concerned with the management of recreational lands.

Damage to primary values of recreational lands stems largely from the wear and tear generated by excessive public use and from a lack of responsibility on the part of the public in the care of such lands [13,43]. Such difficulties vary with different areas, but they are closely related to the degree and character of use, the means of access, the type and location of facilities, and the nature of the land area. Unfortunately, there is little that can be done to erase completely the effects of past overuse or improper planning typical of some recreational lands, but since protection and preservation are among the primary concerns of enlightened recreational land management, it is imperative that administrators make every effort to alleviate overuse and develop public interest in and understanding of their recreational privileges.

The preservation of significant recreational areas is of primary importance, since they are especially subject to damage as a result of overuse. In particular, care must be given to the degree and manner of the development of such areas and the character of public activities on them. Although significant recreational features cannot be fully appreciated by the public unless adequate means for their observation and study are provided, it should be recognized that development of any kind introduces elements of artificiality which adversely affect the interests involved. For this reason physical development of significant recreational lands should be held to a minimum; facilities necessary to the comfort and convenience of visitors should be considered as a means to an end rather than an end in themselves.

Public activities in significant recreational areas should conform to high standards. In most cases an area's unique features, many of which are quite fragile, can be destroyed or seriously modified by ill-advised actions. If the values of significant recreational lands are to be perpetuated for the enjoyment of future generations, public use must be guided by specific protective rules. We may not like it, but uncontrolled recreational activity typical of the days of our forefathers is no longer possible. Regulatory restrictions, some of which may be irksome, will be increasingly necessary as greater numbers of people seek the fulfillment of their leisure-time needs in the outdoors.

Even wilderness areas, although visited by comparatively few people, are not immune to the dangers of overuse. Wilderness values are delicately balanced; they cannot absorb the impact of too many people; it is possible for remote back country to be altered seriously by relatively few travelers, particularly if accompanied by numbers of pack animals and riding stock [46]. Also, the use of aircraft as a means of gaining access to remote regions poses many problems [12,41,42]. Consequently, restrictive rules and regulations relative to the use of specifically defined wilderness areas must be imposed so that the benefits of these lands may be preserved.

The maintenance of the remaining American wilderness involves a great public responsibility. In numerous discussions about the reservation of extensive areas for wilderness recreation, severe criticism has been leveled at those who seek to utilize the natural resources of wild lands commercially. Such criticism is often justified, but wilderness enthusiasts are not entirely guiltless in their use of the outdoors, and the more forward-looking men and women in that group are cognizant of this fact. On too many occasions the natural beauty of remote wild lands has been severely damaged by unthinking or selfish individuals. The impact of use by excessively large groups is particularly severe, but repeated use by smaller parties, if such use is not accompanied by good outdoor manners, can be equally damaging. Too often extensive flower meadows have been severely trampled or overgrazed. In too many instances signs and trail shelters erected for the safe and convenient use of remote areas exhibit various forms of vandalism. Fuel wood, literally scoured from the vicinity of desirable camp sites, is often used with unregulated abandon and with little consideration for the needs of those who may follow. On many occasions boughs have been stripped unnecessarily from living trees; refuse and garbage have not been properly disposed of, and basic sanitary requirements are not always followed. Such evidences of selfishness and poor outdoor manners occasionally result from the activities of those who class themselves as devotees of wilderness recreation. True wilderness enthusiasts, however, because of their greater interest and understanding in such matters, have a responsibility of proper leadership in the alleviation of such problems. They should give tangible evidence of their sincerity in these matters by voluntarily regulating, controlling, or even limiting their activities in remote areas and by working for a more general improvement of public outdoor manners. If they do not accept this obligation of leadership, they should be willing to assume their share of responsibility for the deterioration of wilderness interests, or they should be prepared to abide by an increasing number of arbitrary administrative restrictions and regulations imposed by various land managers for the protection of the inherent values of remote lands.

The basic interests of other recreational lands must be guarded with equal zeal. For instance, the use of beaches for swimming and water

a b

Fig. 8-5a. Disfigured trunk of an aspen. (*Photo by George A. Grant, National Park Service*)

b. A little care would have saved the expense of this roadside cleanup operation. (*Photo by Jean Speiser, National Park Service*)

sports is dependent upon uncontaminated water. Inappropriate development largely destroys the recreational importance of ocean, lake, and stream shore lines. Camping and picnic areas are interesting only so long as they remain neat, clean, and attractive. The litter that too often accompanies public use of roadside attractions is anything but pleasing to the eye. Hunters and fishermen must abide by the true meaning of the word "sportsman." An attractive ski terrain can be ruined for many participants, and the hazards inherent in such areas intensified, by the undesirable behavior of a small handful of skiers.

Public outdoor manners relate directly to the protection of recreational

interests. It is imperative that administrators of recreational lands give careful consideration to ways and means by which public appreciation for and care of recreational interests may be developed. The more people are aware of their responsibility to such lands, the less will be the likelihood of damage.

Poor outdoor manners are also expensive. Improper public attitudes create many disagreeable tasks which invariably fall to employees of recreational areas, and the cost of carrying out these tasks can often be a financial burden if the factors which prompt them are not controlled at their source. Among noteworthy positive examples in this connection is the growing use of litter bags by motorists, a practice which has materially reduced the amount of debris along highways. The Keep America Green program, which has the famous bear, Smokey, as its trademark, is another example. Since its origination in the state of Washington in 1941 [1], this program has been largely responsible for a striking reduction in the amount of forest acreage destroyed by man-caused forest fire.

Poor outdoor manners are largely the result of public ignorance or indifference; they are a reflection of the interests, character, and background of visitors. For example, problems relative to the administration of the Cook County Forest Preserve near Chicago are quite different from those of Mesa Verde National Park in southwestern Colorado. The character as well as the degree of patronage is radically different.

People whose interests and activities are normally cricumscribed by an urban environment often find it difficult to adapt to the requirements of the outdoors; being largely unaware of its demands, they are often unable to appreciate properly the necessity of exercising maximum individual responsibility. Thus through ignorance or indifference they are apt to damage the very interests which served to attract them or to get into difficulties which not only harass the administrative force but often result in severe or even fatal injury to themselves.

Areas of unique interest are particularly vulnerable to the effects of bad outdoor manners. To this end interpretive programs are important, for through understanding of the significant qualities of such areas public cooperation in their protection is encouraged [53].

Specifically, if the archeological importance of a remarkable cliff dwelling is understood and its value to mankind is recognized, one's approach to it, both physically and mentally, will be more in keeping with the dignity which should characterize use of such treasures, and wear and damage will be minimized. Similarly, varied and abundant floral interests will be less liable to modification through selfish removal of plants or thoughtless meandering from developed trails. Further, the danger of fire or acts of vandalism which ravage the beauty of unique forests will be materially reduced. Even features of geological excellence, generally more resistant to such damage, will be more likely to escape defacement if their importance is recognized.

Although originally planned to enhance public enjoyment of significant areas, interpretive programs are receiving increasing recognition as a protective measure. They have been most intensively developed in areas under National Park Service administration, but some state park systems, notably California, Indiana, and Washington, have also recognized their value. Although the more elaborate forms of interpretive activities, such as those typical of National Park Service areas, may not be practical on smaller and less significant recreational lands, similar or related activities are worthy of the most earnest consideration of all recreational land managers, even those concerned with municipal parks.

Provision of Facilities and Services. The nature and extent of facilities and services for each type of recreational area should be governed by the primary purpose of the area as defined by administrative policy. This policy shapes the degree and the type of necessary accommodations, transportation, communications, provisions for outdoor sports, interpretive needs, and similar requirements. In turn these will regulate the necessity for other basic provisions such as water supply, sanitation, refuse disposal, and law enforcement. Consequently, if the primary values of an area are properly diagnosed, its management will set the pattern of use and automatically determine the nature and extent of physical development.

Proper planning and design of physical facilities in outdoor recreational areas are of extreme importance. They promote desired visitor use and enjoyment as well as economy of operation; they facilitate adequate presentation and protection of basic recreational interests, and they promote public safety by minimizing or even eliminating many hazards.

The following factors are given careful consideration in the planning and design of physical facilities.

Harmony. The design of physical facilities must be in accord with the character of the region; cultural and climatic variations in different sections of the country prompt distinctive architectural patterns which should naturally be reflected in the appearance of necessary buildings.

Simplicity. Developments should be functional and should follow natural-use tendencies.

Efficiency. Easy maintenance at all seasons, operation with a minimum of supervision, and use with a minimum of danger, accident, or damage are paramount. Recognition of climatic factors is of obvious importance, for deep snow, excessive heat, and similar factors necessitate adequate consideration of the comfort and safety of visitors and employees.

Unobtrusiveness. Developments should be inconspicuous; since physical facilities in outdoor recreational areas are essentially tools to aid visitors in safe and proper use of such lands, they should blend with rather than dominate their surroundings. They should be no more conspicuous than necessary to indicate their presence.

Preservation. Necessary construction should modify the basic interests of a given area as little as possible. Consideration should also be given the probable effects of public use from the provision of particular facilities; for example, the use of an area recently opened to motor travel may be responsible for greater damage than that caused by the actual construction of the highway.

Utility. Whenever practical, developments should serve the widest possible use.

To a considerable degree, the manner in which visitors move about recreational areas regulates the nature and extent of probable damage. Thus, planning for proper visitor circulation and dispersal of visitor concentrations is of vital importance. The pattern of movement is largely regulated by the location of necessary facilities such as roads, trails, camp and picnic grounds, hotels, and similar developments. It is important that such facilities be planned and located to ensure adequate circulation or free flow of visitor movement. This not only minimizes damage resulting from congestion but facilitates proper use of the area by the maximum number of people.

The development of transportation facilities within recreational areas must be coordinated with the specific purpose for which these areas were established; such facilities must also be properly planned in relation to the values involved. Certain types of recreational lands can accommodate a greater degree of physical development of this kind without material damage to their features of interest than others; in fact, the widespread interests of some areas demand extensive transportation facilities. It is important, however, to recognize that any such development—a road, a trail, a boat landing, an airfield, a ski lift—introduces a degree of artificiality. Thus, such features must be considered in the light of their relation to the character and primary purpose of the area. If they are not so considered, their benefits may be counterbalanced by resultant damage which, in the long run, may be irreparable.

It is also important to recognize that the development of transportation facilities within recreational lands prompts a variety of other needs. Additional camp and picnic grounds, parking areas, water supply and sanitary facilities must be planned, developed, and maintained; the problems of fire control, waste disposal, visitor health and safety, and the protection of basic interests in the area are greatly enlarged; and a staff adequate to handle these matters must be provided. In fact, these varied consequences of improved transportation often involve greater cost and require more careful consideration than the feature which induced them.

Roads and trails, in addition to enabling people to reach a particular destination, should be designed to call attention to interests along the way. In that manner public knowledge of the area is broadened, and the numerous stops thus encouraged serve to alleviate congestion by dispersing travel throughout the area. Loop roads and trails are preferable to those terminating in dead ends; by such means visitors are able to return to their original starting point without retracing their steps, and the capacity of the road or trail is materially increased by eliminating returning traffic. In campgrounds and picnic areas proper traffic control, and consequently reduced congestion and damage to trees and vegetation, is most adequately served by one-way, loop roads.

Hotels and other buildings which serve specific public needs should be located so that they will be readily accessible in accordance with the desired public use of the area. Large developments, however, are undesirable because of the extensive throngs which they attract. Whenever possible, development of several small centers that are properly integrated with one another and separated by suitable buffer zones is preferable to a single large development. Through such an arrangement public interest and use of an area are more evenly distributed, and the likelihood of severe damage is proportionately reduced.

Public congestion is particularly critical in areas of unique quality. In such cases damage to significant features may be alleviated by eliminating crowd-catching facilities or activities from the immediate neighborhood of high-quality interests. Sequoia National Park poses an interesting example of this procedure. The primary feature of interest in Sequoia National Park is the Giant Forest with its numerous magnificent specimens of *Sequoia gigantea.* Since these marvels of the arboreal world, with their tremendous size and great age, can be appreciated and enjoyed best by actually living among them, facilities for public accommodations (e.g., campgrounds, hotels, and related structures) were originally located within the forest itself. With increasing patronage, however, it soon became evident that the normal wear and tear fostered by such a plan would eventually result in material damage to these magnificent trees. National Park policy, although dedicated to the development of public interest in the giant sequoia, is also vitally concerned with the protection of such interests for the benefit of future generations. As a result a long-term program aimed at the eventual removal of all unnecessary facilities from the Giant Forest was developed. Public campgrounds, shops for the maintenance of necessary equipment, horse corrals, and similar utilities were relocated at a distance, and accessibility to the Giant Forest was limited to a modern trail system. This plan permitted enjoyment of these arboreal monarchs but minimized the wear and tear of public use. Today only the lodge and its cabins remain in the Giant Forest; presumably these will be relocated at some future time.

This trend which seeks to eliminate the causes of excessive public concentrations in areas of particular value is a natural result of the difficult problems posed by crowds of people. Even in Yosemite Valley, where the pattern of use has been established for many years and where sweeping changes are made difficult by the staggering investment, considerable thought has been given to the removal and relocation of all but necessary facilities beyond Yosemite Valley or even outside park boundaries. As a result, through the Mission 66 program, approval has been given for the development of a new administrative site for Yosemite National Park; eventually, all but those facilities which directly serve the visitor will be removed from Yosemite Valley [53-*a*,53-*c*]. The Mission 66 program also gives consideration to the alleviation of somewhat similar conditions in other National Park Service areas [53-*b*].

Protection of Visitor Health, Safety, and Property. Whenever outdoor recreational lands are provided for public use, the administrative agency has an obligation to guard patrons, as well as employees and their families, from conditions which may adversely affect their physical well-being or which endanger their property. There are a number of basic reasons for difficulties of this nature on recreational lands. Visitors are in an unfamiliar environment, characterized by hazards which are often unrecognized or improperly understood. Public interest in recreational attractions often develops localized overcrowding which promotes a variety of conditions disadvantageous to public health and safety. Further, these areas are available, without question, to all people; no workable method of preliminary screening of visitors in relation to character and attitude is applicable. In addition, the nature of recreational interests and activities sponsors laxity by visitors in the protection of personal belongings; the outdoors seems to foster a feeling of universal trust which, unfortunately, is not always justified.

In recognition of the foregoing factors, adequate, sensible rules and regulations must be developed; these have the dual objectives of protecting the interests of an area and the people who are attracted to it. The value of such rules and regulations is proportionate to the care and consideration which guided their preparation, the positive manner in which they are presented to the public, and the intelligence by which they are enforced.

Personal conduct of visitors must obviously be governed by accepted laws of decency and propriety; in areas characterized by large heterogeneous crowds, the possibility of thievery must be recognized and controlled; in movement of people throughout an area, certain hazards must be carefully considered and guarded against. In many recreational areas normal traffic dangers are complicated by rough, mountainous terrain responsible for relatively steep, narrow, winding roads. In addition, a variety of interests generally compete for the attention of the driver. Attractive scenic vistas, wild animals, colorful wild flowers, or interesting geological formations along the way often militate against traffic safety.

The behavior of hikers also poses a variety of problems. For instance, rapid descent over a steep trail may develop unsure footing and unsafe speed; short-cutting switchbacks in unfamiliar terrain may lead hikers into dangerous situations; special precautions are required when foot and mounted travelers meet on the trail; rolling of rocks or debris from high

FIG. 8-6. Pauperization of the American black bear through feeding encourages misdirected intimacy, often resulting in bodily harm or property damage. (*Photo by Abbie Rowe, National Park Service*)

places must be stamped out; and smoking, except in safe, designated places, should be banned.

Many other factors must be reckoned with in considering public safety in the outdoors. The peculiarities of climate, such as fog, high winds, lightning, or extremes of temperature, can be dangerous if not properly understood. The unsuspected or changeable power of stream or ocean currents and the hidden dangers of unfamiliar waters are ever-present threats in some areas. The character of the surface over which hikers travel, as in the case of snow, glacial ice, bogs, or the rocky footing of steep, mountainous terrain, often necessitates specific precautions. Consequently, before starting on any potentially hazardous undertaking in the outdoors, individuals should have adequate experience or proper leadership, and on extensive trips, they should carry equipment adequate to meet all foreseeable contingencies.

In many areas the relationship between people and native plant and animal life promotes difficulty. If poisonous plants or animals (e.g., poison ivy, poison oak, rattlesnakes) are likely to be encountered, visitors should know of their existence and, if possible, be informed how to recognize and guard against them. It is also important that the public be aware of the dangers which lurk in overfamiliarity with native animals that have lost their fear of man. Such animals are not tame; their response to unexpected movement or misunderstood actions can often result in severe bodily injury to the uninformed person. Except under certain conditions, such as during the mating season, when females are caring for their young, or when suddenly surprised, truly wild animals are rarely dangerous; their fear of man prevents unnecessary contact with him. Under conditions of complete protection, however, many wild animals lose this fear yet react instinctively when startled, frightened, or bewildered.

Proper disposal of refuse, coupled with regular inspections of water supply and methods of storing and serving food, is also important to public health and safety. Such safeguards are particularly vital in areas characterized by large numbers of people, for crowded conditions increase danger from contamination of food and water sources and from the spread of contagious diseases.

To ensure maximum visitor safety, administration and enforcement of regulations require adequate, trained personnel experienced in the specialized duties for which they are responsible. It is also essential, in case of emergency, that the staff be properly organized so that each member is equipped and able to fulfill his particular emergency obligation. A fundamental safety measure is the availability of first-aid and medical care.

It should be obvious that the basic underlying factor in the promotion of public health and safety, as well as in the protection of property, is public understanding; the proverbial ounce of prevention is always worth the pound of cure. Since recreational areas were established for public benefit, those who use them must recognize that the privilege of such use entails definite personal responsibility. Inconsiderate, selfish, uncooperative, willful, or antisocial acts which affect the interests of an area or violate principles of decency and common sense infringe upon the legitimate rights of others and militate against maximum enjoyment by all.

Relationship between the Administration and Operators of Commercial Facilities. A variety of specific commercial facilities and services is necessary to full enjoyment of many outdoor recreational areas. Hotel accommodations, meals, equipment and supplies, public transportation, and similar needs must be provided. Since most recreational lands are administered by various public agencies which, by law, are often prohibited from engaging in commercial ventures, services of this type must necessarily be handled by companies or individuals experienced in and equipped for such business. These concessionaires usually operate under a franchise or permit granted by the administrative agency.

It is important that the nature of these services be in accord with the purpose of the area, that necessary commercial structures be designed and located to harmonize with its interests and that the public be given maximum value at reasonable cost. Conversely, it is also necessary to ensure the operator opportunity for fair profit, consistent with the quality of service provided and the investment required.

A written agreement or contract between the administration and the operator should define the nature of the service, the quality and standard desired, costs to the public, and similar considerations. In many instances the administrative agency shares in revenues above a determined figure which, although rarely applied directly to the operating costs of the area, nevertheless aid indirectly in its support. By this means, as well as by regular inspection of facilities and financial records, the administration controls the activities of the operator and ensures proper performance of his duties. Inadequate or inappropriate concessionaire activities reflect discredit upon the entire management of a recreational area.

Formerly, in agreements of this nature the operator was required to finance and construct necessary buildings. In recent years some administrative agencies have built and retained title to necessary commercial structures which are leased to suitable bidders who provide required services. This system, since the administrative agency assumes responsibility for major capital investment, facilitates greater control over commercial activity.

Abilities Required of Personnel. Proper management of outdoor recreational lands requires an adequate number of employees who are possessed of a wide variety of interests and abilities. The nature of the personnel of specific organizations is dependent upon the recreational values inherent in the areas under their jurisdiction and, as determined by the administrative policy, the manner in which these values will be offered to the public. Although various national, state, county, and municipal recreational lands differ in details of management which are reflected in the activities of employees, they have common broad objectives. As a result the basic qualities desirable in individual members of a recreational land-management staff are similar. They are:

1. An interest in and an understanding of people. Employees must recognize and understand the reasons for varied public recreational needs, have patience with and insight into the vagaries of human nature, and be able to guide public interests and activities diplomatically in the proper use of a particular area.

2. An interest in, appreciation for, and understanding of the particular

area in which one works. No matter how menial the task, the "feeling" of an employee for an area will be reflected in his attitude. His interest will be reflected in the character of his work, as well as by his relations with people who use the area in which he is employed.

3. An understanding of the recreational values of one's area and the manner in which these values are affected by public use. Employees should willingly accept their share of responsibility in the preservation of an area's interests by aiding in the prevention or correction of causes of damage.

FIG. 8-7. Recreational land management is concerned largely with people; patience, tact, and a friendly manner are primary requisites of employees of such areas. (*Photo by Rex Schmidt, National Park Service*)

4. Capability in the specific tasks to which one may be assigned (e.g., maintenance, engineering, fiscal matters, law enforcement, interpretation, and the like).

5. Ability to recognize the relationship of one's particular responsibilities to the broad objectives of a given recreational program.

The foregoing characteristics are essential. They apply regardless of the type of recreational area involved or how training and experience for a given aspect of recreational land management were obtained.

Until recent years there was little recognition of the need for specific training in the management of recreational areas. Even those favored by a technical background useful in a particular aspect of such work (e.g., engineering, architecture, landscape architecture, business, natural or social science, law enforcement, or the like) had to develop the necessary understanding of the related fields and the broader requirements of recreational land management by experience. Few guideposts necessary to the solution of the problems of these people and the evaluation of their efforts were available. Professionally, outdoor recreation did not begin to come of age until growing public interest in its needs prompted the careful consideration of planning, development, and the use of different types of land for this purpose.[1]

With increased use of outdoor recreational lands and the resultant expansion of related complex problems, academic training for recreational land management is assuming increased importance. Such training should not only develop necessary technical abilities but, through evaluation of the experiences of those who are currently engaged in this field, should also foster proper understanding of outdoor recreational needs and adequate consideration of related basic problems. Such background, whether obtained by means of a stylized academic recreational-land-management curriculum or not, necessitates, first, a broad general educational background which develops an ability to think clearly and communicate ideas, and second, specific technical training in any one of several professional aspects of recreational land management.

The first requirement places emphasis on proper use of the English language in both the written and spoken word, basic psychology as an aid in understanding human nature, and the basic framework of the natural, physical, and social sciences in order that eventual specific training may be properly correlated with the broad objectives of recreational lands. The nature of the second requirement will depend largely upon individual aptitudes and interests, with emphasis on either engineering, architecture, landscape architecture, a natural science (e.g., geology, botany, zoology, forestry), a social science (e.g., history, geography, anthropology, archeology), business, physical education, or law enforcement.

Each of the foregoing technical fields provides different avenues of approach to the requirements of recreational land management and facilitates proper performance of specific tasks which are part of an overall program. Engineering training enables one to supervise the construction and maintenance of necessary physical facilities (e.g., roads, trails, buildings, water, sewer, and communication systems). Planning and

[1] In the early 1930s, at the suggestion of the National Conference on State Parks, the New York State College of Forestry conducted a special course for those engaged in the administration and management of recreational lands. Several years later the first curriculum designed for recreational land management training was organized at that institution. Since that time other colleges and universities have given official recognition to this field of activity and, in varying degrees, have offered many courses tailored to this need [33].

Many agencies administering recreational land, notably the National Park Service, the U.S. Forest Service, and a number of state park organizations, have instituted various types of in-service training programs in order to augment specific abilities of employees and to broaden their perspective with relation to the needs of particular recreational objectives.

design of these developments relates to an architectural background. Landscape architecture not only presupposes an understanding of environmental requirements of plants useful in rehabilitating damaged areas and an awareness of the proper design of recreational lands, but also an understanding of how the natural attractiveness of a recreational area may be maintained in the face of public use. A knowledge of any one of the natural or social sciences qualifies one not only to assist in relating necessary physical developments to the specific interests of certain areas but also to aid in the protection and public interpretation of those interests. Business training develops the skills required in the proper handling of funds, in the purchase of supplies, in personnel matters, and in related tasks. Physical education training, coordinated with the direction of youth and adult group activities, applies primarily to municipal recreational programs and management of organized camps. Maintenance of proper visitor conduct and public safety is predicated upon adequate training in law enforcement.

Certain of the aforementioned abilities are more important in some types of recreational areas than in others. Each is important in its proper relationship to varied recreational needs, but in a given area, if specific abilities are unaccompanied by a proper perspective of the over-all program, their value to management will be materially reduced.

THE FORESTER'S TRAINING IN RELATION TO OUTDOOR RECREATION

Forestry and recreational land management have much in common [4,7,11,55]. It is significant that academic training in the management of recreational lands was first offered by a school of forestry [33], indicating the close relationship between a forester's training and the requirements of recreational land management.

The close affinity between forestry and the management of recreational lands is emphasized further by the fact that many professional foresters are actively engaged in various forms of outdoor recreational work. Many of these men have made notable contributions to the recreational field, and some, like Aldo Leopold and Robert Marshall, are recognized as pioneer leaders. Such a relationship is not accidental. The common denominator of both forestry and recreational land management is interest in the outdoors; consequently both fields of endeavor attract young men who have similar inherent qualities, such as a natural curiosity about living, growing things and a desire to aid in their perpetuation and proper use.

Further, both good forestry and good recreational land management are founded upon an understanding of biological laws pertaining to plants and animals in relation to environment. That the basic interests of many recreational lands are related to their forest cover enhances this relationship. In addition, basic forestry training places emphasis upon forest protection, land planning, land survey, trail and road construction, and related activities which are also of vital concern in the proper management of recreational lands. In short, training in forestry is characterized by breadth, with emphasis upon the fundamentals of natural and physical science, mathematics, and engineering.

However, it must be admitted that in so far as work in outdoor recreation is concerned forestry training has a number of blind spots. The embryo forester soon discovers that his academic schedule aims at widely diverse goals. These embrace, in addition to active outdoor work in caring for forest lands, the control, harvesting, and processing of timber crops; such activities have little interest for those concerned with recreation. Further, certain aspects of academic training, particularly those relating to public relations, must be minimized in the forestry curriculum by reason of necessary emphasis on technical fundamentals.

These weaknesses, while they may foster a lack of proper appreciation for the recreational use of land on the part of some foresters, are outweighed by the advantages of training in biological principles essential to the perpetuation of wild-land resources. They may be alleviated by judicious selection of elective courses, by active participation in certain extracurricular activities, and by experience.

It is important to recognize that all foresters, whatever their particular activities, should have a basic understanding of the importance of recreation in wild-land management. As custodians of extensive areas of forest land, much of which is useful to varied public recreational needs, or as manufacturers of forest products, they have a definite responsibility to provide adequate leadership in this field. In effect, they should be equipped to see the forest as well as the trees.

SUMMARY

A good administrative policy is the basis for the most adequate management of a recreational area. Such a policy is developed by careful planning which considers all land values, both utilitarian and recreational, thereby determining the manner in which the use of an area can serve the best interests of the people. On certain lands the public welfare may dictate the total exclusion of recreational activities, some lands may be adapted to coordinated utilitarian and recreational development, and other areas may be most valuable in the exclusive provision of various types of recreational opportunities.

The good administrative policy also recognizes that the diversity of public leisure-time interests necessitates a wide variety of recreational areas, that radically different types of recreational activity must be provided for on different types of land, and that the management of specific areas should be in accord with the service each can render best. Further, if various types of recreational areas are properly coordinated, maximum and properly diversified public recreational opportunities will be provided and over-all economy of operation will be served.

It is imperative that details of the management of each area be conducted in accordance with its administrative policy, so that the differences in values between specific types of recreational lands will be recognized by the public. Such a program will minimize the problems concerned with recreational land use and, in addition, will facilitate the preservation of different recreational benefits for the future.

Proper solution of varied recreational-land-management problems necessitates a wide variety of skills and technical abilities on the part of various members of specific administrative organizations, basic interest in and understanding of human nature, and ability to relate detailed activities to the broad, over-all plan. The increasing complexity of recreational-land-management problems is placing growing emphasis on the value of adequate academic training. Since the primary interests of most recreational areas are closely related to the character of their forest cover, the broad training characteristic of modern forestry curricula provides a most adequate base for a career in this field.

SELECTED REFERENCES

1. Allen, Shirley W.: "An Introduction to American Forestry," McGraw-Hill Book Company, Inc., New York, 1950, p. 350.
2. Anonymous: Winter Use of National Parks, *National Parks Magazine*, vol. 31, no. 131, pp. 164–165, October–December, 1957.
3. Anonymous: National Parks Association Stand on Winter Use, *National Parks Magazine*, vol. 32, no. 132, p. 21, January–March, 1958.
4. Arnold, F. R.: From Commercial to Recreational Forester, *Journal of Forestry*, vol. 33, no. 7, pp. 662–667, July, 1935.
5. Bassett, Ray E.: Zoning as Applied to Wilderness, *Planning and Civic Comment*, vol. 16, no. 1, pp. 16–19, March, 1950.
6. Bradley, H. C., and David R. Brower: Roads in the National Parks, *Sierra Club Bulletin*, vol. 34, no. 6, pp. 31–54, June, 1949.
7. Brockman, C. F.: A Practical Approach to Forest Recreation Education, *Journal of Forestry*, vol. 50, no. 5, pp. 389–392, May, 1952.
8. Brower, David R.: Scenic Resources for the Future, *Sierra Club Bulletin*, vol. 41, no. 10, pp. 1–11, December, 1956.
9. Chapman, H. H.: Concession Policies in State Parks, "1949 Yearbook, Park and Recreation Progress," National Conference on State Parks, Washington, 1949, pp. 10–12.
10. Coffman, John D.: How Much and What Kind of Forest Land Should Be

Devoted Exclusively to Recreation and to Aesthetics? *Journal of Forestry,* vol. 35, no. 2, pp. 210–214, February, 1937.
11. Coffman, John: The Relationship of Recreational Foresters to the Forestry Profession, *Journal of Forestry,* vol. 33, no. 7, pp. 658–661, July, 1935.
12. Coffman, John D.: The Airplane Problem as It Relates to the National Park System, *Proceedings of the Society of American Foresters Meeting,* Boston, Mass., Dec. 16–18, 1948, pp. 106–109, Washington, 1949.
13. DeVoto, Bernard: Shall We Let Them Ruin Our National Parks? *Saturday Evening Post,* vol. 223, no. 4, pp. 17–19, July 22, 1950.
14. Flick, A. C., and C. C. Adams: Suggestions for a State Policy Relating to Historic and Scientific Reservations, and A Policy for State Historic and Scientific Reservations, *New York State Museum Bulletin,* no. 284, New York State University, Albany, N.Y., 1929.
15. Flint, H. R.: Wasted Wilderness, *American Forests and Forest Life,* vol. 32, no. 391, pp. 407–410, July, 1926.
16. Frank, Bernard: When Can Forest Recreation Be Considered as Exclusive or Dominant? *Journal of Forestry,* vol. 50, no. 4, pp. 314–316, April, 1952.
17. Gilligan, James P.: The Contradiction of Wilderness Preservation in a Democracy, *Proceedings of the Society of American Foresters Meeting,* Milwaukee, Wis., Oct. 24–27, 1954, pp. 119–122, Washington, 1955.
18. Hubbard, H. V.: Landscape Development Based on Conservation as Practiced in the National Park Service, *Landscape Architecture,* vol. 29, no. 3, pp. 105–121, April, 1939.
19. Harris, F. B.: The Sanctity of Open Spaces, *The Living Wilderness,* vol. 22, no. 60, pp. 5–8, Spring, 1957.
20. Heiberg, Svend O.: Preservation of Natural Forest Areas, *Proceedings of the Society of American Foresters Meeting,* Minneapolis, Minn., Dec. 17–20, 1947, pp. 173–177, Washington, 1948.
21. Humphrey, Hubert: The Wilderness Bill, *The Living Wilderness,* vol. 21, no. 59, pp. 13–36, Winter–Spring, 1956–1957.
22. Leopold, Aldo: Conservation Esthetic, *Bird-lore Magazine,* vol. 40, no. 2, pp. 101–109, March, 1938.
23. Leopold, Aldo: Wilderness Values, "1941 Yearbook, Park and Recreation Progress," U.S. National Park Service, Washington, 1941, pp. 27–29.
24. Lieber, Richard: Nature's Balance in Parks and Elsewhere, "1940 Yearbook, Park and Recreation Progress," U.S. National Park Service, Washington, 1940, pp. 82–85.
25. Lutz, H. J.: Soil Conditions of Picnic Grounds in Public Forest Parks, *Journal of Forestry,* vol. 43, no. 2, pp. 121–127, February, 1945.
26. McCulloch, W. F.: "Responsibilities of Resource Managers," Address given at Supervisors' Meeting, Portland, Ore., Mar. 28, 1956, U.S. Forest Service Region 6, Portland, Ore., n.d. (Mimeographed.)
27. Marshall, Robert: The Problem of the Wilderness, *Scientific Monthly,* vol. 30, no. 2, pp. 141–148, February, 1930.
28. Meinecke, E. P.: "Camp Planning and Camp Reconstruction," U.S. Forest Service, California Region, San Francisco, Calif., n.d.
29. Meinecke, E. P.: "The Effect of Excessive Tourist Travel on the California Redwood Parks," California State Printing Office, Sacramento, Calif., 1929.
30. Meinecke, E. P.: "A Campground Policy," U.S. Forest Service, Intermountain Region, Ogden, Utah, 1932.

31. Murie, Olas J.: Wild Country as a National Asset, *The Living Wilderness,* vol. 18, no. 45, pp. 1–29, Summer, 1953.
32. Nason, George: Architecture and Its Relationship to the Design of Parks, "1940 Yearbook, Park and Recreation Progress," U.S. National Park Service, Washington, 1940, pp. 56–58.
33. National Conference on State Parks: "1946 Yearbook, Park and Recreation Progress," Washington, 1946, p. 11.
34. Price, J. H.: The Quetico-Superior Program as It Relates to the Superior National Forest, *Proceedings of the Society of American Foresters Meeting,* Minneapolis, Minn., Dec. 17–20, 1947, pp. 182–188, Washington, 1948.
35. Rogers, John I.: Planning State Parks from the Designer's Viewpoint, "1952 Yearbook, Park and Recreation Progress," National Conference on State Parks, Washington, 1952, pp. 7–11.
36. Roewekamp, F. W.: Landscaping Recreational Areas, *Parks and Recreation Magazine,* vol. 38, no. 12, pp. 15–16, December, 1955.
37. Sauers, Charles G.: The Order of Parks, *Planning and Civic Comment,* vol. 18, no. 1, pp. 1–8, March, 1952.
38. Saylor, John P.: Saving America's Wilderness, *The Living Wilderness,* vol. 21, no. 59, pp. 1–12, Winter–Spring, 1956–1957.
39. Scoggin, L. G.: Planning of State Parks from the Administrator's Viewpoint, "1952 Yearbook, Park and Recreation Progress," National Conference on State Parks, Washington, 1952, pp. 5–7.
40. Shanklin, J. F.: Natural Areas, *Journal of Forestry,* vol. 52, no. 5, pp. 375–383, May, 1954.
41. Sieker, John: Aircraft and Forest Recreation, *Journal of Forestry,* vol. 44, no. 11, pp. 888–892, November, 1946.
42. Sieker, J. H.: Airplanes in National Forest Wilderness, *Proceedings of the Society of American Foresters Meeting,* Boston, Mass., Dec. 16–18, 1948, pp. 104–106, Washington, 1949.
43. Smith, Huntington: Tourists Who Act Like Pigs, *Saturday Evening Post,* vol. 225, no. 48, pp. 36–37, May 30, 1953.
44. Smith, Richard W.: Why I Am Opposed to the Wilderness Preservation Bill, *The Living Wilderness,* vol. 21, no. 59, pp. 44–50, Winter–Spring, 1956–57.
45. Society of American Foresters, Committee on Natural Areas: Report of the Committee on Natural Areas, *Journal of Forestry,* vol. 47, no. 2, pp. 137–147, February, 1949.
46. Sumner, Lowell: Regulation of High Country Pack Stock Use, *Proceedings of the Region IV Park Naturalists' Conference,* Yosemite National Park, Apr. 14–18, 1948, pp. 293–300, U.S. National Park Service, 1948. (Mimeographed.)
47. Teale, Edwin W.: Land Forever Wild, *Audubon Magazine,* vol. 59, no. 3, pp. 106–110, May–June, 1957.
48. Thompson, C. G.: Hiding Yosemite's Visitors, *American Civic Annual,* vol. 4, pp. 26–30, 1932.
49. U.S. Congress, "Hearings of the Senate Committee on Interior and Insular Affairs, National Wilderness Preservation Act, S.1176, June 19–20, 1957," 85th Congress, 1st Session, 1957.

49-*a*. U.S. Congress: Hearing of the Senate Committee on Interior and Insular

Affairs, National Wilderness Preservation Act, S. 4028, July 23, 1958, 85th Congress, 2d Session, 1957.

50. U.S. Department of Agriculture, Forest Service: "Avalanche Handbook," Washington, n.d.
51. U.S. Department of the Interior, National Park Service: "A Study of the Park and Recreation Problem of the United States," Washington, 1941.
52. U.S. Department of the Interior, National Park Service: "Recreational Resources of the Alaska Highway and Other Roads in Alaska," Washington, 1944.
53. U.S. Department of the Interior, National Park Service: "Securing Protection and Conservation Objectives through Interpretation," Memorandum from the Director of the National Park Service to all field offices, Apr. 23, 1953. (Mimeographed.)

53-*a*. U.S. Department of the Interior, National Park Service: "Mission 66 for Yosemite National Park," Washington, n.d.

53-*b*. U.S. Department of the Interior, National Park Service: "Mission 66 for Mount Rainier National Park," Washington, January, 1957.

53-*c*. U.S. Department of the Interior, National Park Service: "National Park Service Announces Purchase of Land for New Administrative Site outside Yosemite Boundary," Nov. 5, 1958. (Mimeographed news release.)

54. Vint, Thomas C.: National Park Service Master Plans, *Planning and Civic Comment*, vol. 12, no. 2, pp. 21–24, April–June, 1946.
55. Wagar, J. V. K.: The Forester's Place in the Field of Recreation, *Journal of Forestry*, vol. 42, no. 7, pp. 496–500, July, 1944.
56. Wagar, J. V. K.: Some Major Principles in Recreation Land-use Planning, *Journal of Forestry*, vol. 49, no. 6, pp. 431–435, June, 1951.
57. Wirth, Conrad L.: Is There a Need for a Comprehensive Recreation Program in the United States? *Planning and Civic Comment*, vol. 21, no. 2, pp. 1–9, June, 1955.
58. Zahniser, Howard: The Need for Wilderness Areas, *The Living Wilderness*, vol. 21, no. 59, pp. 37–43, Winter–Spring, 1956–57.
59. Zalesky, Philip: "Our Economy Can Afford Wilderness," Address given before the Society of American Foresters, Puget Sound Section, Seattle, Wash., Dec. 6, 1957, *North Cascades Conservation Council News*, vol. 1, no. 5, December, 1957.

CHAPTER 9 *Important Outdoor Recreational Facilities and Services*

Many facilities and services are necessary to the proper public use of different types of recreational lands. Such facilities and services include roads and trails, several types of signs, campgrounds and picnic areas, commercial overnight accommodations and related needs, organized camps, facilities for such activities as swimming, boating, winter sports, interpretation, and varied structures required for administration and maintenance.

Detailed planning, design, and construction of such facilities, or the provision and operation of specialized services, are the province of trained technicians who are experts in such matters (e.g., landscape planners, architects, engineers, naturalists). However, it is imperative that all those engaged in the management of recreational lands have a knowledge of basic principles governing the need for and the utility of common recreational facilities and services, for these often determine the character and degree of recreational use on different areas. This chapter, together with specific references noted in the bibliography, is intended to serve as a guide in such matters.

Specifically, principal administrative officers of recreational areas should understand the effects of various developments upon the area with which they are concerned. They should have at least a general idea of proper programming and good design or be able to recognize good design when incorporated into a plan for official approval. They should also be able to relate various physical developments to probable public use, serviceability, cost of maintenance, and public health and safety. To a lesser degree this also applies to employees in the lower echelons of an organization charged with the administration of recreational areas. Since such employees are concerned with details of management, they can better assist supervisory personnel in making proper decisions if they can relate their own activities to specific public needs through an awareness of basic requirements.

Proper public use, as determined by administrative policy, regulates the type and degree of development on various kinds of recreational lands. Facilities, services, or public activities which are not in accord with the primary, long-term purpose of an area should not be permitted. Recreational land managers have a responsibility to future generations in guiding the use of such areas so that their values will be perpetuated.

As noted in previous chapters, necessary facilities should be planned, designed, and developed in a manner that is in keeping with the character of the region. In so far as possible, the works of man should not dominate the natural scene; to this end the use of native materials in proper scale, low silhouettes and irregular lines, colors typical of or harmonious with the immediate surroundings, and proper location in relation to existing trees, other vegetation, and related interests are paramount. Some basic considerations relative to the provision of principal facilities and services of recreational areas follow.

ROADS AND TRAILS

Although roads in recreational areas should conform to sound engineering principles, they should be located, designed, and constructed in a manner which will avoid extensive modification of scenic beauty or damage to natural features of interest. On a smaller scale, the same principle applies to trail development. As noted in Chapter 8, roads and trails in recreational areas are a means to an end, rather than an end in themselves; their primary function is to facilitate proper mobility of visitors.

Extensive cuts and fills should be avoided wherever possible, especially if they result in scars visible from a distance. If they are unavoidable, such scars should be rehabilitated by suitable plantings of native trees and shrubs. The road surface, bridges, culverts and walls, guard rails, and similar features should blend with natural surroundings so as to be unobtrusive. Since roads and trails in recreational areas serve primarily to bring visitors into contact with representative interests of such lands, they should be located with that in mind rather than as direct routes through an area. It is also important to recognize that the existence of a road induces a variety of other needs (e.g., picnic areas, campgrounds, sanitary facilities, interpretive displays); it is desirable that these be considered as adjuncts in the over-all cost of highway construction, just as are necessary bridges, culverts, and similar developments.

SIGNS

Proper use of recreational areas necessitates a variety of signs. These serve to direct public movements, designate features and facilities, identify hazards, denote improper actions or activities, define rules and regulations, or attract attention to or explain particular interests [10,11].

In large measure, signs can indicate the motif of recreational areas. Proper placement, scale, design, materials, size of letters, and nature of the text are important factors in their serviceability; decisions relative to

FIG. 9-1. Some examples of signs.

a. Entrance, Cornet Bay, Deception Pass State Park, Washington. (*Washington State Parks and Recreation Commission*)

b. Explanatory sign, site of Spokane House, Riverside State Park, Washington. (*Photo by Batchelor-Plath, Inc., Washington State Parks and Recreation Commission*)

these factors result from careful consideration of the purpose to be served. The location of signs should be related to the average sight distance for various rates of travel, varying from a few feet for stationary viewing or for foot or horse travel, to approximately 300 feet for fast motor traffic on main highways [10]. Scale, design, and materials used should be in accord with the character of the region, the cost of maintenance, and the cost of occasional replacement. The size of the letters and the extent of the text should relate to the purpose; a few brief words in large, readily visible letters serve the purposes of directional or cautionary signs, while regulatory or informational signs demand more extensive text. In any event brevity, consistent with clarity and completeness, is paramount; unnecessarily wordy signs are ineffective. The possibility of vandalism should also receive careful consideration. Such actions can be minimized by use of materials which do not lend themselves readily to destructive tendencies, by use of massive materials where good taste permits, by affixing signs firmly in place, or by placing them in positions inconvenient to destructive acts.

Improper sign technique can impair the interests of an area and largely nullify otherwise careful recreational planning. If signs are affixed to trees or other natural features, they may cause serious damage to recreational values. Overuse of signs should definitely be avoided; this creates a confusing hodgepodge of information which is largely ineffective.

CAMPGROUNDS

The setting aside of specific areas for camping provides an economical way of controlling and guiding public use of the outdoors, thus facilitating over-all preservation of the attractiveness of recreational lands without too great limitation of visitor use and enjoyment. Limiting camping to specific, well-defined sections within recreational lands, however, often results in large concentrations of people on relatively small areas. Unless campgrounds are properly planned, designed, and developed, such concentrations of people will result in the serious modification of campground interests [12,13].

Destruction of vegetation is one of the first indications of the overuse of campgrounds. In extreme cases herbaceous plants, even shrubs, may be literally tramped out. Indiscriminate use of automobiles may damage trees so severely, through barking and exposure of their roots, that the trees eventually succumb. Studding trees with nails or encircling them with wire for purposes of hanging camping equipment, the use of living trees as backlogs for fires, or building fires in other than designated places are equally damaging.

Lack of vegetation, coupled with a constant search for fuel wood, may seriously affect soil fertility by the elimination of necessary humus. Even at considerable distances from heavily used campgrounds the surface of the ground is often literally scoured of down logs, broken limbs, twigs, and similar arboreal refuse. Excessive packing of soil, a result of trampling and unregulated use of motor vehicles, affects tree vitality through reduced soil aeration, increasing the probability of damage by destructive insects and fungi. Camping refuse, such as piles of ashes from numerous fires and oil and grease from cars, adversely affects the health of shrubs and trees. The likelihood of deliberate vandalism is increased with added numbers of people.

Proper planning and development of campgrounds are vital to the best use of recreational areas. Good planning not only preserves recreational interests for use by future generations but also ensures everyone of an equal opportunity for enjoyment, provides the maximum number of camp spaces consistent with the character of a given area, and fosters maximum efficiency and economy of operation as well as public safety.

Proper selection of an area for a campground hinges upon a number of important factors. These include the interests of the area, its topography (including hazards), proximity and nature of water supply, the type of soil and vegetation, climate, accessibility, expected public use and its seasonal or periodic variations, the general background of those likely to use the campground, the nature of their vehicles or mode of transportation, and the proximity of the campground to public needs and points of interest.

The attractions of a campground, that is, its vegetation and forest cover, lakes or streams, scenic beauty or outlook, and animal life, relate to its hazards as well as to its charm. Consideration must be given to fire hazards, public health and safety in the use of lakes or streams, possible depredations of certain animals (e.g., the American black bear), and, in some cases, the existence of poisonous plants or reptiles. Although level terrain simplifies campground layout and facilitates greater economy of space, selection of a level site is not obligatory; a reasonable degree of irregularity in topography often lends itself to development of a plan which provides maximum individual privacy and which creates an illusion of "wilderness." The nature and proximity of a water supply are important in relation to economy of operation and public health. The reaction of soils and types of vegetation to different degrees of use must be understood, for they react variously to similar conditions; further, some types of vegetation can be more easily replaced than others if excessive use of an area necessitates rehabilitation. Climatic considerations (including elevation, temperature, prevailing winds, rainfall, and snow conditions) and accessibility to centers of population bear strongly upon the degree and fluctuation of campground use, factors which, in addition to topography, are important in determining the location, size, and arrangement of camping facilities.

The mode of transportation generally used by campers must also be considered. For instance, use by trailers necessitates certain modifications in campground design, and campgrounds in remote areas for those traveling on foot or horseback must obviously be developed differently from those adjacent to primary highways. The background and interests of those who use camping facilities will determine, in large degree, the extent of public cooperation in their care and maintenance; people accustomed to outdoor living are generally more cognizant of their responsibilities. Finally, it is also vital to consider the relationship of campgrounds to interesting features or activities in the immediate area, as well as the nature of other developments in the vicinity.

An adequate topographic map of the area, based upon a careful survey, is basic to proper planning and development of campgrounds, particularly those of large size. This is necessary because roads, camp sites, and related developments must be tailored to the terrain and related characteristics. The best campground layout embraces a system of one-way roads which should be 10 feet wide, with an additional 3-foot width to accommodate bordering gutters [11]. The resultant traffic pattern eliminates congestion and minimizes the damage to vegetation and trees that is almost inevitable in a two-way system. If two-way roads are necessary, a 16-foot width, with an additional 3 feet for gutters, is required [11]. Short individual parking spurs branching from the primary campground road give access to single camp sites which, in addition to a parking spur for the car, provide a fixed tent site, table, and outdoor fireplace; approximately 750 square feet of space is required [10]. Maximum efficiency of such individual campsites is accomplished by definitely locating facilities in proper relation to each other, to existing vegetation, and to prevailing winds. Spacing between individual campsites will be dependent upon topography, vegetation, and the degree and character of expected use. Maximum privacy may be provided for each campsite by screens of vegetation; in areas where vegetation is sparse or lacking, an illusion of privacy can sometimes be accomplished by greater spacing of individual units. Each camp unit should be within 200 to 250 feet of safe drinking water, no more than 300 to 400 feet from sanitary facilities, and, if such facilities are provided, within 1,500 feet of washhouse and laundry [10,11].

Protection of trees and other vegetation from damage through undesirable movement of automobiles can be effected by the erection of solid log or rock barriers at critical locations bordering roads and parking spurs. Trees and shrubs which unnecessarily interfere with proper visitor movement in campgrounds should be removed; otherwise the damage which will inevitably occur to such vegetation will set a pattern for more extensive, undesirable modification of the area [13].

Where space is not a major problem, large campground developments sometimes can be planned in distinct but related sections that are separated by suitable buffer zones which permit ready increase or decrease of available camp space according to fluctuations of seasonal travel. Also, under some conditions use of entire sections may be rotated annually in order to minimize the likelihood of damage by distributing public pressures over a wider camping area.

The same basic considerations apply in providing camp space for those using trailers except that trailer areas cannot accommodate as many individual units; individual trailer-camp units necessitate approximately twice the space (about 1,200 square feet) required for nontrailers [10]. Modification in the design of parking spurs is necessary to facilitate handling of this more unwieldly equipment and to permit parking of the trailer without immobilizing the car. Sketches found in "Park and Recreation Structures" [11] depict a number of possible arrangements suitable for cars and trailers which are adapted to various conditions. Basically these variations entail longer or differently arranged parking spurs into which trailer and car can be backed or parking spurs generally parallel to the main camp roadway which allow the trailer and car to be conveniently removed from, but parked in the same direction as, the main camp traffic pattern.

Difficulties may occasionally arise from the fact that many trailers are equipped for connection with various utilities which, because of cost of installation, cannot be made available in most public campgrounds that are provided at little or no cost.

Because of the foregoing factors, it is inadvisable to provide accommodations for both trailer and nontrailer users in the same campground. If it is impossible or undesirable to develop distinct campgrounds for these two types of recreationalists, they can be segregated in specific units of the same area.

PICNIC AREAS

Since those who utilize the outdoors for picnicking are more transient and have different objectives from campers, it is advisable to provide separate areas for camping and picnicking whenever possible. This not only avoids temporary, periodic overcrowding of campgrounds, with resultant ills, but eliminates possible friction between campers and picnickers.

In many cases, because of the larger number of picnickers, natural conditions must be more generally sacrificed in planning adequate picnic areas than in developing campgrounds. Further, design and arrangement of picnic areas are different from that of campgrounds. The one-way road pattern still applies, and for the same reasons, but group rather than individual parking facilities are the rule. These facilities should be located within easy walking distance of permanent tables, outdoor fireplaces, water, and sanitary facilities. The size of parking areas required for a number of cars is computed on the basis of 300 square feet per car; this allows a 10- by 20-foot space for static parking plus the necessary room for backing and turning [10]. Individual picnic spaces, suitable for small groups not exceeding eight individuals in number and including a table, camp stove, and trash can, require an area of 225 square feet [10].

FACILITIES PROVIDED IN CAMPGROUNDS AND PICNIC AREAS

Utility, economy of construction and maintenance, and a design which is in harmony with the region are guiding principles in the construction of tables, camp stoves, and other necessary facilities in campgrounds and picnic areas.

Picnic or camp tables made of sawed or native wood products or different forms of masonry are applicable to different types of recreational lands. The particular form and design used depend upon cost and local conditions, but table proportions generally conform to definite standards. The table surface should be approximately 3 feet wide and 28 to 30 inches above the ground; the seat should be approximately 1

FIG. 9-2. Example of a simple, standard camp or picnic table. (*Photo by Ed Druxman, Washington State Parks*)

foot wide and 16 to 18 inches above the ground, with its front edge from 1 to 3 inches removed from a point corresponding to the edge of the table surface [10,11].

The practice of dragging tables from place to place not only damages ground cover but materially increases the cost of maintenance of the tables. Such practice may be discouraged by using materials of considerable weight or, preferably, by anchoring tables in a fixed position. In campgrounds the fixed table is particularly important. Greater freedom may be permitted in the design of tables for picnic areas, since large groups often require expanded table space which is easily provided by moving several units together. In picnic areas habitually used by sizable groups it is advisable to provide a number of larger tables to eliminate unnecessary, selfish appropriation.

Another important consideration concerns care and maintenance.

Wooden facilities should be adequately protected from the weather by use of proper preservatives. Where weather conditions make seasonal storage necessary, tables should be constructed so that they can be handled by two men or so that they can be dismantled and reassembled readily. Further, rough edges, which are damaging to light clothing, should be avoided, as should small crevices in which food particles may lodge; in this connection table tops should have at least a one-quarter inch space between planks.

Camp stoves must be economical to construct and maintain and must be planned for ease and economy of operation. As in the case of tables, the type and design of camp stoves are largely a matter of local determi-

FIG. 9-3. Example of one type of simple, standard camp stove. (*Photo by Ed Druxman, Washington State Parks*)

nation and should be based upon the nature and degree of their use, as well as the character of the region. The fundamentals of design include a properly proportioned firebox (approximately 14 to 18 inches wide, 9 to 12 inches high and 24 to 30 inches long) with sufficient level surface on top of the firebox walls to serve as a food warmer or to provide auxiliary work space [10,11]. Most fireboxes are enclosed on three sides, but use of fuel in a greater variety of lengths is possible if the back as well as the front is open. Loose grates, chained to the masonry to prevent vandalism, are preferred; these facilitate removal of ashes and, since grates have to be replaced periodically, economy of maintenance.

Increasing use of gasoline stoves by campers does not necessarily eliminate the need for camp fireplaces. Not all people have gasoline equipment, and campfires are often a necessity as well as a pleasure in outdoor living. The same principle does not always apply to picnic areas, especially when they are characterized by excessive use. In heavily used picnic areas campstoves are often replaced by community kitchens with wood stoves or metered gas ranges.

Pure water supply, proper refuse disposal, and adequate sanitary facilities are vital to campgrounds and picnic areas. An uncontaminated water source must be maintained by proper development and regular inspection, and the design of taps and drinking fountains should conform to modern sanitary requirements. A vertical pipe fitted with an upturned tap is the simplest form of drinking fountain. The basic feature of this device can be elaborated in a variety of ways to accommodate greater

FIG. 9-4. Type of cast-steel fireplace favored in the Provincial Parks of British Columbia; when installed for use, legs are embedded in concrete slab. (*Department of Recreation and Conservation, British Columbia, Canada*)

esthetic need and to provide for greater utility and better sanitation [11]. For instance, proper disposal of waste water eliminates muddy ground about a drinking fountain, a separate tap for filling pails can be provided, and steps can be constructed to accommodate children. Such improvements can be enclosed by masonry of suitable design and roofed for protection from the weather if necessary. The nature and degree of development depend upon local conditions. As noted in the "Forestry Handbook" [10], an estimate of water requirements per person per day for picnickers is 3.1 gallons; for campers, 5.5 gallons; for occupants of cabins, 18.4 gallons; and for those in organized camps, 15 gallons.

Adequate refuse and garbage disposal requires a sufficient number of properly placed containers, the development of public responsibility in the proper use of such facilities, and a system of frequent, regular servicing; in this way the beauty of an area, as well as sanitation, is served. Various modifications of the generally undesirable, conspicuous garbage can are used, but each of these has one or more obvious disadvantages. They may be too small or too large, too obvious or too inconspicuous; too often they serve as attractions for many forms of animals; they may be unsanitary, odoriferous, too inconvenient to use, or too difficult to service; or they may be too costly to provide and maintain. One form of container that has received wide interest is a can, properly placed in an appropriately constructed sunken pit, that can be removed readily for servicing and is equipped with some form of snug lid that can be lifted easily by foot pressure.

In many wild-land recreational areas the omnivorous food habits of the American black bear are a constant aggravation. These animals make regular patrols of garbage cans, overturning them and scattering their contents. Containers designed to offer various physical deterrents to the activities of this animal have, at best, been only partially successful. The answer to this problem, and it can rarely be applied because of economic and other limitations, lies in timing regular service of refuse containers with the normal habits of bears and recreationalists; for instance, garbage is collected as soon after the evening meal period as possible, yet before the bears begin their nightly rounds.

It is unlikely that a completely foolproof and adequate solution of the refuse and garbage problem in recreational areas will ever be reached. Doubtless the problem will always be vexatious. Recreational-land managers will have to be content with the answer that best fits their particular situation and budget at any given time.

Sanitary facilities, regardless of whether they are of a modern flush type or not, should conform to regulatory laws governing such features. They should be adequately lighted, properly ventilated, and designed to facilitate regular cleaning and maintenance. Where there is danger of freezing in winter, adequate provision must be made for complete draining of all pipes and related equipment, unless there is sufficient use to justify heating of such buildings. When the foregoing conditions have been met, consideration should be given to the development of an attractive exterior in harmony with the surroundings [3,10,11,21].

FACILITIES NECESSARY TO OPERATORS OF COMMERCIAL SERVICES

Among the more difficult problems of recreational land management are those concerned with the location and design of buildings required by concessionaires. This applies to extensive developments (hotels, lodges, cabins, and related facilities for overnight use) or minor needs (food stores, photo and souvenir shops, and refreshment stands). The primary reason for such difficulties on recreational areas is that, unlike structures which are subsidized by public funds, buildings operated by concessionaires serve commercial enterprises and must necessarily pay their way. Largely because of this, their design and construction often impress themselves too forcefully upon the landscape or are not always in harmony with the area or in keeping with the appearance of other physical developments. Further, the operators of such facilities, because of their understandable interest in profits, often exhibit attitudes which conflict with basic administrative policies.

Harmonious relations between administrators and concessionaires enhance the quality of public service. To remain financially solvent, a concessionaire must attract sufficient patronage. It is to his advantage to seek and obtain a location for his enterprise which is athwart visitor traffic or which commands strategic viewpoints, and to conduct his operations in buildings which readily proclaim the nature of their specific services. In short, if a hotel, restaurant, or food store displays the customary earmarks of such facilities, its wares and services are automatically advertised to prospective patrons.

Although varied types of commercial services and facilities are necessary on many recreational areas, the best long-term interest of both the public and the concessionaire will be served if commercial activities do not usurp the primary values of such lands. While the financial solvency of those who provide necessary commercial services must be considered by the administration, concessionaires must also recognize that the existence of their enterprise depends upon the maintenance of the interests of an area. To this end administrators of recreational lands should:

1. Permit establishment of only those commercial facilities that are in keeping with the character of a given area, and only if they are definitely necessary to its proper public use. For instance, overnight accommodations should not be provided if they merely offer a convenient stopping point in an extended itinerary, or if adequate services of this kind are available nearby.

2. Give proper consideration to all factors concerned in preparation of an operating contract. If a given commercial development is acceptable on an area, there should be a clear understanding between the administration and operator as to their respective responsibilities.

3. If possible, locate, design, and construct necessary commercial facilities for lease to suitable operators. By assuming responsibility for capital investment and holding title to buildings, the administration can better control the location and design of commercial buildings, as well as the character and propriety of the operation which they are designed to serve.

Overnight facilities take a variety of forms; they vary from large hotels to simple lodges with sleeping accommodations in adjacent cabins [11]. The nature of any hotel development depends upon local conditions, but large hotels, because of their dominating size and lack of adaptability to modern travel habits, are usually undesirable in most types of recreational areas. On the other hand, lodges can be equally disadvantageous if they present a uniform arrangement of closely crowded cabins reminiscent of hastily constructed barracks. Uniform arrangement favors economy of construction and operation, but modern thinking in design of overnight facilities attempts to adapt the economical advantages of a regimented plan to a more pleasing design with several low, properly related, rambling structures. In such cases one section is designed as the main lodge building (including lounge, dining room, and related facilities), while other sections contain multiple cabin units grouped informally to conform to the terrain and connected with the main building by protected walkways. Such a plan not only eliminates undesirable structural characteristics of large hotels but provides accommodations for visitors in different economic brackets. Without materially modifying their exterior appearance or their relation to the over-all development, different blocks of cabin units can be designed to accommodate either simple or luxurious tastes.

Hotels and other structures serving commercial objectives in recreational areas must be planned so as not to detract from natural interests; their design should reflect the character of the region. Native materials are usually preferred, but their use must be carefully gauged in relation to economy of construction, since greater amounts of handiwork entail higher costs than when commercial materials are utilized. Careful consideration of this factor is important, since commercial buildings must pay their way; their cost is reflected in charges for the public services which they provide.

Economy may dictate eliminating the use of many native materials because of the expensive handwork involved, but this need not necessarily result in buildings out of character with their locale. Proper design and skillful use of less expensive materials can often produce proper results.

ORGANIZED CAMPS

Camps designed to accommodate organized groups have an important place in outdoor recreation. Sponsored by a wide variety of organizations (churches, lodges, schools, clubs, and even towns and cities), they serve equally diverse purposes, catering to specific age groups, boys or girls, families, the infirm, or the underprivileged.

The nature and the extent of facilities, as well as the camp layout, should be in accord with the purpose to be served. For instance, the facilities and layout of family camps differ from those required by youth groups. Further, many camps must necessarily be used consecutively by several organizations; in such cases it is necessary that they be designed to satisfy diverse needs.

Proper layout of an organized camp is important for efficiency of operation, maximum enjoyment of the recreational interests of an area, and proper care of the health and physical well-being of its patrons [11]. Regimented arrangement of barrackslike structures, promoting close confinement of many individuals on a small area, is impractical and undesirable; instead, large camp populations are broken up into small groups having similar interests or abilities. This is accomplished best by an arrangement consisting of a central headquarters in which all campers have a common interest and supplemented by a number of separate but closely coordinated sleeping units. Occupants of different sleeping units engage in activities as specific groups, frequently joining in over-all camp programs.

The camp headquarters embraces the main lodge (including dining hall, kitchen and related facilities, camp store, office, and the like), the service road, visitor parking area, and the central washhouse and laundry. In large camps a separate administration building may be needed. The lodge kitchen should be so related to the service road that refuse and bulky supplies may be handled conveniently, unobtrusively, and with dispatch. Parking space for visitors should be so located that a pleasing approach to the camp is provided. Two or more units of sleeping accommodations, each with necessary sanitary facilities and with responsible supervision and leadership, augment camp headquarters; small specific units of from four to eight tents or cabins, each housing four individuals, are recommended as a means of reducing behavior problems, especially in youth camps. Each of these group facilities should be located so as to provide satisfactory privacy and yet be convenient to the central lodge and features of special interest. Finally, the infirmary should be suitably isolated from the main body of the camp.

The development and operation of camps for organized groups should give careful consideration to the following:

1. *Adequate, experienced leadership and supervision.* This is extremely important. Qualified leadership should be provided for the development of all values typical of the region wherein the camp is located, including various forms of physical activity (e.g., swimming, boating, hiking, riding) and cultural interests (e.g., nature study, handicrafts, dramatics). Poor, unqualified, or inadequate administrative supervisory personnel greatly reduce the value of individual camping experience.

2. *Character of buildings.* Building design should be attractive and, in so far as possible, should reflect the spirit of the region. Permanent structures should be designed for economy of operation and ease of maintenance. The main lodge, at least, should be well constructed, since it is a permanent building usually used for winter storage of equipment. The use of tents for sleeping quarters, although desirable in many ways, has the disadvantage of high maintenance cost. Small buildings and tent platforms should be provided with masonry foundations and should be sufficiently elevated above the ground to provide ready access to the area beneath them.

3. *Fire hazard.* Electrical wiring, flues, and other details of building construction should conform to accepted safety regulations. If it is necessary to use lanterns, these should be carefully controlled, and campfires should be permitted only in safe, designated places.

4. *Health and safety.* Clean, healthful surroundings, personal cleanliness, good food, and proper supervision of activities are basic to the health and safety of any group. Adequate sanitary facilities (one toilet for a maximum of ten individuals) and showers (one for eight campers) are required [11]. Food must be well balanced and nourishing. Hazards should be eliminated or guarded against. Experienced first-aid and medical attention, if not provided in camp, must be readily available.

FACILITIES FOR SWIMMING AND BOATING

An understanding of the hazards involved, proper supervision, and provision of adequate facilities for public health and safety are necessary wherever swimming, boating, and related water sports are made available on public lands.

Bathhouses must be designed in accordance with proper sanitary practice and in such manner that varied public needs may be accommodated efficiently. The former practice of renting private dressing rooms for the duration of a visitor's stay is outmoded because of extensive space requirements. Where beaches and pools are used by large numbers of people, temporary private dressing rooms are provided (at least for women), together with some suitable method of safeguarding wearing apparel and valuables, such as small individual lockers or containers to be checked at the bathhouse office.

Adequate shower facilities are also necessary, particularly when swimming is done in pools, for bathing with soap and water before entering the pool is mandatory. Showers are usually provided in a central room, but in some cases (especially for women), it may be desirable to place them in individual dressing rooms. To reduce the spread of foot infections a foot bath should be provided at some location which makes its use unavoidable en route to the pool. In all cases, sanitary facilities should be located so that their use may be encouraged before the swimmer enters the water. Adequate ventilation can be most easily accomplished by generous use of louvers or in certain cases even by eliminating the roof, except over dressing rooms.

The degree to which these basic requirements are expanded depends upon local conditions. Staff lockers and dressing rooms and first-aid facilities are desirable; in addition, drinking fountains, public telephones, wringers, hair driers, facilities for the sale or rental of equipment and refreshments may also be necessary.

Floats for swimming should be mobile in order that they may be moved and securely anchored at various locations; this also facilitates their removal from the water, if necessary, for repair or winter storage.

Fig. 9-5. Marine boat dock on shore of Sucia Island, Fossil Bay State Park, Washington. (*Washington State Parks and Recreation Commission*)

Docks and piers should be designed in some sort of enclosed form in order to limit the activities of children or those of different abilities. A dock in the form of the letter "H" is often used for this purpose.

The construction of docks, either for use by swimmers or boating enthusiasts, should be accompanied by careful selection of proper materials. This applies particularly to the foundations of the docks which should be treated with suitable preservatives; otherwise the life of such structures will be materially reduced. Fluctuating water levels, ice, marine animals, and many other factors which affect the serviceability of docks should also be considered.

In areas subject to excessive changes in water level, such as tidal marine locations, it is convenient to have an attached float accessible to the dock platform by a ladder, which is readily available to those using boats. Where water levels do not fluctuate so severely, a hinged dock with the outer end floating on the surface will usually suffice. Broad, shallow beaches necessitate use of a floating dock connected to the shore by a catwalk. Another system employs inclined railed runways into deep water; a wheeled cart operating on these rails transports the boat to the necessary depth by gravity. Boats are returned, after being maneuvered into position on the cart, by means of a cable in the boathouse.

Since canoes and racing shells must be removed from the water when not in use, suitable racks for their storage are necessary. Transportation

FIG. 9-6. Boat-launching ramp. (*Washington State Parks and Recreation Commission*)

of this equipment to and from the water, whether related to current use or seasonal storage, is facilitated by large overhead or barn-type doors in the boathouse.

WINTER SPORTS FACILITIES

In relatively recent years skiing has dominated the winter sports picture, but skating, tobogganing, sledding, sleighing, and ski jumping have long been important outdoor recreational activities.

The basic requirements of a ski area are proper terrain, snow conditions, and climate. Snow must be of dependable depth and quality. In order to reduce the probability of accidents materially, topography must be sufficiently varied to permit the development of different sections of the ski area for expert skiers, those of intermediate ability, and beginners; the ratio of steep slopes to gentle ones depends upon the number and proficiency of the users of a given area. The designation of specific zones, defined by natural topographical boundaries or small patches of trees, most easily separates groups of skiers of varying ability.

Patch cutting on heavily timbered terrain sometimes provides a suitable substitute for natural ski slopes. The expense of such an operation, however, is often excessive, for in many parts of the country timber found on such areas is not readily marketable.

Climate, in addition to affecting visitor enjoyment of ski areas, is responsible for numerous hazards. Storms and heavy fog create considerable danger. Extremes of temperature or prolonged periods of high wind often develop a dangerous surface crust on snow slopes. Wide variations in altitude have equally diverse snow conditions owing to differences in temperature and wind velocity at varying levels. The probability of avalanches or slides is increased by certain combinations of climate, snow conditions, and topography.

Careful evaluation of proposed ski areas should be made by experienced skiers before development is undertaken. Further, before a final decision is reached, areas under consideration should be examined carefully during the summer as well as during winter. Often the presence of

FIG. 9-7. Ski areas should be designed to facilitate safe use by participants of varying proficiency; Berthoud Pass, Arapaho National Forest, Colorado. (*Photo by George K. Brown, U.S. Forest Service*)

large stumps, boulders, and related ground debris makes it impossible to use an area safely except during the relatively limited period of greatest snow depth.

Accessibility of ski areas and types of transportation used in reaching them will largely determine the character and degree of their development. Access roads should be located and constructed so as to minimize the difficulty, hazard, and expense of snow removal. Highways which ascend a slope by a series of switchbacks, one above the other, are almost impossible to maintain, since snow cleared from the upper sections accumulates in recently cleared portions below. Cost of road maintenance due to winter sports developments may be materially reduced by locating ski areas along or near highways which are regularly maintained for general winter travel.

The ski area itself will require parking areas, various buildings to serve public needs, some sort of uphill transportation for skiers, and adequate, experienced personnel. Since parking an individual car necessitates a space of 10 by 20 feet, an additional width of 20 feet on each side of the highway will provide for single rows of cars parked at right angles to the flow of traffic. Parking space for more than one row of cars in a specific area is not advisable, since this increases the difficulty of snow removal. Roads and parking areas, invariably bordered by precipitous snowbanks, should not be immediately adjacent to the center of activity, as they represent a serious hazard to unwary skiers.

Necessary buildings, although located conveniently to the ski area, should be sufficiently removed from ski runs to avoid any danger of collision between skiers and buildings or groups of spectators gathered about them. Buildings should also be constructed with full regard to snow depths and prevailing winds in order to assure accessibility and easy maintenance at all times. It is usually advisable to provide such basic needs as shelter, comfort stations, and a first-aid room under one roof, since this permits the use of one heating plant. Overnight accommodations are necessary only when ski areas are located at a considerable distance from centers of population, and if such facilities are not already available nearby.

Some form of uphill transportation, varying from a simple rope tow to some type of permanent lift, is necessary on most modern ski areas. Rope tows are desirable on areas where there is not sufficient patronage to justify extensive development or where it is necessary to preserve significant or scenic values, such as in national parks.

Personnel concerned with the public use of ski areas should be experienced skiers with a thorough, first-hand knowledge of the area and its hazards; they should also be capable of discharging basic requirements of first aid and rescue.

INTERPRETIVE FACILITIES AND SERVICES

Interpretive activities are designed primarily to enhance visitor enjoyment of outdoor recreational areas by developing public understanding of their varied interests [6,7,20,27]. Further, as noted in Chapter 8, a good interpretive program also contributes to the protection of recreational lands, since the program develops an awareness of visitors' responsibilities in preserving a recreational heritage by fostering recognition of its values.

Interpretation may embrace such features as museums, roadside and trail-side exhibits, self-guiding nature trails, wild-flower gardens, informative lectures or campfire programs, field trips, libraries, and publication of material pertinent to a given region for distribution and sale.

Museums are generally but one part in a broader interpretive program. They are to a recreational area what a table of contents is to a book or a display window is to a department store; they inform and stimulate interest in the area [7,27]. Well-planned museum exhibits in a strategically located and attractively designed building present, outline, and briefly explain the significance of an area's interests, and encourage people to go afield and observe such interests first hand. They should not be so complete that visitor interest becomes jaded; the area itself is the primary interest, and museums should merely assist in proper public use, enjoyment, and understanding. Consequently, the scope of the museum "story"

FIG. 9-8. Well-planned museum exhibits tell a story; Fort Columbia Historical State Park, Washington. (*Washington State Parks and Recreation Commission*)

should not go beyond the immediate area involved except when necessary for perspective or in the interest of reasonable completeness. Obviously, extraneous material should not be included; for instance, regardless of its interest or value, a display of weapons of modern warfare would be inappropriate in an area of unique biological significance.

A successful museum project in a recreational area is dependent upon the following:

1. The quality of the scientific foundation of the museum project or the character of the research program which develops such a foundation. Factual misrepresentation of an area's interests in an interpretive program cannot be condoned; for this reason the museum, in more significant recreational areas, serves as a center of research activities and contains adequate facilities necessary to such a program (e.g., library, study collections).

2. An understanding of public psychology on the part of those who

FIG. 9-9. Mariposa Grove Museum, Yosemite National Park. (*National Park Service*)

plan and prepare the exhibits. Since the displays will be available to people of all ages, interests, and backgrounds, their effectiveness will be dependent to a great degree upon the manner in which scientific fact is simplified and dramatized. Modern museum displays borrow considerably from good advertising technique, for their objectives are similar in spite of radically different "products." Eye-catching arrangements and judicious use of color have great value. Careful preparation of explanatory texts, often given too little attention, is very important; no matter how attractive an exhibit, it will not completely fulfill its purpose unless necessary labels are concise and couched in language understandable to the layman.

3. The location of the museum building. Since museums are designed to foster public understanding of an area, they must be strategically located in relation to public activity.

4. The design and plan of the building. In addition to an attractive

FIG. 9-10. Obsidian Cliff Wayside Exhibit, Yellowstone National Park. (*National Park Service*)

appearance, a museum building should have public display rooms arranged to foster proper visitor circulation. Adequate space for necessary staff activities must also be provided. It is extremely important that the design and plan of the building be adapted to the exhibit plan; reversal of that procedure will invariably result in lowered efficiency in the presentation of the story of an area.

Roadside and trailside exhibits are actually small-scale museum developments applied to detailed, on-the-spot interests. They vary from simple, attractive, informative signs to more elaborate semienclosed structures; the latter contain exhibit cases with interpretive displays concerning specific localized interests (e.g., fossil remains, a biological association of particular note, or a geological feature). Since, by comparison to museums, these developments are relatively inexpensive, they often shoulder the entire burden of interpretive programs in many types of recreational areas.

Self-guiding nature trails involve so little cost and effort and are so adaptable that they should be included in recreational areas wherever possible. A short trail that is readily accessible to centers of public concentration, offers typical views of the area, and provides opportunity for observation of special features of interest usually serves this purpose. Two systems of development prevail. In one system individual features of interest along the way (e.g., trees, flowers, and the like) are marked by small movable signs attached to stakes [9]. In the second system a small mimeographed leaflet describes specific interests found at points along the trail, points which are marked by relatively permanent, numbered stakes. The descriptive leaflets are made available in a container located at the beginning of the nature trail; these may be retained by visitors or returned after they have served their purpose.

Wild-flower gardens. Many areas contain a wide variety of habitats, and consequently plants, not readily accessible to the public. To make these interests more readily available to visitors, wild-flower gardens are sometimes developed to simulate the natural setting of varied plant associations. Many plants, however, do not adapt themselves to such treatment; this, together with the cost of development and maintenance, usually militates against the use of wild-flower gardens as an interpretive facility.

Informal lectures or campfire programs on varied interests characteristic of recreational areas are often important interpretive features [28]. Such activities generally require campfire circles or outdoor amphitheaters of different type and design, constructed in accordance with certain basic considerations [11,30]. Their location must be readily accessible but in a setting which will inspire the visitor and arouse his interest in the topics discussed. Surroundings should be typical of the area and should emphasize its principal interests. The site should be as free as possible from distractions which will destroy the mood of the program; forests, topographical features, water surfaces, and other characteristics of a natural setting have varied acoustical properties which must be taken into account. Since it is desirable to illustrate such programs, proper visibility by the audience is essential, and provision must be made for the convenient use and safe storage of projection equipment. If large crowds are the rule, an adequate amplifying system may be necessary. Seating arrangements and stage should be designed to blend into the surroundings. If parking space is necessary and programs are given during the evening, care should be taken that headlights from cars do not impair the quality of projection.

In certain instances programs may have to be given indoors. In such cases community buildings and related suitable structures, or even hotel lobbies, may be utilized.

Guided field trips may vary in duration from one hour to several days; they may involve a hike on foot or a trip by auto caravan, bus, boat, or horseback. The success of such ventures is largely dependent upon the qualifications and experience of the leader; his background in the scientific aspect of interests along the way, his understanding of people, and

FIG. 9-11. Field trips under trained leadership reward one by fostering an understanding of what is seen along the way; naturalist-conducted hike in Rocky Mountain National Park, Colorado. (*National Park Service*)

his technique of presenting various subjects to his group are vitally important [29]. Each type of trip involves specific problems. Since the audience is a mobile one, a running commentary is out of the question. The leader should confine explanations to specific points, properly spaced along the way in accordance with the capabilities of the group or the location of special attractions. While the main purpose of such trips is interpretation, it is also necessary that the group be impressed with the importance of good outdoor manners. The leader should also understand the hazards of the route to be taken, see that his party has proper respect for safety precautions, and in the event of unavoidable accidents, know how to cope with emergencies.

Libraries are of value to the general administrative staff, as a research tool for interpretive workers, and as a source of information to visitors [7].

While most people who use and enjoy outdoor recreational areas have merely a casual interest in various detailed features, a small percentage have a much deeper perception. For these people, as well as for the administrative and interpretive staff, a well-chosen collection of books about the region is of great value. However, a general library is seldom necessary unless considerable numbers of people remain in an area for long periods.

Publication, distribution, and sale of literature dealing with the area may also be desirable, particularly where recreational lands have diverse interests. In addition to serving as acceptable souvenirs, such publications promote a broader understanding of a region and contribute to the visitor's continual interest after his return home. In some cases such activities may be handled directly by the administrative agency; in others by approved subsidiary organizations established specifically for such purposes.

Various natural history and museum associations which operate in many national parks and monuments are outstanding examples of such subsidiary organizations [7]. In addition to selling more elaborate books obtained at the regular bookseller's discount from established publishers, these organizations also publish small, popular, inexpensive booklets on specific subjects (e.g., wild flowers, animal life, geology, or history). They are organized so that accumulated small profits derived from their operation accrue to the benefit of the local interpretive program rather than to the park in general or to any individual.

MISCELLANEOUS STRUCTURES

In addition to the specific facilities and services previously outlined, many recreational areas require a number of other structures and developments which must be carefully related to the particular environment involved. These include park entrances, checking stations, administration buildings, quarters for the seasonal and year-round staff, trail shelters, community buildings, buildings necessary for storage and maintenance of equipment, facilities for fire control, pack or riding stock, and a variety of utilities such as telephone and radio communication, power and light, sewage and water systems, and the like [11].

Within the physical limitations of this chapter it would be impractical even to outline specific criteria which would guide the development of these miscellaneous but vital needs. The functions of these facilities and services are too diverse, and the nature of the interests in the areas involved is too varied to permit more than a general summation. Some of these facilities and services (e.g., entrances, checking stations, administration buildings, trail shelters, community buildings) serve purposes which necessarily bring them in close contact with users of recreational lands;

consequently greater care must be exercised in their location and design. Other miscellaneous needs (e.g., various utilities, structures for storage and maintenance) are such that public contact is either extremely limited or unlikely; because they are rarely observed by the public, the requirements of location, layout, and design need not be so rigid. For instance, the design and location of a checking station at a park boundary, since it is viewed by all visitors and thus introduces the general concept of an area, must be more carefully considered than the design and location of a warehouse, maintenance shop, or corral, which visitors rarely have occasion to observe. In like vein the installation of light and power cables serving an area such as Carlsbad Caverns National Park is accompanied by more difficult problems than those typical of a heavily forested region. Cables and electrical fixtures serving underground areas are difficult to locate so that they are properly camouflaged and yet are available for necessary servicing. In heavily forested country necessary light and power lines can be erected parallel to highways, readily accessible to those who must make periodic adjustments and repairs but screened from view by native forest growth.

Suffice it to say that these miscellaneous but vital facilities must be planned and developed so that they will fulfill the requirements of their particular purpose efficiently. However, man's works must necessarily be subjugated to natural values on most recreational lands and must also adhere to basic standards applicable to developments which are more intimately related to general public use. In short, the location and design of these works must be harmonious with their environment. Such basic criteria permit varied approaches to specific problems, approaches which will meet the needs of specific situations due to differences in terrain, plant cover, and other factors. Techniques such as screening by vegetation, use of harmonious colors, employment of native materials in proper scale, maintenance of low silhouettes, and a handicraft style of construction are generally followed.

SUMMARY

Proper use of different types of outdoor recreational lands necessitates a variety of facilities and services adapted to diverse recreational interests and activities. Growing recognition of the fact that various types of recreational areas serve different purposes has been coupled with a better understanding of the character and design of facilities and the nature of services which serve varied purposes. Better design and the more functional quality typical of modern recreational facilities, as well as better planning of recreational services, have replaced haphazard development of such needs.

While details of planning, construction, and development of facilities and services are necessarily the province of trained technicians, it is imperative that all administrative personnel have a well-rounded understanding of the fundamentals of such activities, since responsibility for decisions rests in their hands.

SELECTED REFERENCES

1. American Institute of Park Executives and Michigan State College: "Park Automobile Barriers," *Park Management Series Bulletin,* no. 1, Chicago, 1954.
2. American Institute of Park Executives and Michigan State College: "Picnic Tables," *Park Management Series Bulletin,* no. 2, Chicago, 1954.
3. American Institute of Park Executives and Michigan State College: "Park Sanitary Facilities," *Park Management Series Bulletin,* no. 4, Chicago, n.d.
4. Anderson, Ralph: Information Please, *In-service Training Series,* U.S. National Park Service, Washington, 1955.
5. Brower, David: "Manual of Ski Mountaineering," University of California Press, Berkeley, Calif., 1947.
6. Bryant, H. C., and W. W. Atwood: "Research and Education in the National Parks," U.S. Government Printing Office, Washington, 1936.
7. Burns, Ned: "National Park Service Field Manual for Small Museums," U.S. Government Printing Office, Washington, 1941.
8. Butler, George D.: "Recreation Areas: Their Design and Equipment," 2d ed., The Ronald Press Company, New York, 1957.
9. Dalby, George W., and George H. Hamilton: Labeling Plants in the Niagara Parks System, *Parks and Recreation,* vol. 38, no. 11, pp. 4–5, November, 1955.
10. Forbes, Reginald D., and Arthur B. Meyer (eds.): "Forestry Handbook," edited for Society of American Foresters, The Ronald Press Company, New York, 1955.
11. Good, A. H.: "Park and Recreation Structures" (part I, Administration and Basic Service Facilities; part II, Recreational and Cultural Facilities; part III, Overnight and Organized Camp Facilities), U.S. National Park Service, Washington, 1938.
12. Meinecke, D. P.: "The Effect of Excessive Tourist Travel on the California Redwood Parks," California State Printing Office, Sacramento, Calif., 1929.
13. Meinecke, D. P.: "Camp Planning and Camp Reconstruction," U.S. Forest Service, California Region, San Francisco, n.d.
14. National Conference on State Parks and U.S. National Park Service: "Park Practice," Periodic loose-leaf service, edited by Ira Lykes, Chief of Park Practice, Washington, v.d.
15. National Conference on State Parks and U.S. National Park Service: "Park Practice Guide Line," Periodic loose-leaf service, edited by Ira Lykes, Chief of Park Practice, National Park Service, Washington, v.d.
16. Newton, Norman T.: "An Approach to Design," Addison-Wesley Press, Cambridge, Mass., 1951.
17. Outboard Boating Club of America and Socony Mobil Oil Company, Inc.: "Outboard Marinas," Chicago, n.d.
18. Sears, Bradford G.: "Building and Construction References for Landscape

Architects," Bulletin, no. 30, Syracuse University, New York State College of Forestry, Department of Landscape and Recreational Management, Syracuse, N.Y., n.d.

19. Scott, Robert G.: "Design Fundamentals," McGraw-Hill Book Company, Inc., New York, 1951.
20. Tilden, Freeman: "Interpreting Our Heritage," University of North Carolina Press, Chapel Hill, N.C., 1957.
21. U.S. Department of Agriculture, Forest Service: "Recreation Handbook" (various regions), n.d. (Mimeographed.)
22. U.S. Department of Agriculture, Forest Service: "Avalanche Handbook," Washington, n.d.
23. U.S. Department of Agriculture, Forest Service: "Forest Trail Handbook," Washington, 1935.
24. U.S. Department of Agriculture, Forest Service: "Camp Stoves and Fireplaces," Washington, 1937.
25. U.S. Department of Agriculture, Forest Service: Building with Logs, *Miscellaneous Publication*, no. 579, Washington, 1954.
26. U.S. Department of the Interior, National Park Service: "Instructions for the Preparation of Master Plans," U.S. National Park Service Administrative Manual, current revision, vol. 12, chap. 1, Washington, n.d. (Mimeographed.)
27. U.S. Department of the Interior, National Park Service: "Information and Interpretation in the Field," U.S. National Park Service Administrative Manual, current revision, vol. 25, Washington, n.d. (Mimeographed.)
28. U.S. Department of the Interior, National Park Service: Talks, *In-service Training Series*, Washington, 1953.
29. U.S. Department of the Interior, National Park Service: Conducted Trips, *In-service Training Series*, Washington, 1954.
30. U.S. Department of the Interior, National Park Service: Campfire Programs, *In-service Training Series*, Washington, 1955.
31. Vinal, W. G.: "Nature Recreation," McGraw-Hill Book Company, Inc., New York, 1940.

CHAPTER 10 *Principal Wild Land Recreational Areas in Other Parts of the World*

Establishment of wild-land areas for public outdoor recreational use in the United States was followed by similar action in many other countries of the world. This was first manifest in Canada. In 1885, only thirteen years after the formation of Yellowstone National Park in the United States, an area of 10 square miles surrounding the hot springs at Banff, in the Canadian Province of Alberta, was designated as a health resort [26,79]. Two years later this area was enlarged to 260 square miles and christened Rocky Mountains, later Banff, National Park. Later it was to become the nucleus of the extensive, present-day Canadian National Park System [25,26].

Today many nations have some form of national park system, have established game reserves, wildlife sanctuaries, recreational forests and the like, or have placed sites of archeological and historical importance under the protection of public agencies. Although details of administrative philosophy of such lands differ, largely owing to variations in cultural background, density of population, and economic conditions typical of different parts of the world, the fundamental idea underlying the management of such lands is similar. Preservation of basic recreational interests is a primary objective.

Interest in the preservation of significant wild-land values on an international level began to develop early in the present century [10,14,32,50, 94,101], although such interest did not become formally organized until 1948. In October of that year the International Union for the Protection of Nature was formed at an International Conference held at Fontainebleau [33,101]. This conference was called by the French government with the joint sponsorship of UNESCO. Subsequent meetings of this and related organizations broadened and developed the scope of world-wide conservation activities [14,34,62,63,64,65,67,68,101].

The following brief summary of principal wild-land recreational areas in various foreign countries is included to emphasize that international recognition is now accorded the national park idea and to provide a means of comparison between the basic administrative policies of such lands in other parts of the globe and those of the United States.

RECREATIONAL USE OF WILD LANDS IN AFRICA

Interest in the preservation of significant wild lands was manifest at an early date in several parts of Africa. Initial efforts in this direction were made in 1846 [63], at which time attempts were made to prohibit the ruthless slaughter of wildlife in Transvaal, now part of the Union of South Africa. Early areas specifically set aside for the protection of native African wildlife were the Hluhluwe Game Reserve, established in 1877 in Natal [115], a small reserve established in 1889 by King Leopold of Belgium in the Belgian Congo, primarily for the protection of elephants [12], and Sabie Game Reserve in Transvaal, forerunner of Kruger National Park, established in 1898 [63].

Belgian Congo. The Belgian Congo has four magnificent national parks [12,63]. The first of these had its origin in 1925 when King Albert issued a decree establishing the original area of Parc National Albert. This original decree concerned only a small part of the present park, set aside for the protection of a band of gorillas; it was prompted by King Albert's interest in the national parks of the United States, an interest gained on his visit to this country in 1919. Parc National Albert was later enlarged to 2.5 million acres, bordered on both east and west by the great escarpments of the Albertine Rift, a huge natural trench several hundred miles long that is characterized by a series of great African lakes. Natural topographical boundaries thus serve as serious barriers to botanical and zoological migration, rendering Parc National Albert unique for biological study.

Special features of Parc National Albert include active and extinct volcanoes, a wide variety of plant life (ranging from equatorial to alpine vegetation), a diversity of animal interests (elephant, hippopotamus, numerous carnivores, and gorilla), and several groups of pygmies, whose villages are permitted in the area.

The other three national parks of the Belgian Congo are Parc National de la Kagera (established 1934; area 750,000 acres), Parc National de la Garamba (established 1938; area 1,250,000 acres), and Parc National de l'Upemba (established 1939; area 2,932,000 acres). All were set aside primarily to preserve varied unique animal interests.

Broad administrative policies concerning these parks are determined by the Institut des Parcs Nationaux du Congo Belge. Local administration of specific areas is entrusted to one or more commissioners, with each area being divided into sections under supervision of a staff of keepers. Administrative policy is strongly flavored by the natural-reserve concept, and only limited sections of each area are open to the general public. Those wishing to enter these national parks must have permission from the proper authorities. The boundaries have been so drawn that all

FIG. 10-1. Visitor accommodations at Camp Ruindi, a point of departure for journeys into parts of Parc National Albert, Belgian Congo. (*Photo by G. Felix, Congopresse, Belgian Congo Tourist Bureau*)

areas suitable for colonization are excluded. Native population in park areas has been reduced to a minimum; in some cases it was necessary to move native populations to new areas beyond the confines of the reserves.

Kenya. Numerous highly significant national parks, together with areas of somewhat similar character, have also been established in various units of the British Commonwealth in Africa. In general their basic administrative policy is similar to that of the national parks of the United States in that it recognizes the desirability of limited development which facilitates public use and enjoyment. Such development of course is carried out with true regard for the preservation of features of interest.

Kenya has six national parks (see Table 10-1) and six national reserves.[1] Both types of areas are established by proclamation of the Gov-

[1] Text, as well as accompanying Table 10-1, derived from bibliographical references 35, 36, and 74, together with personal correspondence of Jan. 5, 1955, from M. H. Cowie, Director, Royal National Parks of Kenya, Nairobi.

ernor with the consent of the Legislative Council of the colony, as provided in the National Parks Ordinance passed by the Legislative Council in 1945. Likewise, both types of areas are administered by the Kenya National Parks Trustees, a corporate body of fourteen individuals. In national parks the development of permanent habitations and the disturbance of natural features are prohibited. Kenya's national reserves, although somewhat similar to national parks, are administered under a more liberal policy which recognizes that the legitimate rights and needs of indigenous people take precedence over preservation of game and vegetation.

Kenya's national reserves are Marsabit, approximately 10,000 square miles; Amboselli, approximately 1,000 square miles; Mara, approximately

Table 10-1. Summary of National Parks in Kenya, 1955

National park	Year est.	Area, acres	Principal features of interest
Nairobi.	1946	28,160	Wide variety of native African animal life
Tsavo.	1948	5,164,160	Wide variety of native African animal life
Mount Kenya. . . .	1949	145,920	Scenic mountain area; includes Mt. Kenya (17,040 ft.)
Aberdare.	1950	145,920	Scenic mountain area, interesting animal life
Gedi.	1948	107	Ancient ruined city of Islamic origin
Olorgesallie.	1949	53	Only known living site of "hand-ax man"

200 square miles; West Chyulu, approximately 250 square miles; Ngong, approximately 200 square miles; and Tsavo Road and Railway. The last named area includes railways and public roads extending through Tsavo National Park; it has been excluded from the national park for administrative reasons. All of these national reserves were established in 1948 and 1949.

Federation of Rhodesia and Nyasaland.[2] A number of areas have been designated as national parks in the Federated States of Northern and Southern Rhodesia and Nyasaland (see Table 10-2). Those in Southern Rhodesia were established prior to the federation by the government of Southern Rhodesia under provisions of the National Parks Act, passed in 1949. Under the new Federal Act, 1955, national parks are designated by the Governor General of the Federation, with the consent of the governor

[2] Text, as well as Table 10-2, derived from bibliographical references 107 and 108 and from personal correspondence, Jan. 8 and Mar. 23, 1955, and Feb. 10, 1956, from L. H. Stewart, Director, Department of National Parks, Salisbury, Southern Rhodesia.

FIG. 10-2. Reticulated giraffe in Marsabit National Reserve, Kenya. (*Photo copyright by Mervyn Cowie, Director, Royal National Parks of Kenya*)

of the territory concerned; they are administered by the Department of National Parks, in the Ministry of Home Affairs, with the assistance of an advisory board. Local administration of specific areas is in charge of wardens. Funds for administration and development are provided by the government of the Federation.

In Southern Rhodesia, the National Parks Act of 1949 was the result of a growing public interest in national parks. This interest first achieved tangible form in 1928 when the Game and Fish Preservation Act was passed and Wankie Game Reserve was established. In 1944, with the passage of the Monuments and Relics Act, the Natural and Historical Monuments and Relics Commission was established. This body, in addition to being responsible for the care and administration of national monuments, now assists the Department of National Parks in archeological matters within the national parks and is represented on the National Parks Advisory Board.

Table 10-2. Summary of National Parks in the Federation of Rhodesia and Nyasaland

National park	Year est.	Area, acres	Principal features of interest
Victoria Falls	1952	132,250	Victoria Falls, native African wildlife
Wankie	1949	3,365,600	Wide variety of native African wildlife
Matopos	1953	245,000	Scenic area; aboriginal rock paintings
Rob't McIlwaine	1952	13,875	Artificial lake; recreation area
Inyanga	1949	84,000	Important scenic area in eastern highlands
Mtarazi Falls	1953	4,400	Scenic area adjoining Inyanga National Park
Chimanimani	1949	20,213	Rugged mountains; primitive wilderness area
Zimbabwe Ruins	....[a]	1,789	Archeological area
Ewanrigg	....[a]	700	Aloe and cycad garden
Mushandike	1955	32,000	Artificial lake; recreation area

[a] Date of establishment unavailable.

Among the national parks in Rhodesia, Victoria Falls has long been world famous. In addition to its great cataract, this national park also includes a small game reserve on the banks of the Zambezi River. Wankie, particularly noteworthy for variety and abundance of native African wildlife, is said to rival the famous Kruger National Park in the Union of South Africa. Development of Wankie National Park is somewhat similar to that of Kruger National Park, although on a smaller scale; a number of roads and several comfortable overnight camps are available to visitors during the open season, from June to November.

The Federation of Rhodesia and Nyasaland also has a number of game reserves or sanctuaries, controlled by the Game Department. A limited number of visitors are allowed in these areas. Most noteworthy of these game reserves is Kafue in Northern Rhodesia; it embraces an area of over 5.5 million acres, provides a habitat for a wide variety of native African wildlife, and fulfills many of the requirements of a national park. In addition, large forest areas have been reserved by the Federation government, but these, administered by the Forestry Commission, are not open to the general public.

Tanganyika. In Tanganyika the national park idea first achieved tangible form in 1940 when a vast area of the Serengeti Plains and adjacent Ngorongoro Crater region was declared a national park under the Game Ordinance.[3] In 1951, following the passage of the National Park Ordinance, the boundary of this area was revised and its control was vested in a Board of Trustees. In 1954 administrative responsibility was transferred to a Director of National Parks.

Serengeti National Park (established 1951; area 5,600 square miles), varying in elevation from 4,000 to 10,000 feet, is noteworthy for its abundant and varied animal life. About two-thirds of the park lies within the traditional grazing land of the Masai, a proud, independent-minded, picturesque people; they have been granted certain rights, since their evacuation from the area was impractical. The Masai are not a hunting tribe and own great numbers of cattle, sheep, and goats; the problem of keeping the numbers of these animals within the carrying capacity of the park is an extremely difficult one.

Tanganyika also has a number of game reserves, aggregating about 29,000 square miles in area. In addition, the famous Olduwai Gorge in the southeast corner of the Serengeti Plains is also protected, and since 1947, a few of the many sites characterized by prehistoric art have been opened to the public.

Uganda. National parks in the Uganda Protectorate are, by authority of the National Parks Ordinance of 1952, established by proclamation of the Governor, after consultation with the African local government in whose area the proposed park is situated, and with the consent of the Legislative Council.[4] Boundaries of Uganda national parks cannot be altered without consent of both the Legislative Council and the Board of Trustees. The Board of Trustees, appointed by the Governor, determines the broad administrative policies of the Uganda national parks and appoints the Director and Chief Warden, together with his assistants, including a warden for each national park. Funds required for administration and development are derived from government appropriations.

Uganda has two national parks. Queen Elizabeth National Park (established 1952; area 800 square miles) adjoins Parc National Albert in the

[3] Information relative to Tanganyika prepared from personal correspondence, Jan. 24, 1955 and Mar. 6, 1956, from the Public Relations Department, Dar es Salaam, Tanganyika.

[4] Information relative to the national parks of Uganda obtained from bibliographical references 112, 113, and 114, together with personal correspondence, Feb. 5, 1955, and Mar. 15, 1956, from the office of the Director and Chief Warden of Uganda National Parks, Lake Katwe, Uganda Protectorate.

Belgian Congo. It is noted for its abundant native animal life and includes the famous crater area near the base of the Ruwenzori Range, known as the Mountains of the Moon. Murchison Falls National Park (established 1952; area 1,200 square miles), astride the Victoria Nile, has abundant native African wildlife as well as famous Murchison Falls.

Three game reserves, aggregating about 500 square miles in area, and eight game sanctuaries, with an area of over 1,500 square miles, have also been established in Uganda.[5] In game reserves hunting is prohibited except by permission of the Governor, and settlement is banned. Game sanctuaries are more specific and restricted in purpose; they are set aside to maintain characteristic wildlife near population centers or to assist rare species to recover and establish themselves. Neither the game reserves nor the sanctuaries provide facilities for visitors.

Union of South Africa. National parks, game reserves, and related areas in the Union of South Africa are among the most significant in the world. Their administration is in charge of various specifically designated authorities, as determined by different provincial governments of the Union.

The five national parks of Cape Province and Transvaal are administered by a National Board of Trustees consisting of ten members appointed by the Governor General [116]. Most noteworthy of these national parks is Kruger National Park in Transvaal, world famous for its abundant and varied native African fauna. This area, originally established as Sabie Game Reserve in 1898, received national park status in 1926 and embraces an area of 8,000 square miles [116]. It is completely open to visitors from May 15 to October 15 (one section throughout the year), and although accessibility is fostered by a system of roads and overnight camps, visitor movement and the type of vehicles used are carefully regulated [116]. The four other national parks in Cape Province and Transvaal, parks which also contain significant wildlife interests, are Kalahari Gemsbuck National Park (established 1931; area 3,650 square miles), Bredasdorp Bontebok National Park (established 1931; area 1,800 acres), Mountain Zebra National Park (established 1937; area 4,500 acres), and Addo National Park (established 1931; area 17,000 acres) [116].

The six game reserves in Transvaal are Pafuri (established 1933; area 40,639 acres), Rust-der-Winter (established 1937; area 13,432 acres), Marico Bosveld (established 1937; area 17,257 acres), Honnet (established 1939; area approximately 5,000 acres), Vaal-Hartz (established 1939; area approximately 63,000 acres), and Loskop (established 1940; area approximately 30,000 acres). These game reserves are administered by the Provincial Game Department. In addition, three municipal game

[5] Personal correspondence, Jan. 11, 1955, with Game and Fisheries Department, Entebbe, Uganda Protectorate.

Table 10-3. Summary of National Parks and Related Areas in Natal

National park or reserve	Year est.	Area, acres	Principal features of interest
Natal:			
Giant's Castle Game Reserve and Park	1903	59,605	In Drakensberg Range; includes variety of native animal life; accessible by road; visitor accommodations available
Royal Natal National Park	1916	20,000	Scenic area in Drakensberg Range; interesting flora and fauna; hotel accommodations
Rugged Glen Nature Reserve[a]	1950	1,882	
Oribi Gorge Nature Reserve	1950	3,700	Varied interesting native flora and fauna
Krantzkloof Nature Reserve	1950	1,108	Varied interesting native flora and fauna; facilities for picnicking
Kamberg Nature Reserve	1951	5,515	Varied interesting native flora and fauna
Loteni Nature Reserve[a]	1953	3,160	
Zululand:			
Hluhluwe Game Reserve	1897	57,000	World famous for varied, abundant native wildlife; visitor facilities available
Ndumu Game Reserve	1924	25,000	Varied, abundant animal life; accessible by road
Umfolozi Game Reserve	1897	72,000	Interesting native wildlife, especially the square-lipped rhinoceros
Mkuzi Game Reserve[a]	1912	62,000	
St. Lucia Game Reserve	1897	81,090	Coastal area, originally established for protection of native birds
Richard's Bay Game Reserve	1935	2,000	Coastal area, originally established for protection of native birds
Enselini Game Reserve[a]	1948	725	
Umlalazi Game Reserve	1948	2,240	Varied native wildlife of interest; fishing; camping facilities available
Kosi Bay Nature Reserve	1950	50	Excellent fishing; also variety of interesting native mammals
St. Lucia Park	1939	31,000	Fishing; native wildlife; camping facilities
Richard's Bay Park	1945	975	Fishing; native wildlife; camping facilities
False Bay Park	1944	5,553	Fishing; native wildlife; camping facilities
Sordwana Bay National Park	1950	1,020	Coastal area; excellent fishing; camping facilities
Dhlinza Forest Nature Reserve[a]	1952	461	

[a] Information incomplete.

SOURCE: Prepared from data included in bibliographical reference 82, together with information contained in personal correspondence, Jan. 20, 1955, and Feb. 7, 1952, from the Director of Wildlife Conservation, Natal Parks, Game and Fish Preservation Board, Pietermaritzburg.

reserves, aggregating nearly 30,000 acres, are administered by the City Council of Pretoria [116].

National Parks and related areas in the Province of Natal, including Zululand (see Table 10-3), are administered by the Natal Parks, Game and Fish Preservation Board [82]. This board, composed of nine members, operates under authority of an ordinance passed in 1947 [81].

Subject to certain rules and regulations, national parks and reserves in Natal are open to visitors; many are accessible by road and have camping and hotel facilities. A number are world famous for their abundant and varied native animal life; one of the most noteworthy is Hluhluwe Game Reserve, wherein nearly every species of animal native to Zululand may be seen [116].

The Orange Free State has two game reserves administered by the provincial government. However, neither of these is strictly a game reserve, since game-management activities are conducted on these areas, and certain animal species are occasionally captured for distribution to zoological gardens [116].

Finally, numerous areas classed as natural or historical monuments, relics, and antiquities, have been established in the Union of South Africa. Responsibility for their administration and protection rests with the Historic Monuments Commission [116].

Other National Parks and Reserves in Africa. A number of other countries in Africa, particularly those under the French sphere of influence, have made substantial progress in the establishment of national parks and natural reserves. Such areas in the northern part of Africa were established primarily to preserve botanical interests, while those in the southern portion were set aside largely because of their faunal values.

Since 1923 *Algeria* has established fourteen national parks aggregating an area of about 70,000 acres.[6] Two national parks, with a total area of approximately 85,000 acres, exist in *Morocco.*[7] *Tunisia* has one national park of about 12,000 acres.[7]

French Equatorial Africa (see Table 10-4) has five national parks with a total area of nearly 5 million acres, as well as a specifically designated strict natural reserve of about 370,000 acres.[7] In addition, eight partial reserves, totaling nearly 17 million acres, have been established in which hunting is prohibited except by special scientific permit [63,101]. Personnel and procedures for adequate administration and protection of these areas have not been completely organized, and their development for

[6] Personal correspondence, June 6, 1955, from Agricultural Attache, American Embassy, Paris, France, including an unpublished statement on national parks and natural reserves in France and the Overseas Territories [45], supplied by Mr. Henri Morel, Service des Eaux et Forêts, French Ministry of Agriculture (also see bibliographical reference 101).

[7] *Ibid.*

general public use, as in Kruger National Park in the Union of South Africa, is still pending [63,101].

French Equatorial Africa has also established a partial hunting reserve (approximately 370,000 acres) in which hunting is permitted under certain regulations. In addition there are a number of forest reserves, and certain sites of historical importance are given protection [63,101].

Table 10-4. National Park and Strict Natural Reserves in French Equatorial Africa

National park	Year est.	Area, acres	National park	Year est.	Area, acres
Saint-Floris	1940	98,840	Vassako Bola[a]	....	370,650
Bamingui-Bangoran	1940	2,471,000	(Strict Natural Reserve)		
Odzala	1949	1,111,950			
Okanda	1946	469,490	l'Ofue	1946	370,650

[a] Established as a strict natural reserve in 1940; date of transfer to national park status not given.

SOURCE: Prepared from information contained in bibliographical reference 45 (included in personal correspondence, June 6, 1955, from American Embassy, Paris) and from information contained in bibliographical references 63 and 101.

In *French West Africa* a number of reserves have been established for the regulation of hunting, as well as for the protection of native forests, flora, and animal life. Among these areas are a strict nature reserve (Monts Nimba) of about 45,000 acres, established in 1944, and two national parks (W. du Niger and La Comoe et Reserve de Bouna) with a total of nearly 2.5 million acres.[8] Neither national parks nor strict natural reserves are found in the *French Cameroons;* however, there are twelve game reserves with a total area of approximately 5 million acres[8] and a number of forest reserves [101]. *French Somaliland* has two national parks with a total area of more than 25,000 acres,[8] as well as several game reserves [101].

On the island of *Madagascar,* in addition to a proposed national park, there are numerous reserves of different types, including twelve strict natural reserves with a total area of approximately 1.5 million acres [101].

Mozambique has two areas of particular note. The Maputo Reserve, located in the region of the Mozambique–Natal border, serves primarily for the protection of elephants. Gorongosa National Park adjoins Kruger National Park in Transvaal, Union of South Africa; in many respects it is an extension of that famous wildlife preserve and embodies similar floral and faunal interests in great variety [101].

[8] *Ibid.*

In *Ethiopia* the Mengasha Forest, a 6,000-acre area set aside as a game and forest preserve by Emperor Menelik early in the present century, now serves primarily as a recreational area and is considered as Ethiopia's first national park. It is administered by the Department of Game and Forests in the Ministry of Agriculture.[9]

Finally, the *Sudan*, in addition to two national parks, has established eleven game reserves and three game sanctuaries. The Sudan also has a Commission of Archeology, responsible for the preservation and investigation of historic and prehistoric sites in that country [35,101].

RECREATIONAL USE OF WILD LANDS IN ASIA

Although the recreational use of wild lands in Asia has not developed to the degree typical of North America or Africa, a number of Asiatic nations have taken steps in this direction.

Burma. Although national parks have not yet been established in Burma, twelve game sanctuaries aggregating an area of about 600,000 acres have been designated by authority of the Burma Wildlife Protection Act of 1936. These sanctuaries were formed primarily for the protection of rare or interesting native animal species and are administered by the Burma Forest Service [66].

Limited facilities for the accommodation of visitors are found only in Pidung Game Sanctuary but long-range plans call for further developments of this nature. It has also been proposed that Pidung Game Sanctuary, together with some other area nearer Rangoon, be designated as national parks and managed somewhat like Kruger National Park in South Africa or Yellowstone National Park in the United States [66].

India. For some time portions of certain forest reserves in India have been designated as game reserves or wildlife sanctuaries, but the nature of protection given these areas was largely dependent upon the interest of individual forest officers.

In 1952 public interest in wildlife protection, which developed as a result of past unregulated hunting and consequent rapid depletion of faunal resources, culminated in the formation of the Indian Board for Wild Life [5]. Subsequently, stringent game laws were enacted and measures were taken for their enforcement, specific protection was given certain species, the number of game sanctuaries was increased, and one national park was established [5].

Most noteworthy of more than forty game sanctuaries in India are Rajaji in Uttar Pradesh, Jaldapara in West Bengal, Kaziranga in Assam, Madumalai in Madras, Bandipur in Mysore, Periyar in Travancore-

[9] Personal correspondence, Feb. 2, 1955, from the American Embassy, Addis Ababa, Ethiopia.

Cochin, and Banjar Game Reserve in Madhya Pradesh [5]. In some of these areas limited facilities are available for public use; future plans call for an extension of visitor needs [46]. In addition to game sanctuaries an area of 200 square miles in Uttar Pradesh, noteworthy for its sub-Himalayan fauna, has been designated as Hailey National Park.[10] All of these areas are administered and protected by the Indian Forest Service [5,46,63]. Game sanctuaries are designated by government order and may be similarly modified or opened to hunting; a national park, established by legislative act, has a more permanent status [5].

Indonesia. Interest in the preservation of the natural scene was manifest in Indonesia during the days of its Dutch Colonial period. In 1889 a section of the primeval jungle forest on the slopes of Mount Tjibodas, on the island of Java, was placed under the protection of the Botanical Institute of Buitenzorg [16], primarily to serve as a natural laboratory for scientific research. In 1912 the Society for Nature Protection was founded, and as a result of efforts by this organization, the government began to take steps toward the protection of plant and animal life. The first natural reserve was established in 1912, and by 1940 the number of such areas had been increased to 120 [47].

Since the formation of the Republic of Indonesia, nature reserves and nature parks have been under the joint control of the Biological Research Service of the Botanic Garden (Djawatan Penjelidikan Alam) at Bogor, and the Indonesian Forest Service. By cooperative agreement between these two agencies the Biological Research Service gives advice on questions of research, while the administration and management of the reserves are the responsibility of the Forest Service. The Forest Service also assists in the solution of wildlife problems through its Bureau of Wildlife Management and Nature Protection, established in 1951.[11]

In 1956 there were in the Republic of Indonesia 104 strict nature reserves and 12 nature parks[11] aggregating an area of over 4 million acres. Most of these areas are found on the islands of Java, Sumatra, Borneo, and Celebes. Strict nature reserves were established for the protection of significant botanical, zoological, geological, historical, and scenic interests typical of Indonesia; nature parks are essentially game reserves set aside for the protection of animal species.

Japan. The most extensive and highly developed national park system in Asia is in Japan. Nineteen national parks (see Table 10-5), aggregating a gross total of 4,360,000 acres, are included, the first having been established in 1934 [71]. Supplementing these national parks are fourteen

[10] Although only one area in India has been specifically designated as a national park, the term "national park" appears in the name of several game sanctuaries [5].

[11] Personal correspondence, Jan. 7, 1956, from the Chief of the Division of the Protection of Nature of the Forestry Department, Bogor, Indonesia.

Table 10-5. Summary of Japanese National Parks

National park	Year est.	Area, acres	Principal features of interest
Akan	1934	216,216	Volcanoes, *caldera* lakes, extensive forests, hot springs
Aso	1934	180,605	Volcanoes, varied plant life, hot springs
Bandai-Asahi	1950	506,607	Volcanoes, lakes, forests, alpine flora
Chichibu-Tama	1950	300,486	Rugged mountains, forests, animal life
Chûbu-sangaku	1934	419,514	Rugged mountains, varied flora, dense forests
Daisetsuzan	1934	573,120	Volcanoes, alpine flora, extensive forests
Daisen	1936	30,649	Volcanoes, extensive forests, historical interests, skiing
Fuji-Hakone-Izu	1936	243,295	Mt. Fuji and other mountains, waterfalls, lakes, varied plant life, hot springs
Ise-Shima	1946	128,586	Marine views, pearl fisheries, historical interests
Jôshinyetsu-Kôgen	1949	466,829	Volcanoes, varied forests, hot springs, skiing
Kirishima	1934	52,277	Volcanoes, forests, flora, historical interests, hot springs
Nikko	1934	347,419	Volcanoes, lakes, alpine flora, waterfalls
Rikuchyu-kaigan	1955	21,250	Rugged coastal landscape, forests, flora, birds
Saikai	1955	60,107	Coastal islands, forests, flora, historical interests
Seto-naikai	1934	163,060	Marine scenery, varied forests, historical interests
Shikotsu-Tôya	1949	243,799	Volcanoes, lakes, forests, varied animal life
Towada-Hachimantai	1936	205,969	Lake Towada, volcanoes, varied forests and flora, hot springs
Unzen-Amakusa	1934	63,260	Rugged mountains, varied flora, hot springs
Yoshino-Kumano	1936	136,845	Rugged mountains, seascapes, historical interests

SOURCE: "National Parks of Japan," National Parks Association, c/o Ministry of Health and Welfare, Tokyo, 1956.

quasi-national parks[12] with an aggregate area of over 1 million acres, the National Gardens, including the Outer Garden of the Imperial Palace, and numerous hot springs [71]. The Japanese national park system, except for the quasi-national parks,[13] is administered by the National Parks Division of the Ministry of Health and Welfare [71].

[12] Areas of scenic beauty not fully qualified for national park status; all quasi-national parks have been established since 1950.

[13] Although designated by the Minister of Health and Welfare, quasi-national parks are administered by prefectural governors.

The establishment of national parks in Japan was suggested before the end of the last century by Nagonori Okabe, a member of the House of Peers who had developed an interest in Yellowstone National Park during a period of study in the United States [69]. However, it was not until 1931 that the National Parks Law was adopted[14] by both houses of the Japanese Diet and became effective through Imperial edict [69]. This action resulted largely from public interest developed by the Japanese National Parks Association, formed in 1927 [69].

FIG. 10-3. Mt. Fuji as viewed from Hakone, Fuji-Hakone-Izu National Park, Japan. (*Japan Tourist Association*)

Because of Japan's large population and limited space, national parks in that country must be formulated and managed differently from similar areas in the United States. Establishment of a national park in Japan does not change the existing ownership or jurisdiction of land within its boundaries, but sections of such areas may be specifically designated for the protection of the natural landscape; in such instances public use and activities which affect scenic beauty may be restricted [71].

The national parks of Japan, which typify the scenery, geological interests, plant and animal life, and historical associations of that country, preserve the natural beauty and significant interests of areas selected as representative of the Japanese scene and provide for public use and enjoyment. They offer opportunity for a wide variety of activities including boating, camping, hiking, mountain climbing, fishing and, in winter,

[14] Revised in 1950.

skiing. Most of these national parks are readily accessible by boat, rail, or highway from principal cities, and hotel accommodations may usually be found in or adjacent to these areas.

Lebanon. An area regarded as a national park, about 80 miles from Beirut, protects one of the remnants of the formerly extensive stands of Labanon cedar (*Cedrus libani*), a historic tree species which flourished in this part of the world in the pre-Christian era [43]. It includes about 400 of these trees and is administered by the Department of Forestry of the Ministry of Agriculture.[15]

Malaya. In the Federation of Malaya, King George V National Park embraces an area of 1,677 square miles [76], including portions of the states of Pehang, Kelantan, and Trengganu [42]. It was established in 1939 and contains impressive scenery, vast areas of virgin Malayan forests, significant floral interests, and abundant native animal life in wide variety.[16]

Administration of this area is vested in a Board of Trustees, including the High Commissioner and the Sultans of the three states concerned.[16] In 1948 the Chief Game Warden of the Federation of Malaya was appointed by the trustees as ex-officio officer in charge; local administration of the park is entrusted to a resident European superintendent and his staff (including a Malay assistant superintendent, 15 Malay park rangers, and 20 Malay laborers), all employees of the Game Department.[16]

King George V National Park is accessible only by motorboat, and only one section is available to visitors during the open season, from March to September [76]. Limited accommodations are available at park headquarters located at Kuala Tahan, 70 miles from the nearest roadhead at Kuala Lipis. Permits are required for entrance to King George V National Park, and regulations prohibit the introduction of plants or animals or the disturbance of plant or animal life therein.

In addition to its national park the Federation of Malaya has established a number of game reserves and wildlife sanctuaries aggregating over 1,000 square miles in area [41].

New Caledonia. One national park and one natural reserve have been established on the island of New Caledonia. Area, dates of establishment, and principal features of interest in these areas are unknown [45].

Philippine Republic.[17] The national park system in the Philippine

[15] Personal correspondence, Apr. 14, 1958, from the Consulate General of Lebanon, New York.

[16] Personal correspondence, 1953, from H. J. Kitchener, Chief Game Warden, Klang, Federation of Malaya.

[17] Text and Table 10-6 prepared from information contained in personal correspondence, June 2, 1956, from Mr. Vicente de la Cruz, Officer in Charge of Parks and Wildlife, Manila, Philippine Republic.

Republic dates from 1932. In that year the act providing for the establishment of such areas, previously passed by the Philippine Legislature, was approved. Subsequent acts also established commissions for the purpose of marking historical sites and objects of antiquity.

By 1956 the Philippine Republic had established thirty-nine national parks (see Table 10-6) typifying the flora, fauna, geology, history, and

Table 10-6. Summary of National Parks in the Philippine Republic, 1956

National park	Year est.	Area, acres	National park	Year est.	Area, acres
Makiling	1933	9,400	Mayon Volcano	1938	13,100
Roosevelt	1933	3,550	Mount Isarog	1938	24,270
Mount Ararat	1933	8,800	Tirad Pass	1938	15,170
Libmanan	1934	48	Fuyot Spring	1938	1,965
Bicol	1934	12,480	Pagsanjan Gorge	1939	364
Kanlaon	1934	58,920	Basilan	1939	15,485
Quezon	1934	2,350	Mado Hot Springs	1939	115
Bulusan	1935	8,820	Rizal	1940	25
Callao Cave	1935	456	Manleluag Hot Springs	1940	220
Sohotan Natural Bridge	1935	2,016	Hundred Islands	1941	4,425
Sudlon	1936	1,670	Mt. Banahaw-San Cristobal	1941	26,720
Mount Apo	1936	186,000	Bataan	1945	74,400
Mount Data	1936	13,220	Quezon Memorial Park	1954	487
Kuapnit-Balinsasayao	1937	873	Manila Bay Beach	1954	1,159
Tagonan Hot Springs	1937	652	Tiwi Hot Springs	1954	116
Mahagnao Volcano	1937	1,526	Bessang Pass	1954	751
Central Cebu	1937	36,948	Luneta[a]	1955	40
Bongabon, Baler	1937	13,622	Lake Naujan	1956	53,488
Biak-na-bato	1937	5,080	Total (39)	....	598,781
Mount Dajo	1938	519			
Caramoan	1920	832			

[a] Established by Section 64(e) of the Revised Administrative Code and under the administration of the Commission on Parks and Wildlife.

scenic values of the Philippine Islands. Originally administered by the Philippine Bureau of Forestry (to 1953) and the Commission on Parks and Wildlife of the Executive Department (to June 30, 1956), responsibility for these areas was transferred to the Parks and Wildlife Office of the Department of Agriculture and Natural Resources on July 1, 1956.

RECREATIONAL LAND USE IN AUSTRALIA AND NEW ZEALAND

Extensive systems of outdoor recreational areas are found in both Australia and New Zealand. The administrative machinery concerned with these lands, however, as well as the broad policies which guide their management, is radically different.

Each of the six Australian states has established its own park system, based upon distinct legislation and managed, in accordance with specific objectives, by different organizations set up by the individual states. Outdoor recreational areas in the Australian states of New South Wales, South Australia, Victoria, and Western Australia lean heavily toward the outdoor-playground concept, with emphasis on the development of facilities for various outdoor sports. Queensland and Tasmania, however, place much greater emphasis on the maintenance of natural conditions in the management of their national parks.

Table 10-7. Summary of More Important Recreational Areas in New South Wales, 1956

Name of area	Approximate area, acres	Principal features of interest
Kosciusko State Park	1,500,000	Mt. Kosciusko, 7,305 ft., highest point in Australia; rugged mountains, largest snowfield in Australia, skiing, and other outdoor sports
National Park	36,880	Coastal area with fine beaches and sports facilities
Ku-ring-gai Chase	38,000	Outdoor recreational area
Blue Mountains Sights Reserves	12,000	Rugged mountains, outdoor recreational area
New England National Park	42,000	Rugged mountains, outdoor recreational area
Shoalhaven Morton Primitive Area[a]	45,000	
Bulli Pass and Lady Fuller National Park	725	Magnificent coastal views from summit of Bulli Pass
Yarrangobilly Caves Reserve	3,000	Interesting caverns, warm springs, fishing, snow sports
Jenolan Caves Reserve	6,000	Interesting caverns, wildlife sanctuary

[a] Information incomplete.

In New Zealand, national parks are administered by the National Park Authority, and policies which guide the management and use of these areas are somewhat similar to those of the U.S. National Park Service. In addition to national parks, New Zealand has also established other areas for the preservation of scenery or the conservation and protection of flora and fauna. These are generally subject to the authority of the Lands and Survey Department with local administration often delegated to other bodies in which control is vested; for example, some notable areas are managed by Scenic Reserve Boards.

Australia. Of the many areas established for various types of outdoor recreation in *New South Wales,* those noted in Table 10-7 are most important.[18] Each of these is administered by a Board of Trustees designated by the Department of Lands. State grants, as well as revenue derived from such sources as rents, leases, and royalties, provide funds for operation and maintenance. Except for Kosciusko, all of these areas owe their origin to the Public Trusts Act of 1897, the Public Parks Act of 1912, or the Crown Lands Consolidation Act of 1913; Kosciusko State Park was established by special act of Parliament in 1944 [117].

Table 10-8. Summary of Important National Parks in Queensland, 1956

National park	Area, acres	National park	Area, acres
Lamington	48,824	Shaw and Lindeman	8,697
Springbrook	3,518	Hook and Hayman	13,814
Tamborine	857	Molle and Conway	4,102
Mount Barney	12,980	Conway Range	48,640
Mount Glorious	1,345	Magnetic	6,260
Numinbah	477	Mount Elliot	60,000
Mount Tibrogargan	720	Mount Spec	18,560
Noosa	760	Dunk	1,805
Bunya Mountains	24,230	Hinchinbrook	97,232
Cunningham's Gap	7,470	Palmerston	6,315
Ravensbourne	224	Tully Falls	730
Mount Walsh	7,380	Lake Barrine	1,213
Carnarvon	66,480	Lake Eacham	1,200
Queen Mary Falls	193	Crater	900
Heron	127	Green	30
Keppel	2,287	Barron Falls	7,000
Eungella	122,799	Chillagoe Caves	4,733
Whitsunday	32,342	Bellenden Ker	80,140

Queensland has a national park system[19] of more than 200 areas of varying sizes aggregating nearly 800,000 acres (see Table 10–8). The first of these areas was established in 1908. Practically all are located in the eastern part of Queensland, most being on or adjacent to the coast or comprising islands or island groups in the Great Barrier Reef. They were established by authority of the State Forests and National Parks

[18] Text and Table 10-7 prepared largely from information contained in personal correspondence, May 2, 1956, from office of Under Secretary for Lands, Sydney, New South Wales, Australia.

[19] Text, as well as accompanying Table 10-8, derived from bibliographical reference 98 and from information contained in personal correspondence, Dec. 20, 1954, and Feb. 21, 1956, from Department of Forestry, Brisbane, Queensland, Australia.

Acts because of their outstanding scenic, scientific, or recreational qualities and are maintained as nearly as possible in their natural condition.

The philosophy upon which Queensland's national parks have been established is akin to that of similar areas in the United States. Each is regarded as a fragment of original Australia, and once constituted, they cannot be alienated except by authority of an act of Parliament. They are controlled by the Forestry Board, and administration is vested in the State Department of Forestry, which also supervises their development from funds derived from state appropriations.

Some of Queensland's national parks are particularly noteworthy. Lamington National Park contains inspiring views, numerous waterfalls, and a wealth of plant and animal life; the rare dormouse possum is found here, and Antarctic beech (*Nothofagus antarctica*) reaches the northernmost extent of its range in this area. Eugella and Bellenden-Ker National Parks are characterized by tropical forests. Bunya Mountains National Park includes a variety of botanical interests, varying from subtropical coastal forests to drier inland vegetation; the Bunya pine (*Araucaria bidwillii*) is the most interesting tree species in this area. Carnarvon Range National Park, most westerly national park in Queensland, has a varied forest cover and evidence of former aboriginal inhabitants. Hinchinbrook, the largest island national park in Queensland, has characteristic scrub forest with a backbone of serrated peaks. Barrine and Eacham National Parks include lakes in extinct volcanic craters set in tropical forests, and Bellenden-Ker National Park embraces two of the highest peaks in Queensland. Tully Falls National Park is most famous for its waterfall, 900 feet high.

The state of *South Australia* has but one national park [106]. It embraces an area of 2,000 acres located in the Mount Lofty Ranges about 8 miles from Adelaide. Established by act of Parliament in 1891, it serves primarily as a recreation ground for citizens of South Australia; a portion is retained in a natural condition, but on other sections varied sports facilities are made available. Control is vested in a Board of Commissioners, including the Lord Mayor of Adelaide, five other Government officials, and six representatives from interested organizations. The national park is self-supporting; funds required for operation and maintenance are derived from rents or leases of sports facilities and equipment [106]. The National Park Act, amended in 1955, now permits the commissioners to accept other areas to be set aside for recreation or as reserves for the protection of flora and fauna.[20] By early 1956 two areas, with a total of over 2,000 acres, had been so established.

A number of other outdoor recreational areas have been established

[20] Personal correspondence, Apr. 6, 1956, from Secretary to the Commissioners of the National Park and Wild Life Reserves, Belair, South Australia, Australia.

in the vicinity of Adelaide [106]. These include such reserves as Morialta Falls (539 acres), Waterfall Gully (103 acres), Mount Lofty Summit (58 acres), Brownhill Creek (120 acres), Greenhill (64 acres), Obelisk Estate (1,753 acres), The Knoll (4½ acres), and Horsnell Gully (282 acres). In addition, an area of approximately 8 acres has been acquired for the protection of a grove of eucalyptus, and Fort Glanville (12 acres) is considered as a historical monument.

The island state of *Tasmania* has eight national parks,[21] aggregating an area of more than 500,000 acres (see Table 10–9). Selected because

Table 10-9. Summary of National Parks in Tasmania, 1954

National park	Year est.	Area, acres
Freycinet Peninsula	1916	16,050
Mount Field	1916	42,020
Cradle Mountain–Lake St. Clair	1940	333,106
Mount Barrow	1940	1,134
Ben Lomond	1947	39,460
Frenchman's Cap	1951	25,380
Hartz Mountains	1952	23,000
Lake Pedder	....	59,000

SOURCE: "Annual Report 1953–54," Tasmania Scenery Preservation Board, Government Printer, Hobart, Aug. 27, 1954, together with additions provided by the Superintendent of Scenic Reserves in personal correspondence, Dec. 2, 1954.

of the beauty of their mountains, lakes, alpine meadows, forests, and moorlands, these national parks are typical examples of the Tasmanian scene, as well as sanctuaries for the protection of native plant and animal life; some provide opportunity for winter sports. There is little development which interferes with their natural character. Tasmania has also established about fifty reserves for the protection of scenic beauty, flora and fauna, geological interests, and historical values; total area of these reserves in 1954 was approximately 50,000 acres [110].

The Scenery Preservation Board, established by authority of the Scenery Preservation Act of 1915, administers the act and is responsible for the maintenance of all scenic reserves in Tasmania. This board is comprised of eleven members, including heads of government departments and especially qualified citizens. Administrative responsibility for some areas has been delegated by the Scenery Preservation Board to subsidiary boards composed of representatives of walking and naturalists' clubs, municipal councils, and similar organizations. Funds required for operation and maintenance of these areas are derived from government

[21] Personal correspondence, Dec. 2, 1954, from the Superintendent of Scenic Reserves, Hobart, Tasmania, Australia.

appropriations, together with miscellaneous revenues acquired from rents, leases, and similar sources.[22]

In the Australian state of *Victoria,* national parks and similar reserves embrace an area of over 300,000 acres[23] (see Table 10-10). These areas, varying from highly developed tourist centers to sanctuaries lacking

Table 10-10. Summary of National Parks and Similar Reserves in Victoria, 1958

National parks and reserves	Year est.	Approximate area, acres	Principal features of interest
Wyperfield	1909	139,000	Primitive area; native flora and fauna
Kinglake	1928	14,000	Mountain scenery, forests, native animal life
Fern Tree Gully	1882	900	Popular picnic area
Wilson's Promontory	1898	102,000	Scenic coastal reserve; native flora and fauna
Mount Buffalo	1898	27,000	Popular summer and winter recreational area
Sperm Whale Head	1927	2,700	Native plant and animal life sanctuary
Lind[a]	1926	3,200	
Alfred	1926	5,000	Tree ferns, varied forests
Wingen Inlet[a]	1909	4,500	
Mallacoota Inlet	1909	11,000	Native animal life sanctuary
Tarra Valley	1909	200	Tree ferns and other vegetation
Bulga	1904	91	Native forests and flora
Tower Hill	1866	1,300	Geological area; extinct volcano
Buchan Caves	1916	950	Beautiful caverns
Werribee Gorge	1907	573	Geological area; glacial striation
Churchill	1930	476	Popular recreational area
Phillip Island	1937	553	Sanctuary for koala bear; two areas
Sir Colin Mackenzie	1929	427	Native animal life sanctuary

[a] Information incomplete.

facilities for general public use, were established from unalienated Crown Land Reserves by authority of various land acts.[24] They are

[22] *Ibid.*

[23] Text, as well as Table 10-10, prepared from information contained in bibliographical references 118 and 120 and personal correspondence, Nov. 23, 1954, and Mar. 7, 1958, from the Office of the Secretary for Lands, Melbourne, Victoria, Australia.

[24] Many reserves of various kinds were established under authority of these acts but only a few were specifically reserved as national parks or areas which might be considered in that category.

administered by separate Committees of Management appointed by the government. However, after several unsuccessful attempts to obtain parliamentary approval of a consolidated form of management for all national parks in Victoria, the government finally passed the National Parks Act of 1956 [120]. This act provides for the appointment of a National Parks Authority, including a Director, with the Premier or some other minister nominated by him as Chairman; the other members include the permanent heads of five named government departments and four other persons representing organizations interested in national parks. This Authority is now starting to function on a long-range program of development and preservation according to the particular suitability of the various parks.

Financial support for the operation and maintenance of such lands in Victoria is derived from a variety of sources, including state grants, local council grants, revenue from fees, rentals, and licenses, and funds provided by the State Tourist Committee. In a few instances bequests or similar endowments have been made by individuals having an interest in a specific area.

Western Australia has established nearly 160 national parks and related areas, which vary in size from a few acres to several hundred thousand.[25] The purpose and function of these reserves are equally varied. Some were established to protect significant flora, fauna, and related natural interests; others provide opportunity for a variety of outdoor sports. Many are inaccessible and totally undeveloped, while a number are located within easy access of population centers and offer a variety of recreational facilities.

Administration of these areas is also greatly varied. Based upon the Parks and Reserves Act (1885–1897), administrative responsibility may be vested in special boards created for a particular purpose, in local authorities, in the Minister for Lands, in the National Parks Board of Western Australia (established in 1920), in the Conservator of Forests, in the Manager of State Hotels, or in the Minister for Water Supply. Funds for operation and maintenance are derived from state grants and, in certain cases, returns from rents, leases, admission and parking fees, and the like. Brief outlines of the more popular areas follow.

Yanchep National Park (7,700 acres), located on the coast about 32 miles north of Perth, is characterized by interesting flora and fauna, a rugged coastline, coastal flats and lagoons, and limestone caves. Roads and trails, modern hotel accommodations, a reef-protected swimming pool and varied sports facilities are available. National Park (approxi-

[25] Information relative to Western Australia derived from personal correspondence, Dec. 21, 1954, and Aug. 29, 1956, from the office of the Under Secretary for Lands, Perth, Western Australia, Australia.

mately 5,000 acres) in the Darling Ranges features a rugged, mountainous terrain and varied plant and animal life. Porongorup National Park (5,400 acres) includes forests of karri (*Eucalyptus diversicolor*) and related vegetation; its rugged terrain is of interest to mountain climbers. Nornalup Reserve (approximately 5,000 acres), a heavily forested coastal area as well as a popular fishing center, is a favorite of campers. Rottnest Island (approximately 20,000 acres) is an area of historical significance as well as a favored holiday resort; it lies a short distance from the mainland near Perth.

FIG. 10-4. Ngauruhoe (7,515 feet), an active volcano, is one of the interests of Tongariro National Park, New Zealand. (*New Zealand Government Department of Tourist and Publicity*)

New Zealand. There are eight national parks in New Zealand, aggregating an area of about 6,000 square miles. These areas are administered in accordance with the National Park Act of 1952 by the National Park Authority, consisting of nine members; five are government officials and four, appointed by the Minister of Lands, represent especially interested organizations [90].

The New Zealand national park system began with the establishment of Tongariro National Park by special act in 1894. Later specific legislation established additional national parks, each controlled by specific boards or government departments and administered under independent and unrelated policies. Passage of the National Park Act of 1952 correlated administrative procedures and effected uniform policies of management for existing and future national parks. Individual park boards established under earlier acts are still operative, but they now function under the National Parks Act of 1952 and are represented by one member of the National Parks Authority.

Policies which guide the use and development of national parks in New Zealand are similar to those of the U.S. National Park Service. Each of New Zealand's national parks contains scenery of such quality, or features of such unique interest, that their preservation in a natural state is in the national interest. Facilities for public use are provided consistent with the policy of maintaining, in so far as possible, natural conditions typical of these lands. Funds for their administration, protection, and maintenance are derived from government appropriations.

Table 10-11. Summary of National Parks in New Zealand, 1957

National park	Area, acres	Year est.	Principal features of interest
Abel Tasman....	40,622	1942	Coast (cliffs, inlets, islands, beaches) and adjacent uplands; largely undeveloped
Arthur Pass......	239,152	1929	Mountains, glaciers, ski terrain
Egmont.........	80,681	1900	Mount Egmont (extinct volcano) with permanent snowfields, waterfalls, forests, ski terrain
Fiordland........	2,959,793	1892[a]	Coast and adjacent uplands, forests, lakes, waterfalls, fiords; largely undeveloped
Mount Cook.....	151,800	1953 [86]	Highest mountains in New Zealand, glaciers, ski terrain
Nelson Lakes....	139,833	1956 [89]	Mount Robert and adjacent ranges, lakes, fishing, skiing; largely primitive
Tongariro........	161,538	1894	Active volcanoes, hot crater lake, waterfalls, forests, glaciers, ski terrain
Urewera.........	119,617	1953 [86]	Waterfalls, lakes, mountains, forests, historical values

[a] Originally established under the Land Act, 1892, and administered by the Lands and Survey Department for many years.

SOURCE: Compiled from information contained largely in the New Zealand National Parks Authority, "New Zealand National Parks," Government Printer, Wellington, 1957.

The National Park Authority, in cooperation with the New Zealand Forest Service, has also formulated a plan for the development of the higher portions of the Tararua Range (245,000 acres) as a forest park [88].

In addition to the national parks, New Zealand has also reserved 922 *public domains* (aggregating 81,995 acres); 1,370 *scenic and historic reserves* (aggregating about 893,700 acres); and *several miscellaneous areas*—including the Trounson Kauri Park (1,241 acres) and four prin-

FIG. 10-5. Mount Pembroke (6,710 feet) and Milford Sound, Fiordland National Park, New Zealand. (*New Zealand Government Department of Tourist and Publicity*)

cipal bird sanctuaries (aggregating 11,692 acres). Such areas, set apart for the preservation of scenery or the conservation and protection of flora and fauna, are subject generally to the authority of the Lands and Survey Department.[26]

RECREATIONAL USE OF WILD LANDS IN EUROPE

Although the natural characteristics of extensive European areas have been greatly modified by centuries of use, interest in the natural scene and conservation of natural resources have long been associated with the culture of many European peoples. However, only in relatively recent years has the national park idea been instituted in Europe. An early manifestation of growing interest in this regard was a proposal, in 1880, by a Finnish scientist, that certain areas be reserved in their natural state for posterity [73]. However, this idea did not assume tangible form until 1909 when laws relative to the establishment of national parks and monuments were passed in Sweden [109].

In accordance with the most recent available information this portion of Chapter 10 briefly outlines the nature of those areas in the principal European countries which have made the most significant progress in establishing national parks.

[26] Personal correspondence, Mar. 20, 1956, from the Director General of Lands and Chairman of National Parks Authority, Wellington, New Zealand.

Belgium [101]. Protection of specific areas in Belgium having historic, artistic, esthetic, or scientific values of national interest is guided by the law of August 7, 1931, providing for the establishment of monuments and "sites."

In 1947 the Royal Commission of Monuments and Sites proposed the establishment of eight natural reserves, each typical of a specific biogeographic region of the country; in addition, on May 20, 1950, the Commission classified over 200 sites which were subsequently placed under state protection.

Belgium has five small areas known as national parks, acquired by lease or purchase by l'Association Ardenne et Guame, with a total of about 470 acres; public use of these areas is carefully regulated, and a permit must be obtained before they may be entered. There are also a number of other sites administered by l'Association Ardenne et Guame, as well as a few forest reserves and bird sanctuaries.

Finland. The establishment of various kinds of areas for the protection of nature in Finland is based upon the Nature Protection Act of 1923.[27] Such areas include national parks, nature parks, and natural monuments.[28] National parks and nature parks are administered by the Forest Research Institute; the protection of natural monuments is the concern of the agency administering the land on which specific natural monuments are located [73].

In 1938 ten national parks and nature parks were established in Finland, but only four of these areas remained under Finnish control following the Russo-Finnish War (1939 to 1944). Pisavaara Nature Park (approximately 20,000 acres) is noteworthy for its extensive spruce forests, Malla Nature Park (approximately 12,000 acres) has richer alpine plant life than any other area in Finland, Pallastunturi National Park (approximately 200,000 acres) is noteworthy for its impressive Lapland panoramas, and Pyhatunturi National Park (approximately 12,000 acres) contains barren rocky hills which were the object of worship by ancient Laplanders.[29] In addition to the foregoing parks Finland had also established 150 natural monuments by 1950.[29]

Establishment of a number of additional national parks and nature parks was recommended by leading Finnish natural science societies in 1948 [73]. In 1950 the Finnish government appointed a committee to study the nation's need concerning this form of land use; the report of

[27] As early as 1880 a famous Finnish scientist recommended the reservation of areas for the preservation of typical Finnish landscapes [73].

[28] Areas reserved exclusively for scientific research are termed nature parks; national parks are open to general public use, and natural monuments are small areas containing features of interest or scientific significance which are worthy of protection [73].

[29] Personal correspondence, June, 1956, from Dr. Reino Kalliola, Forest Research Institute, Helsinki, Finland.

this committee, published in 1953, recommended the establishment of seven additional national parks and twelve additional nature parks.[30]

The Nature Protection Act also provides for the protection of most nongame animal species and prohibits the erection of advertising signs along scenic highways [73].

France. Although national parks, as such, do not exist in France, a number of botanical and faunal reserves have been established for the protection of rare or interesting biotopes.[31] Administrative responsibility for these areas is entrusted to a variety of organizations. Reserves of botanical interest are administered either by the National Forest Service or by specifically designated private societies; those of faunal interest by the Conseil Supérieur de la Chasse (Hunting Council) or by the Fédération Départsmentale des Chasseurs (Departmental Federation of Hunters Associations).

FIG. 10-6. Tarn Hows in England's Lake District. (*British Travel Association*)

In addition to these reserves, numerous areas of outstanding beauty within public forests have been designated by the National Forest Service as "artistic series" for the preservation of their scenic values. Further, the Ecole Nationale des Eaux et Forêts (National Forestry School) controls an area in the Hautes-Alpes Department characterized by a remarkable stand of junipers.

Great Britain. Interest in the establishment of public outdoor recreational lands in Great Britain has developed rapidly in recent years. Ten areas have been designated as national parks in England and Wales [4]. These include Dartmoor (365 square miles), Exmoor (265 square miles), Lake District (866 square miles), North York Moors (553 square miles), Peak District (542 square miles), Pembrokeshire Coast (225 square miles), Snowdonia (837 square miles), and Yorkshire Dales (680

[30] *Ibid.*

[31] Text relating to France developed from unpublished material, "Note on National Parks and Natural Reserves in France and the Overseas Territories," supplied by Mr. Henri Morel, Service des Eaux et Forêts, French Ministry of Agriculture; included in personal correspondence, June 6, 1955, from Agricultural Attache, American Embassy, Paris.

square miles).[32] Among more recently established national parks in England and Wales are Northumberland[33] (400 square miles) and Brecon Beacons (515 square miles); establishment of several other areas is in prospect [4].

National parks in England and Wales are established by authority of the National Parks and Access to the Countryside Act of 1949 [49]. This act also set up the National Parks Commission, members of which are appointed by the Minister of Housing and Local Government [49]. National parks must be of extensive size and of the finest landscape quality, and their preservation must be in the national interest; they must also afford opportunity for outdoor recreation. Such areas are selected by the National Parks Commission. After consulting with local authorities, the Commission submits a designation order to the Minister of Housing and Local Government, who either accepts, modifies, or rejects the proposal.[34] Areas approved as national parks are administered by local planning authorities, subject to general supervision by the National Parks Commission [49].

Planning and development of national parks are conducted with special regard for the preservation or enhancement of natural beauty and the promotion of facilities for public use [49]. Designation of a national park, however, does not change the character of land ownership in the area; moreover, no right of access is automatically granted to the general public [1]. Access to "open country,"[35] which the planning authority may decide is necessary, is provided by agreement negotiated between the planning authority and land owners or by order of the planning authority. Such orders are open to objection and hearing of such objection by the Minister of Housing and Local Government before they are confirmed, modified, or rejected. In short, users of national parks must recognize that the farmers' fields within such areas are, and will remain, private and that they, the users, must remain on specifically designated routes of travel.

The national park movement in Great Britain originated in 1884 when James Bryce, a member of the House of Commons, introduced the Access to the Mountains Bill [49]. It applied only to Scotland and was prompted by the fact that, through the years, public rights of access to certain types of "open country" had been seriously curtailed. Bryce's proposal

[32] Personal correspondence, May 3, 1954, and Jan. 17, 1956, from the National Parks Commission, London.

[33] News release from National Parks Commission and Forestry Commission, Sept. 20, 1955; also Manchester Guardian, Sept. 22, 1955.

[34] Personal correspondence, May 3, 1954, and Jan. 17, 1956, from the National Parks Commission, London.

[35] Agricultural lands other than rough grazing areas, railways, tramways, golf courses, quarries, air fields, and the like are specifically eliminated from the designation of "open country."

did not become law, but its objective was not forgotten. From time to time similar bills were introduced; these were either defeated or failed to accomplish the desired results. The National Parks and Access to the Countryside Act of 1949 represents the culmination of Bryce's dream.

In addition to the national parks of England and Wales, certain public forest lands in England, Wales, Scotland, and Northern Ireland have been made available for recreational use. These areas, administered by the Forestry Commission (established 1919), are known as National Forest Parks.[36] Such areas usually embrace lands of several public forests and contain campgrounds, hostels, and other related outdoor recreational facilities. Including New Forest, which is administered under a special act of Parliament, they are ten in number.

Argyll National Forest Park (designated 1935; area 58,000 acres), northwest of Glasgow, embraces some of the wildest country in western Scotland [51]. Forest of Dean (designated 1938; area 22,000 acres) has been Crown property since before the Norman Conquest; its forests are more nearly characteristic of early-day Britain than those of any other area [52]. Glen More National Forest Park (designated 1947; area 12,500 acres) is in the eastern Scottish Highlands [54]. Glen Trool National Forest Park (designated 1945; area 110,000 acres), in addition to the scenic charm of the southern Scottish Highlands, includes historic associations with Robert Bruce [56]. Hardknott National Forest Park (designated 1943; area 7,275 acres) is typical of the scenery of northern England; it also includes geological, botanical, and historical interests [55]. New Forest (designated 1947; area 144 square miles) in southern England includes noteworthy forests, varied plant and animal life, and prehistoric and Roman relics [57]. Queen Elizabeth National Forest Park (designated 1951; area 40,000 acres) is in southern Scotland, embracing a portion of the southern Highlands and extending to the shores of romantic Loch Lomond [58]. Snowdonia National Forest Park (designated 1937; area 21,000 acres) in Wales is noteworthy for the scenic beauty of its hill country and tablelands and is highlighted by prehistoric relics, evidences of the Roman period, medieval architecture, and floral and faunal interests [53]. Border National Forest Park (designated 1955; area 123,000 acres), along the historic borderland of England and Scotland, includes portions of the Cheviot Hills and the dales of the Teviot, Liddel, Rede, and North Tyne Rivers, famous for their ancient peel towers and ballads of border battles.[37] Tollymore Forest Park

[36] Information derived from personal correspondence, May 13, 1954, and Apr. 6 and 13, 1956, from offices of Forestry Commission in London and Edinburgh, as well as from the particular guidebook covering each national forest park; see bibliographical references 51 to 58.

[37] News release from National Parks Commission and Forestry Commission, Sept. 20, 1955; also personal correspondence, Apr. 6, 1956, from Forestry Commission, London.

(established 1955; area 1,200 acres) in Northern Ireland embraces landscapes of beauty and variety with splendid views of the Mourne Mountains and the sea at Newcastle [91].

Greece. The establishment of five national parks in Greece was authorized in 1937 [102], largely through interest generated by the Hellenic Alpine Club. As a result, Mount Olympus and Mount Parnassus National Parks came into being in 1938. Interest in such matters was suspended during World War II but has since been revived with the proposal of a third national park on Mount Parnes [101,102].

Iceland. An area on the Plain of Thingvellir including the site of the old meeting place of the Icelandic parliament or Althing, which dates back to 930, has been reserved as a national park [63]. The Plain of Thingvellir is a huge lava field covered with moss and grass and partly surrounded by abrupt rocky walls about 100 feet high. It is approximately 30 miles east of Reykjavik.

Italy. In addition to innumerable historic sites and monuments, Italy has established four national parks.[38] These are Parco Nazionale del Gran Paridiso (established 1922; approximately 138,000 acres), Parco Nazionale D'Abruzzo (established 1923; approximately 72,000 acres), Parco Nazionale del Circeo (established 1934; approximately 13,000 acres), and Parco Nazionale Dello Stelvio (established 1935; approximately 235,000 acres).

Italian national parks were established primarily to protect native plant and animal species, to provide centers for biological studies, to develop public interest in nature, to illustrate to the public the damage to natural resources resulting from modification of nature's balance, and to create centers of tourist education.

Norway. In the accepted sense neither national parks nor natural reserves exist in Norway. However, a number of small areas of historic or scientific interest are protected by authority of the conservation law passed in 1910 [63].

Poland. In 1954 Poland had eight or ten national parks typified by mountains, forests, and seashore, with a total area of between 175,000 and 200,000 acres [66,101]. These included such national parks as Tatras (42,000 acres),[39] Pieniny (3,000 acres), Babia Gora (5,000 acres), Gory Swieto Krzyskie (3,000 acres), Bialowieza (11,600 acres), and Wolin Island (21,000 acres) [101]. At the same time Poland also had over 500 reserves established to protect specific natural objects, with an aggregate area of about 50,000 acres and nearly 500 monuments [101].

While Polish laws protecting native animals and rare plants date back to the thirteenth century, present-day national parks in Poland are an

[38] Derived from information obtained through the assistance of the Consolato D'Italia, Seattle, Washington; personal correspondence of Nov. 19 and 22, 1954, and November, 1955.

[39] Areas given for Polish national parks noted are approximate.

outgrowth of the Provisional Government Commission for the Protection of Nature, created in 1919. However, it was not until 1934, following passage of a law authorizing establishment of such areas, that the first Polish national parks came into being. Although this activity naturally languished during World War II, the Government Council for Nature Protection was revitalized after that conflict, and the development of the Polish national park system was renewed [101].

Soviet Union. Forty preserves are distributed throughout the European and Asian parts of the Soviet Union, the first having been established in 1919.[40] These reserves were established to maintain natural conditions in areas typical of the principal geographic zones of the U.S.S.R., as well as for the protection of rare plants and animals. In addition, preserves in the Soviet Union provide opportunity for biological research related to various aspects of the national economy and are used by university biology students as outdoor laboratories. They are also designed to serve the general public by means of organized excursions and tourist trips, scientific lectures on nature research, exhibitions, and natural museums.

The total area of the preserves of the U.S.S.R. is nearly 4 million acres. The U.S.S.R. Academy of Sciences is currently working jointly with corresponding government departments on the expansion of the present system to an eventual total of seventy to seventy-five preserves, with an aggregate area of approximately 25 million acres.

Spain. There are two national parks, known as Covadonga and Ordesa Valley, in Spain. Both of these areas were established in 1918, approximately two years after the law authorizing such areas became effective (December 7, 1916). In addition to national parks, seven scenic areas of national interest have been placed under state protection, and a number of natural areas, serving primarily as game refuges, have been set aside [101].

Sweden. Many of Sweden's laws and ordinances, dating back several centuries, were designed to prevent mismanagement of natural resources by regulation of fishing, hunting, mining, and cutting of timber.[41] The idea of conservation with scientific, esthetic, cultural, or social objectives, however, did not materialize until 1909; in that year the first laws rela-

[40] Data in the text, and accompanying Table 10-12, derived from an unpublished article, "USSR Preserves," by G. Burdin, Assistant Chief of the Central Administration of hunting grounds and preserves under the Council of Ministers of the RSFSR. This article was provided by the Soviet Information Bureau, Moscow, through the assistance of the Embassy of the Union of Soviet Socialist Republics, Washington, (personal correspondence of June 22, Aug. 16 and 30, 1956, and June 24 and Sept. 27, 1957; also see bibliographical reference 72).

[41] Information in the text, together with that in Table 10-13, derived from material provided by Board of Crown Lands and Forests (Kungl. Domänstyrelsen), Stockholm (personal correspondence, Sept. 14, 1954, and Apr. 6, 1956; also see bibliographical reference 109).

Table 10-12. Summary of Preserves in the Soviet Union, 1956

Name and location	Year est.	Approximate area, acres
Astrakhan, Astrakhan region (delta of the Volga River, RSFSR)	1919	100,000
Ilmen, Chelyabinsk region (RSFSR)	1920	75,000
Ascania Nova, Kherson region (Ukrainian SSR)	1921	1,200
Caucasian, Krasnodar territory (RSFSR)	1923	250,000
Kyedrovaya Pad, Primorye territory (RSFSR)	1924	38,000
Stolby, Krasnoyarsk territory (RSFSR)	1925	116,000
Aksu-Jabaglinsky, South Kazakhstan region (Kazakh SSR)	1926	180,000
Barguzin, Buryat-Mongolian ASSR (RSFSR)	1926	130,000
Khumutovskaya Step, Stalin region (Ukrainian SSR)	1926	2,500
Azov-Sivash, Kherson region (Ukrainian SSR)	1927	17,000
Voronezh, Voronezh region (Usman River, RSFSR)	1927	76,000
Chernomorsky, Kherson region (Black Sea coast, Ukrainian SSR)	1927	30,000
Zakataly, Azerbaijan SSR	1928	71,000
Crimean, Crimean region (Ukrainian SSR)	1928	75,000
Mikhailovskaya Tselina, Sumy region (Ukrainian SSR)	1928	450
Repetek, Charjou region (Turkmen SSR)	1928	46,000
Tsentralno-Chernozemny, Kursk region (RSFSR)	1930	10,000
Gasan-Kuli, Krasnovodsk region (Turkmen SSR)	1932	173,000
Kandalaksha, Murmansk region (islands of the White and Barents seas, RSFSR)	1932	60,000
Suputinka, Primorye territory (RSFSR)	1932	40,000
Pechoro-Ilychsky, Komi ASSR (RSFSR), upper reaches of the Pechora	1934	230
Lagodekhi, Georgian SSR	1935	33,000
Mordovian, Mordovian ASSR (RSFSR)	1935	75,000
Oka, Ryazan region (flood lands of the Oka River, RSFSR)	1935	56,000
Sikhote-Alin, Primorye territory (middle Sikhote-Alin, RSFSR)	1935	273,000
Hopyor, Balashov region (RSFSR)	1935	40,000
Teberda, Stavropol territory (RSFSR)	1936	172,000
Zuvintas, Latvian SSR	1937	7,500
Tigrovaya Balka, Tajik SSR	1938	67,000
Barsa-Kelmes, Kzyl-Orda region (Kazakh SSR)	1939	45,000
Byelovezhskaya Pushcha, Brest and Grodno regions (Byelorussian SSR)	1939	178,000
Kzyl-Agach, Azerbaijan SSR	1939	211,000
Badkhiz, Mary and Ashkhabad regions (Turkmen SSR)	1941	185,000
Darvinsky, Vologda region (fish preserve, RSFSR)	1945	425,000
Kivach, Karelian ASSR (RSFSR)	1945	26,000
Prioksho-Terrasny, Moscow region (RSFSR)	1945	12,000
Denezhkin Kamen, Sverdlov region (North Urals, RSFSR)	1946	88,000
Gorno-Lesnoi, Tashkent region (Uzbek SSR)	1947	28,000
Streletskaya Step, Voroshilovgrad region (Ukrainian SSR)	1948	1,200
Pushkinsky, Pskov region (RSFSR)	1949	1,500

tive to the establishment of Swedish national parks and monuments were passed. A more recent development is the Law on Conservation of Nature (1953), aimed at the preservation of beautiful natural scenery in general by defining penalties for littering, objectionable advertising, and related undesirable activities.

Table 10-13. Summary of Swedish National Parks, 1956

National park	Area, acres	Year est.	National park	Area, acres	Year est.
Abisko	12,300	1909	Hamra	50	1909
Stora Sjofället	320,000	1909	Ängsö	195	1909
Sarek	470,000	1909	Garphyttan	269	1909
Muddus	121,000	1942	Gotska Sandön	1,000	1910
Peljekaise	36,000	1913	Norra Kvill	70	1927
Sonfjället	6,600	1909	Blå Jungfrun	114	1926
Töfsingdalen	3,370	1930	Dalby Söderskog	84	1918
Vaddetjåkko	6,000	1920			

National parks in Sweden are established by the Riksdag for the purpose of preserving certain large scenic areas in a natural or essentially unaltered condition. They typify the significant geological, biological, and, in certain cases, historical heritage of that country. Many national parks are used in the study of natural science. Some, like Abisko, are readily accessible; others, more remote, have an appeal based primarily upon their inaccessibility and wilderness character. In three national parks (Dalby Söderskog, Ängsö, and Garphyttan) certain measures are necessary to preserve their character of cultural monuments.

Three other types of reserves are also found in Sweden. National monuments, about 200 in number, are established by the County Councils and include objects of scientific or scenic interest. Nature parks, also established by County Councils, originated as a consequence of the 1953 Law on Conservation of Nature; because of their own special character, or the character of the surrounding country, they are considered valuable for familiarizing the public with nature. Crown Reserves are set aside by the Board of Crown Lands and Forests to protect interesting areas and objects in the public domain; about 500 areas (forest types, plant communities, marshes, sand dunes) and objects (ancient graves and monuments, peculiar or interesting trees) are included in this category.

Switzerland. An upland-alpine area of approximately 39,000 acres, located in the lower Engadine section of the Canton of Grisons, was established as Swiss National Park in 1914 [80,101]. It is administered

by the Federal National Park Commission. Features of interest include the peaks of the Engadine Dolomites (maximum elevation 9,515 ft.), a few glaciers, and plant and animal life typical of that section of Europe.

Switzerland also has about six reserves established for the preservation of natural scenery and native plant and animal species and thirty-two districts along portions of the Swiss boundary which are closed to hunting [101].

Yugoslavia. National parks and public parks are established in Yugoslavia by decree of individual People's Republics, as prescribed by

FIG. 10-7. Durmitor National Park, Montenegro, Yugoslavia, embraces a rugged mountainous region. (*Yugoslav State Tourist Office*)

Federal law.[42] Eighteen areas of this type have been established by the People's Republics of Croatia, Macedonia, Montenegro, Bosnia and Herzegovina, and Serbia. These areas are administered by special National Park Boards, assisted by advisory committees, under the supervision of the Republic's Forest Administration. A policy of nearly complete preservation is applied in some of these areas; in others certain development favoring general public use and limited timber management, consistent with the maintenance of natural beauty, is permitted.

[42] Text and Table 10-14 prepared from unpublished material provided by the Secretariat of State for Foreign Affairs, Belgrade, and the College of Forestry, Belgrade, through assistance rendered by the American Embassy, Belgrade, and the Embassy of the Federal Peoples Republic of Yugoslavia, Washington (personal correspondence, Jan. 11, Feb. 10, Feb. 14, Mar. 22, Apr. 5, and June 8, 1955, and May 10, 1956).

Table 10-14. Summary of National Parks in Yugoslavia, 1956

National park	Year est.	Approximate area, acres	Principal features of interest
Plitvicka jezera[a]	1949	47,000	Scenic area, lakes, waterfalls, forests
Paklenica[a]	1949	9,900	Mountainous area near Adriatic; canyons, caves, forests
Risnjak[a]	1953	8,500	Karst phenomena of scientific value; pine and beech forests
Medvednica[a]	1954	11,950	Mountainous resort area near Zagreb
Mavrovo[b]	1949	170,000	Artificial lake; beech and pine forests; historical sites from War of Liberation
Pelister[b]	1949	18,000	Scenic glacial lakes; native pine forests
Durmitor[c]	1952	79,000	Lakes, canyons, alpine highlands, native animal life, forests
Lovcen[c]	1952	5,000	Mountainous area near Adriatic; historical area
Biogradska Gora[c]	1952	5,000	Pine and juniper forests, lakes, native animal life
Perucica[d]	1952	3,500	Forests of fir, juniper, pine, beech; waterfalls; native animal life
Lom u Klekovaci[d]	1951	700	Forests of pine, juniper, beech
Janj[d]	1951	500	Forests of pine, juniper, beech
Hutovo Blato[d]	1954	1,500	Lake with marshes famous for bird life; reservation pending establishment as national park
Trebevic Jahorina[d]	1954	7,400	Resort area; international winter sports center
Fruska Gora[e]	1948	57,000	Recreational area; native forests
Avala[e]	1928	2,600	Monument to Unknown Soldier surrounded by forests
Grmija[e]	1949	....	Résort area; oak and beech forests
Decani[e]	1949	1,400	Resort area; beech, pine, chestnut forests; historical monastery

[a] Croatia. [b] Macedonia. [c] Montenegro. [d] Bosnia and Herzegovina. [e] Serbia.

National parks do not exist in Slovenia. However, this People's Republic has undertaken measures to establish several areas of this kind. In all Republics there are several smaller reservations, established to protect natural beauties and rarities.

RECREATIONAL USE OF WILD LANDS IN NORTH AMERICA

In addition to the United States, many other North American countries have given tangible expression to their interest in varied recreational

values of wild lands by setting aside for public welfare national parks and other areas of similar character.

Canada. There are eighteen national parks in Canada (see Table 10-15) [26]. These areas, established by statute for the use and enjoyment of the people, are administered under provisions of the National Parks

Table 10-15. Summary of Canadian National Parks, 1957

National park	Year est.	Province	Area, acres	Principal features of interest
Banff	1885	Alberta	1,640,960	Massive mountains, glaciers, lakes, plant and animal life; winter sports center
Glacier	1886	British Columbia	333,440	Snow-capped peaks, glaciers, alpine flora
Yoho	1886	British Columbia	324,480	Rugged mountains, glaciers, waterfalls, lakes
Waterton Lakes	1895	Alberta	130,560	Scenic mountains, lakes, plants and animals
Jasper	1907	Alberta	2,688,000	Majestic peaks, ice fields and glaciers, lakes, plant and animal life; winter sports
Mount Revelstoke	1914	British Columbia	64,000	Rolling alpine plateau
Kootenay	1920	British Columbia	347,520	Rugged mountains, glaciers, hot mineral springs
Elk Island	1913	Alberta	48,000	Plains buffalo, other mammals and birds
Wood Buffalo	1922	Northwest Territories and Alberta	11,072,000	Woods bison, other mammals and birds
St. Lawrence Islands	1914	Ontario	172	Recreational area
Point Pelee	1918	Ontario	3,865	Fine beaches, interesting flora, birds
Georgian Bay Islands	1920	Ontario	3,456	Camping and recreational area
Prince Albert	1927	Saskatchewan	957,440	Forests, lakes, streams; summer resort
Riding Mountain	1929	Manitoba	734,720	Lakes, game sanctuary; summer resort
Cape Breton Highlands	1936	Nova Scotia	249,600	Rugged coastline and picturesque mountains
Prince Edward Island	1937	Prince Edward Island	4,480	Fine beaches; golf course
Fundy	1948	New Brunswick	50,880	Interesting rugged coastline; upland woods
Terra Nova	1957	Newfoundland	96,000	Atlantic headlands; undeveloped

SOURCE: Prepared from data derived from bibliographical references 18 to 30.

Act by the National Park Service, one of four divisions[43] in the National Parks Branch of the Department of Northern Affairs and National Resources, with headquarters at Ottawa. The Canadian Wildlife Service of

[43] In addition to the National Park Service, the National Parks Branch of the Department of Northern Affairs and National Resources includes three other divisions: the National Historic Sites Division, the Engineering Services Division, and the Canadian Wildlife Service [26].

the National Parks Branch and the Forestry Branch assist the National Park Service by providing technical advice. The Engineering Services Division of the National Parks Branch carries out various engineering projects in the national parks, while major highway contracts and other major engineering projects are supervised by the Department of Public Works [26]. Administration of each of the eighteen national parks is in charge of a resident superintendent, assisted by professional, technical, and administrative personnel [26]. During the fiscal year 1956–1957 a total of 3,529,976 people visited the national parks of Canada [26].

FIG. 10-8. Lake Louise, Banff National Park, Canada. (*Canadian Pacific Railway*)

Canadian national parks may be most readily grouped into three basic categories—the large scenic areas in the Rocky Mountains and Selkirks of British Columbia and Alberta, noteworthy for their significant geological and biological interests; the scenic wild-animal parks of the prairie region, established primarily to protect native Canadian fauna; and those national parks which are essentially recreational in character. Most of these areas are readily accessible, usually by road. Wood Buffalo National Park, a vast region of forest and plain between Athabaska and Great Slave Lakes, may be reached by river boat from Waterways, terminus of the Northern Alberta Railway which extends north from

Edmonton [18]. Cape Breton, Prince Edward Island, St. Lawrence Islands, and Georgian Bay National Parks are accessible by ferry or boat [24].

Campgrounds, hotels, and related facilities are available in practically all the Canadian national parks.

In addition to eighteen national parks, Canada has also established a number of National Historic Parks (see Table 10-16). Responsibility for the care and administration of these areas, as well as for over 500 national historic sites and plaques, is vested in the National Historic Sites Division of the National Parks Branch [26].

In addition to the national parks administered by the Dominion government, the Canadian provinces of British Columbia, Saskatchewan, Ontario, and Quebec have established provincial park systems.

The Provincial Park System of British Columbia had its origin in 1911 when the Provincial Legislature established Strathcona Park, a great wilderness area in the central part of Vancouver Island.[44] Today British Columbia has over 117 provincial parks, together with a considerable camp- and picnic-site system.[45] These areas vary in type from small roadside picnic areas near centers of population to extensive wilderness lands which are accessible only by trail; their aggregate area is in excess of 8 million acres [92]. Provincial parks in British Columbia, until 1957 in charge of the British Columbia Forest Service, are now administered by the Provincial Parks Branch, Department of Recreation and Conservation,[46] with headquarters at Victoria, B.C. [122].

Ontario's Provincial Park System originated in 1893 with the establishment of Algonquin Provincial Park (2,750 acres). By 1944 five additional provincial parks had been established in Ontario; most noteworthy of these later areas was Quetico Provincial Park (established 1913, area 1,750 square miles), located along the Canadian–United States boundary and adjoining the Superior National Forest in Minnesota. A survey of provincial park needs, initiated in 1954, resulted in the expansion of this system of provincial parks to 122 areas, varying in size from a few acres to 2,750 square miles. The provincial park system of Ontario is administered by the Division of Parks (established 1954) in the Department of Lands and Forests with headquarters at Toronto [59].

In Saskatchewan nine provincial parks have been established.[47] They vary in size from 16 acres to 152 square miles and have a total combined

[44] Personal correspondence, Jan. 7, 1955, from E. G. Oldham, Forester, Parks and Recreation Division, British Columbia Forest Service, Victoria, B.C.

[45] Personal correspondence, Mar. 26, 1958, from S. E. Park, Director, Provincial Parks Branch, Department of Recreation and Conservation, Victoria, B.C.

[46] *Ibid.*

[47] Personal correspondence, Feb. 24, 1955, from R. O. Houseman, Assistant Director of Parks, Department of Provincial Secretary, Regina, Saskatchewan, Canada.

Table 10-16. Summary of National Historic Parks in Canada, 1958

National historic park	Year est.	Province	Area, acres	Principal features of interest
Fort Anne	1917	Nova Scotia	31	Reconstruction of fort associated with early Acadian history; museum
Fort Beausejour	1926	New Brunswick	81	Site of French military post; museum
Prince of Wales Fort	1941	Manitoba	50	Ruins of fort, built 1733–1771, on Hudson Bay
Fort Malden	1941	Ontario	5	Site of fort built 1797–1799; museum
Fort Wellington	1941	Ontario	8.5	Fort built during War of 1812; museum
Fort Chambly	1941	Quebec	2.5	Restored French military post; museum
Fort Lennox	1941	Quebec	210	Site of important military post during French and Indian War and American Revolution
Port Royal	1941	Nova Scotia	17	Reconstruction of first Canadian settlement
Fortress of Louisbourg	1941	Nova Scotia	340	Ruins of French fortifications, built 1720–1740; museum
Fort Battleford	1951	Saskatchewan	36.7	Former Royal Northwest Mounted Police Post, established 1876; museum
Lower Fort Garry	1951	Manitoba	12.75	Stone fort built by Hudson's Bay Company
Woodside	1954[a]	Ontario	11.5	Boyhood home of Wm. Lyon Mackenzie King, former Prime Minister of Canada
Grand Pre[b]	.....	Nova Scotia	......	Associated with principal events relative to expulsion of Acadians
Halifax Citadel[c]	1957	Nova Scotia	......	Early nineteenth century fortress; museum
Alexander Graham Bell Museum[b]	.....	Nova Scotia	......	Museum with relics associated with experiments of Alexander Graham Bell
Signal Hill[b]	.....	Newfoundland	......	Rocky headland; site of last battle of Seven Years' War
Batoche Rectory[c]	.....	Saskatchewan	......	Museum commemorating events associated with Riel Uprising and Battle of Batoche, 1885
Sir Wilfred Laurier's Birthplace[d]	.....	Quebec	......	House where this famous Canadian statesman was born
Fort Langley[b]	.....	British Columbia	......	Site of early Hudson's Bay Post, built 1827

[a] Personal correspondence, Apr. 14, 1958, from Department of Northern Affairs and National Resources, Ottawa.

[b] Administered by the National Historic Sites Division, National Parks Branch, Department of Northern Affairs and National Resources but not yet officially designated as a National Historic Park; also lands still in process of acquisition.

[c] Data incomplete.

[d] Property including house where Sir Wilfred Laurier was born was acquired by the Department of Northern Affairs and National Resources in 1937 and 1939; it is open to the public, but since it embraces but one-third of an acre, it has not been declared a National Historic Park.

SOURCE: Prepared from data derived from bibliographical references 18 to 30 and from personal correspondence, Apr. 14, 1958, from Department of Northern Affairs and National Resources, Ottawa.

area of over 300,000 acres. They are administered by the Parks Branch in the Department of the Provincial Secretary with headquarters at Regina [103].

In addition to marking numerous historic sites the Province of Quebec has established five provincial parks, as well as a number of reserves.

Among these are such well-known areas as Laurentide Park north of the city of Quebec, Mont Tremblant Park northwest of Montreal, and Gaspé Park on the Gaspé Peninsula [96,97].

Mexico. The Republic of Mexico has approximately fifty national parks varying in size from less than 100 to more than 500,000 acres;[48] their combined area exceeds 2.5 million acres (see Table 10-17). With but

Table 10-17. Summary of National Parks in Mexico, 1954

National park	Year est.	Area, acres	National park	Year est.	Area, acres
Alejandro de Humboldt	1936	2,700	Grutus de Cacahuamilpa	1936	3,000
Balneario de los Novillos	1940	127	Historico Coyoacan	1938	1,400
Barranca de Cupatitzio	1938	1,300	Insurgente Miguel Hidalgo y Costilla	1936	1,900
Barranca de Chapultepec	1937	50	Insurgente Jose Maria Morelos	1939	4,500
Benito Juarez	1937	6,700	Iztaccihuatl-Popocatepetl	1935	64,000
Bosencheve	1940	37,500	Lago de Camecuaro	1940	35
Canon de Rio Blanca	1938	136,000	Lagunas de Zempoala	1936	11,500
Cerro de las Campanas	1937	145	Lagunas de Chacahua	1937	35,000
Cerro de Garnica	1936	2,750	La Malinche	1938	41,800
Cumbres de Majalca	1939	11,900	Lomas de Padierna	1938	1,775
Cerro de la Estrella	1938	2,700	Los Marmoles	1936	58,000
Cofre de Perote	1937	29,000	Los Remedios	1938	805
Cumbres de Agusco	1936	2,300	Molino de Belen	1952	240
Cumbres de Monterey	1939	616,000	Molino de las Flores	1937	190
Desierto del Carmen	1942	1,300	Nevado de Toluca	1936	165,000
Desierto de los Leones	1917	4,700	Pico de Orizaba	1936	48,700
El Chico	1898	4,500	Pico de Tancitaro	1940	73,000
El Contador	....	860,000	Rayon	1952	85
El Gororron	1936	62,500	Sierra de San Pedro Martin	1947	157,000
El Potosi	1936	5,000	Volcan de Colima	1936	43,700
El Sabinal	1938	22	Xicotencatl	1937	1,480
El Sacromonte	1939	25	Zoguiapan y Anexas	1937	4,900
El Tepevac	1937	3,700			
El Tepozteco	1937	60,000			
Fuentes Brotantes de Tlalpan	1936	320			

two exceptions, all of these national parks have been established since 1935. El Chico dates from 1898; it embraces a scenic forested area of about 4,500 acres in the state of Hidalgo. Desierto de los Leones, established in 1917, is approximately 4,600 acres in size and is located in the Federal District; it serves as a source of water supply for Mexico City and includes pine forests and the ruins of the Carmelite Convent, constructed in 1607.

[48] Text, and accompanying Table 10-17, derived from personal correspondence, Oct. 18, 1954, from the office of the Secretary of Agriculture and Livestock, Mexico, D.F. (also see bibliographical references 9, 32, 104, and 121).

The national parks of Mexico are administered by the Department of National Parks (Departamento de Zonas Protectoras, Vedas y Parques Nacionales), a unit of the Division of Forestry and Game (Recursos Forestales y de Caza) in the office of the Secretary of Agriculture and Livestock (Secretaria de Agricultura y Ganadería). Although only a few of Mexico's national parks provide for general public use, many of these areas contain noteworthy interests. Within their boundaries one finds impressive volcanoes, rugged mountain ranges, beautiful lakes and waterfalls, deep canyons, mineral springs, caverns, a wide variety of flora and fauna, and historic sites which symbolize or contain evidence of Mexico's significant past.

Among the more outstanding national parks of Mexico are Iztaccihuatl-Popocatepetl, which contains two of Mexico's most famous and picturesque volcanic peaks; Pico de Orizaba, which includes the great snow-clad volcano Orizaba—second highest mountain in North America; El Tepozteco, an archeological area containing ruins of pre-Hispanic pyramids; Volcan de Colima, including a great volcanic peak surrounded by forests which vary from tropical to arctic-alpine types; Lagunas de Chacahua, including tropical forests and lakes of great beauty, together with ruins of the Mixtex kingdom; and Cumbres de Monterey, with rugged mountainous terrain representative of the eastern Sierra Madre.

Additional areas are also being considered for national park status by the Republic of Mexico, including an international park (Sierra del Carmen) adjoining Big Bend National Park in Texas.

Other North American Countries. Many parts of Central America and the West Indies are characterized by significant interests that are worthy of preservation, but only a few countries in those regions have made more than token efforts in that direction.

By 1955 Honduras had established two small national parks and had plans for several more;[49] these areas are administered by the Forest Service of the Ministry of Agriculture [123]. In Guatemala a number of archeological sites pertaining primarily to ancient Mayan culture have been declared national monuments [9]. The Dominican Republic, located on the island of Hispaniola, has also reserved certain land areas for national forests, national parks, wildlife sanctuaries, and historical monuments [9].

RECREATIONAL USE OF WILD LANDS IN SOUTH AMERICA

This continent embraces tropical jungles, expansive plains, frigid wastes, rugged mountains, great rivers, impressive waterfalls, unique

[49] Personal correspondence, Feb. 23, 1955, from the American Embassy, Tegucigalpa, Honduras.

plant and animal life, and evidences of early civilization. It is not surprising that a number of South American countries—notably Argentina, Brazil, Chile, and Venezuela—have established national parks and related areas for the protection of many significant features.

Argentina. The Republic of Argentina has established eight national parks, two national reserves, and one natural monument (see Table 10-18), which embrace a total of over 6 million acres.[50] All are accessible by highway, rail, or air. Nahuel Huapi, the first of Argentina's national parks, was established in 1903.

Table 10-18. Summary of National Parks and Reserves in Argentina, 1957

Area	Size, acres	Principal features of interest
National Parks:		
Iguazú	136,000	Iguassú Falls, subtropical jungle forest, variety of plants and animals
Rio Pilcomayo	700,000	Subtropical jungle with typical flora and fauna
Laguna Blanca	27,000	Established principally for the protection of the black-necked swan (*Cygnus melanocoryphus*)
Lanin	976,000	Rugged mountains, forests, lakes, animals
Nahuel Huapi	1,950,000	Rugged mountains, glaciers, forests, picturesque lakes, varied plant and animal life; important winter sports center
Los Alerces y Anexo Puelo	706,000	Rugged mountains, forests, lakes, animals
Perito Morena	284,000	Rugged mountains, glaciers, extensive meadows, animal life
Los Glaciares	1,482,000	Rugged mountains, glaciers, lakes, forests, animals
National Reserves:		
Finca el Rey	111,000	Picturesque mountain region with subtropical plants and animals
Chaco	37,000	Established principally for protection of tropical tree species (*Schinopsis balansae* Engl.)
Natural Monument:		
Bosques Petrificados	24,000	Petrified cone-bearing trees

Six of the Argentine national parks are located along the eastern slope of the Andes, two additional national parks and two national reserves are found in the subtropical zone in the northern part of the country, and the natural monument includes a portion of the Patagonian plateau. Because of varied climate and topography these areas include a multitude

[50] Text and accompanying Table 10-18 derived from information contained in bibliographical references 6, 7, and 8, together with personal correspondence, Nov. 10, 1956, and June 25, 1957, from the office of the National Parks Administration, Ministry of Agriculture and Livestock, Buenos Aires (also see references 63 and 101).

of interests. A portion of Iguassú Falls, one of the world's great water spectacles, is found in one of these national parks, adjoining a reserve of similar character in Brazil. Other areas are famous for their spectacular mountain scenery, extensive forests, lakes of great beauty, large glaciers, and interesting plants and animals; one is an important winter sports center.

All these reserved lands are administered by the National Parks Administration (Dirección de Parques Nacionales) of the Ministry of Agriculture and Livestock (del Ministerio de Agricultura y Ganadería de la Nación), with headquarters in Buenos Aires.

FIG. 10-9. Rugged Andean peaks form a spectacular backdrop for this hotel in Nahuel Huapi National Park, Argentina. (*Administración General de Parques Nacionales, Buenos Aires*)

Brazil. Federal reserves established by the Brazilian government[51] include four national parks, a wildlife sanctuary, and a national forest (see Table 10-19); expansion of this program is being considered. All these areas are administered by the Forest Service of the Ministry of Agriculture.

National parks were set aside primarily to preserve representative sections of the country in their natural state for scientific investigation, for the development of public interest in the educational and esthetic values of the areas involved, and for the purpose of organizing museums and regional herbariums. Although regulations forbid the destruction or

[51] Text and accompanying Table 10-19 prepared from information contained in bibliographical references 37 and 66.

molestation of plants, animals, and related features, collections for scientific study may be made, provided permission is granted by local park authorities.

The national parks of Brazil contain hotels and other types of visitor accommodations and are accessible throughout the year by highway, rail,

Table 10-19. Summary of National Parks and Related Areas in Brazil, 1954

Name	Year est.	Approximate area, acres	Principal features of interest
National Parks:			
Itatiáia	1937	30,000	Flora and fauna, waterfalls, interesting mountainous terrain; highest tourist road in Brazil
Iguaçú	1929	500,000	Iguassú Falls, tropical plants and animals
Serra dos Orgãos	1939	25,000	Magnificent scenery, high mountains, plant and animal life
Paulo Alfonso	1948	42,000	Paulo Alfonso cataract, canyons, interesting flora
Wildlife Sanctuary:			
Sooretama	....	74,000	Tropical flora and fauna
National Forest:			
Araripe-Apodi[a]	1946	....	First national forest established in Brazil; includes remnants of representative flora of northeastern Brazil and serves as wildlife refuge
State Parks:			
Campos do Jordão	1941	13,000	Game reserve, high altitude flora
Rio Doce	1944	74,000	Varied terrestrial and aquatic flora, luxuriant forests, animal life, lakes, waterfalls
Monte Pascoal[a]	1943	....	Plant and animal life, historical interests

[a] Information incomplete.

or air. Of particular interest is Iguaçú National Park on the Paraná and Iguassú Rivers, which form a part of the Brazil–Argentina boundary. This area adjoins a similar reserve in Argentina and, in addition to diverse tropical flora and fauna, embraces a portion of Iguassú Falls, one of the three great cataracts in the world (210–230 feet high and about 2 miles wide).

In addition to the Federal reserves a number of states in Brazil have established state parks.

Chile. National parks established by this South American republic have an aggregate area of nearly 750,000 acres [101]. About ten or twelve in number, they are located in various parts of the country from the slopes of the Andes to Cape Horn at the southernmost tip of the South American continent; consequently, they embody a wide variety of representative examples of Chilean flora, fauna, and scenery.[52] Some of these areas are important winter sports centers.

So that laws and regulations protecting the flora and fauna of Chile may be better coordinated, the government has established the National Commission for the Protection of the Living Wilderness [101].

FIG. 10-10. A portion of spectacular Iguassú Falls, Iguazú National Park, Argentina. (*Administración General de Parques Nacionales, Buenos Aires*)

Peru. In addition to Pachácamac National Park, the Peruvian Government has established several island reserves for the protection of various species of birds valuable for guano deposits [101].

Venezuela. Several national parks, natural monuments, and reserves have been established by the government of Venezuela, and the reservation of areas of a similar nature is planned for the future.

While two of the national parks (El Pinar and Augustin Codazzi) are small and, being within or adjacent to large population centers, serve primarily as municipal parks [101], others are of extensive size and fulfill a more typical national park function. Henri Pittier (formerly Rancho

[52] According to Atwood, Chile has also designated Easter Island, famous for its weird stone figures, and the San Juan Fernandez Islands, important for the study of vulcanism, as national parks [9].

Grande) National Park was established in 1937 [3,101]. It embraces an area of 210,000 acres along the coastal range in the state of Aragua and offers diverse native floral and faunal interests; good roads make it accessible from Caracas, and a biological research station is maintained there by the Venezuelan government [3]. Sierra National Park, located in the heart of the Andes in the states of Mérida and Barinas, embraces an area of 470,000 acres; it is distinguished by peaks over 16,000 feet in elevation, semitropical to high-altitude forests, many lakes of great beauty, and a wide variety of native plant and animal life.[53] The Grand National Park of the East, established in 1950, is in the Sucre district of the state of Miranda and is one of the more beautiful natural areas east of Caracas [101].

There also exist two natural monuments aggregating an area of approximately 4,500 acres and several reservations for the protection of forests and aquatic fauna [101].

SELECTED REFERENCES

1. Abrahams, Harold M.: "National Parks Progress," National Parks Commission of Great Britain, Jan. 13, 1954. (Mimeographed.)
2. Anonymous: National Parks of Canada, *National Parks Magazine*, vol. 22, no. 94, pp. 6–30, July–September, 1948.
3. Anonymous: National Park Turned into Huge Research Center, *Venezuela Up-to-date*, vol. 4, no. 9, pp. 16–17, October, 1953.
4. Anonymous: British National Park Problems, *Planning and Civic Comment*, vol. 24, no. 1, pp. 36–37, March, 1958.
5. Anonymous: "With Gun and Rod in India," Ministry of Transport, Tourist Traffic Branch, New Delhi, India, 1956.
6. Argentina, Ministerio de Agricultura y Ganadería de la Nación, Administracion General de Parques Nacionales: "Nahuel Huapi National Park," Buenos Aires, July 10, 1952.
7. Argentina, Ministerio de Agricultura y Ganadería de la Nación, Administracion General de Parques Nacionales: "Parque Nacional Nahuel Huapi," Buenos Aires, 1953.
8. Argentina, Ministerio de Agricultura y Ganadería de la Nación, Administracion General de Parques Nacionales: "Los Parques Nacionales Argentinos," Buenos Aires, 1953.
9. Atwood, Wallace W.: Protection of Nature in the Americas, *National Parks Bulletin*, vol. 15, no. 68, pp. 7–10, July, 1940.
10. Belgian Congo, Institut des Parcs Nationaux: "National Parks in the Belgian Congo," Office National du Tourisme de Belgique, Section du Tourisme Colonial, Brussels, n.d.
11. Belgian Congo, Institut des Parcs Nationaux: "Premier Rapport Quinquennal, 1935–1939," Brussels, n.d.

[53] Photostatic copy of magazine article (presumably from *Venezuela Up-to-date*, July–August, 1952) received with personal correspondence, Mar. 15, 1955, from Venezuelan Information Service, Embassy of Venezuela, Washington.

12. Belgian Congo, Institut des Parcs Nationaux: "The Belgian Congo National Parks," Brussels, n.d.
13. Belgian Congo, Institut des Parcs Nationaux: "Les Parcs Nationaux et la Protection de la Nature," Brussels, 1937.
14. Belgian Government, Commission for Technical Co-operation in Africa South of the Sahara: *Proceedings of the Third International Conference for the Protection of the Fauna and Flora of Africa,* Bukavu, Belgian Congo, Oct. 26–31, 1953, Ministry of the Colonies, Brussels, n.d.
15. British Columbia, Province of: "Provincial Park Regulations, December, 1943," King's Printer, Victoria, B.C., 1944.
16. Buitenzorg Scientific Centre: "Buitenzorg Scientific Centre," Archipel Drukkerij en 't Boekhuis, Buitenzorg, Java, 1948.
17. Bulcock, Emily H.: "Queensland's Wonderland of National Parks," Government Printer, Brisbane, Australia, n.d.
18. Canada, National Parks Bureau, Department of Mines and Resources: "Playgrounds of the Prairies," Ottawa, Canada, n.d.
19. Canada, Parliament: "An Act Respecting National Parks," King's Printer, Ottawa, Canada, 1947.
20. Canada, Department of Mines and Resources, Lands, Parks, and Forests Branch: "Report on Lands, Parks and Forests Branch for the Fiscal Year Ended March 31, 1946," King's Printer, Ottawa, Canada, 1947.
21. Canada, Department of Mines and Resources, Lands and Development Services Branch, National Parks Service: "National Historic Parks and Sites in the Province of Quebec," Ottawa, Canada, 1948.
22. Canada, National Parks Branch, Department of Resources and Development: "Canada's Historic Heritage," Queen's Printer, Ottawa, Canada, 1952.
23. Canada, National Parks Branch, Department of Resources and Development: "Playgrounds of the Prairies of Canada," Queen's Printer, Ottawa, Canada, 1953.
24. Canada, National Parks Branch, Department of Resources and Development: "Playgrounds of Eastern Canada," Queen's Printer, Ottawa, Canada, 1953.
25. Canada, National Parks Branch, Department of Northern Affairs and National Resources: "Canada's Mountain Playgrounds," Queen's Printer, Ottawa, Canada, 1954.
26. Canada, Department of Northern Affairs and National Resources: "Annual Report: Fiscal Year 1956–57," Queen's Printer, Ottawa, Canada, 1957.
27. Canada, Department of Northern Affairs and National Resources: "National Parks of Canada," Queen's Printer, Ottawa, Canada, 1957. (Folder.)
28. Canada, Department of Northern Affairs and National Resources: "National Parks of Canada: Maritime Provinces," Queen's Printer, Ottawa, Canada, 1957. (Folder.)
29. Canada, Department of Northern Affairs and National Resources: "National Parks of Canada: Prairie Provinces," Queen's Printer, Ottawa, Canada, 1958. (Folder.)
30. Canada, Department of Northern Affairs and National Resources: "National Parks in British Columbia, Canada," Queen's Printer, Ottawa, Canada, 1958. (Folder.)
31. Cahalane, Victor: Proposed Italian Park for Protection of Bears, *National Parks Magazine,* vol. 26, no. 108, p. 34, January–March, 1952.

32. Colom, Jose L.: Pan American Policy for Nature Protection, *National Parks Bulletin*, vol. 15, no. 69, pp. 5–13, February, 1941.
33. Coolidge, Harold J.: The Birth of a Union: Fontainebleau, October, 1948, *National Parks Magazine*, vol. 23, no. 97, pp. 35–38, April–June, 1949.
34. Cowie, M. H.: "General Report on Preservation of Wild Life Including National Parks and Game Reserves," Third International Congress of African Touring, Nairobi, Kenya, October, 1949. (Mimeographed.)
35. Cowie, M. H.: "Preservation in Kenya," Kenya National Parks, Nairobi, Kenya, January, 1951.
36. Cowie, M. H.: "National Parks and National Reserves in Kenya," Nairobi, Kenya, Dec. 22, 1954. (Mimeographed.)
37. de Barros, Wanderbilt Duarte: Parques Nacionais do Brasil, *Sirie Documentaria*, no. 1, Ministerio da Agricultura, Servico de Informacas Agricola, Rio de Janeiro, 1952.
38. De Saeger, Z. H.: "Exploration du Parc National de la Garamba," Institut des Parcs Nationaux du Congo Belge, Bruxelles, 1954.
39. Drury, Newton B.: South Africa's Park Problems Like Ours, *National Parks Magazine*, vol. 22, no. 93, pp. 26–28, April–June, 1948.
40. Dunn, E. J., and D. J. Mahony: "Mt. Buffalo National Park, Victoria: A Geological Survey," Victorian Railways, Melbourne, Australia, November, 1930.
41. Federation of Malaya: "Map Showing the National Park, Game Reserves, and Sanctuaries," Survey Department, Federation of Malaya, 1952.
42. Federation of Malaya: "King George V National Park," Survey Department, Federation of Malaya, 1953. (Map.)
43. Ferry, Philip: Where Are the Cedars of Lebanon? *Natural History*, vol. 66, no. 3, pp. 130–131, March, 1957.
44. Foster, John: Progress in Britain's Peak District National Park, *National Parks Magazine*, vol. 29, no. 120, pp. 16–20, January–March, 1955.
45. France, Ministry of Agriculture, Service des Eaux et Forêts: "Note on National Parks and Natural Reserves in France and the Overseas Territories," Paris, n.d.
46. Gee, E. P.: Preserving Indian Wildlife, *Country Life* (London), vol. 66, no. 3020, Dec. 2, 1954.
47. Gille, Alain: "Education for the Conservation and More Efficient Use of Natural Resources: An Enquiry," UNESCO, Paris, July, 1949.
48. Great Britain, Forestry Commission: "The Forestry Commission in Scotland," Edinburgh, n.d.
49. Great Britain, Ministry of Town and Country Planning and Central Office of Information: "National Parks and Access to the Countryside," His Majesty's Stationery Office, London, n.d.
50. Great Britain, Parliament, House of Commons: "International Convention for the Protection of Fauna and Flora (with protocol), Treaty Series No. 27 (1936), London, November 8, 1933," His Majesty's Stationery Office, London, 1936.
51. Great Britain, Forestry Commission: "Argyll," Scottish National Forest Park Guides, no. 1, His Majesty's Stationery Office, London, 1947.
52. Great Britain, Forestry Commission: "Forest of Dean," National Forest Park Guides, His Majesty's Stationery Office, London, 1947.
53. Great Britain, Forestry Commission: "Snowdonia," National Forest Park Guides, His Majesty's Stationery Office, London, 1948.

54. Great Britain, Forestry Commission: "Glen More," National Forest Park Guides, His Majesty's Stationery Office, London, 1949.
55. Great Britain, Forestry Commission: "Hardknott," National Forest Park Guides, no. 5, His Majesty's Stationery Office, London, 1949.
56. Great Britain, Forestry Commission: "Glen Trool," National Forest Park Guides, His Majesty's Stationery Office, London, 1950.
57. Great Britain, Forestry Commission: "New Forest," Forestry Commission Guide, Her Majesty's Stationery Office, London, 1951.
58. Great Britain, Forestry Commission: "The Queen Elizabeth Forest Park Guide," Her Majesty's Stationery Office, Edinburgh, 1954.
59. Greenwood, W. B.: Ontario's Provincial Parks, *Planning and Civic Comment,* vol. 22, no. 4, pp. 43–45, December, 1956.
60. Hoier, R.: "Exploration du Parc National Albert," Institut des Parcs Nationaux du Congo Belge, Bruxelles, 1950.
61. Holz, Peter: Kruger's Animal Fair, *Natural History Magazine,* vol. 64, no. 1, pp. 42–47, January, 1955.
62. International Union for the Protection of Nature: *Proceedings and Papers of the International Technical Conference on the Protection of Nature,* Lake Success, N.Y., 1949, UNESCO, Brussels, 1950.
63. International Union for the Protection of Nature: "The Position of Nature Protection throughout the World in 1950," Brussels, 1951.
64. International Union for the Protection of Nature: "Technical Meeting: Caracas, 1952," Brussels, 1954.
65. International Union for the Protection of Nature: *Proceedings and Papers of the Fourth Technical Meeting,* Salzburg, Austria, 1953, Brussels, 1954.
66. International Union for the Protection of Nature: "The Position of Nature Protection throughout the World in 1950 (Addendum)," Brussels, 1954.
67. International Union for the Protection of Nature: "The Ambuklao Symposium: Hydroelectricity and Protection of Nature," Brussels, 1954.
68. International Union for the Protection of Nature: *Proceedings and Papers of the Fifth Technical Meeting,* Copenhagen, 1954, Brussels, 1956.
69. Japan, National Parks Association: "Chronological History of the National Parks of Japan," National Parks Association, c/o Welfare Ministry, Tokyo, August, 1952.
70. Japan, National Parks Association: "The National Parks Portfolio of Japan," National Parks Association, Tokyo, 1954.
71. Japan, National Parks Association: "National Parks of Japan," National Parks Association, c/o Ministry of Health and Welfare, Tokyo, 1956.
72. Jones, Ralph A.: Nature Protection Behind the Iron Curtain, *National Parks Magazine,* vol. 28, no. 118, pp. 116–123, July–September, 1954.
73. Kalliola, Reino: Protection of Nature, *Soumi: A General Handbook on the Geography of Finland,* vol. 72 of Fennia Series, No. 17, pp. 274–284, Geographic Society of Finland, Helsinki, Finland, 1952.
74. Kenya, Royal National Parks: "Annual Reports," Royal National Parks of Kenya, Nairobi, Kenya, v.d.
75. Kitchener, H. J.: "King George V National Park," n.p., n.d. (Mimeographed.)
76. Kitchener, H. J.: "King George V National Park," Government Printer, Kuala Lumpur, Federation of Malaya, 1953.
77. Knapp, Doris Carlton: Notes on the British National Parks, *Planning and Civic Comment,* vol. 23, no. 3, pp. 8–13, September, 1957.

78. Lyons, C. P.: New Boundaries for Tweedsmuir Park, *National Parks Magazine,* vol. 30, no. 125, pp. 53–58, April–June, 1956.
79. MacKay, B. R.: "Geology of the National Parks of Canada in the Rockies and Selkirks," Department of Mines and Resources, Lands, Parks, and Forests Branch, National Parks Bureau, Ottawa, Canada, n.d.
80. Menzi, W., and D. Feuerstein: "Kleiner Führer durch den Schweizerischen Nationalpark," 2d ed., Verkehrsverin für Graubünden, Chur, Switzerland, 1948.
81. Natal, Province of: "Ordinance, no. 35, 1947," n.p., n.d.
82. Natal, Province of: "Fourth Report of the Natal Parks, Game and Fish Preservation Board for the Period 1st April, 1951 to 31st March, 1952," Natal Parks, Game and Fish Preservation Board, Pietermaritzburg, Natal, n.d.
83. New South Wales Government Tourist Bureau: "Kosciusko above Everything in Australia," Sydney, Australia, n.d.
84. New South Wales Government Tourist Bureau: "The National Park," Sydney, Australia, n.d.
85. New Zealand Government: "National Parks Act, 1952," Government Printer, Wellington, New Zealand, 1952.
86. New Zealand Government: "Reserves and Domains Act 1953," Government Printer, Wellington, New Zealand, 1954.
87. New Zealand, Department of Lands and Survey: "Annual Report of the Department of Lands and Survey, 1954," Government Printer, Wellington, New Zealand, 1954.
88. New Zealand, Department of Lands and Survey: "Annual Report of the Department of Lands and Survey, 1956," Government Printer, Wellington, New Zealand, 1956.
89. New Zealand, Department of Lands and Survey: "Annual Report of the Department of Lands and Survey, 1957," Government Printer, Wellington, New Zealand, 1957.
90. New Zealand National Parks Authority: "New Zealand National Parks," Government Printer, Wellington, New Zealand, 1957.
91. Northern Ireland, Ministry of Agriculture: Tollymore Park, *Northern Ireland Forest Park Guide,* Her Majesty's Stationery Office, Belfast, Northern Ireland, 1955.
92. Oldham, E. G.: "Wilderness Areas in British Columbia," Address presented at the Conference on Northwest Wilderness, sponsored by the Federation of Western Outdoor Clubs, Portland, Ore., Apr. 5–6, 1956. (Mimeographed.)
93. Orpen, James H.: The National Parks of the Union of South Africa, *National Parks Magazine,* vol 29, no. 120, pp. 23–27, January–March, 1955.
94. Pan American Union: "Nature Protection and Wildlife Preservation in the Western Hemisphere," Convention between the United States of America and Other American Republics, Washington, 1940, *Treaty Series* 981, U.S. Government Printing Office, Washington, 1943.
95. Petrides, George A.: "Kenya's Wild-life Resource and the National Parks: A Report," Trustees, Royal National Parks of Kenya, Nairobi, Kenya, Mar. 15, 1955.
96. Quebec, Provincial Tourist Branch: "Map of La Province de Quebec," Provincial Tourist Branch, Quebec, Canada, n.d.

97. Quebec, Department of Game and Fisheries, Fish and Game Branch: "The Provincial Parks of La Province de Quebec," Quebec, Canada, 1954.
98. Queensland: "Queensland's National Parks," Government Printer, Brisbane, Australia, 1947.
99. Rai, Lakhpat: Wildlife Conservation, *Indian Forester,* vol. 80, no. 2, pp. 72–77, February, 1954.
100. Richey, Charles A.: National Parks of Japan, *National Parks Magazine,* vol. 23, no. 97, pp. 16–20, April–June, 1949.
101. Robin, Louis: "Le Livre des Sanctuaries de la Nature," Payot, Paris, 1954.
102. Santorineos, Jacques: National Parks of Greece, *National Parks Magazine,* vol. 25, no. 106, pp. 99–101, July–September, 1951.
103. Saskatchewan, Bureau of Publications, Tourist Branch: "Saskatchewan's Provincial Parks," Regina, Canada, n.d.
104. Sosa, Antonio H.: "Parque Nacional Iztaccihuatl Popocatepetl," Secretaria de Agricultura y Ganaderia, Direccion General Forestal y de Caza, Mexico, D.F. 1948.
105. South Africa, National Parks Board of Trustees: "National Parks in South Africa," n.p., n.d. (Mimeographed.)
106. South Australia, Commissioners of the National Park: "National Park and Reserves: An Account of the National Park and Reserves Situated near Adelaide, South Australia," Government Printer, Adelaide, Australia, 1953.
107. Southern Rhodesia: "Annual Reports of the National Parks Advisory Board," Government Stationery Office, Salisbury, Southern Rhodesia, v.d.
108. Southern Rhodesia: "National Parks Act, 1949," Government Printer, Salisbury, Southern Rhodesia, 1949.
109. Sweden, Domänverket: "Naturvård I Statens Skogar," (Protection of Nature in State Forests), Domänverket, Stockholm, 1951.
110. Tasmania, Scenery Preservation Board, Lands and Survey Department: "Annual Report, 1953–54," Government Printer, Hobart, Tasmania, 1954.
111. Tercinod, Guido: National Park Trouble in Italy, *National Parks Magazine,* vol. 24, no. 101, p. 72, April–June, 1950.
112. Uganda Protectorate: "The National Parks Ordinance, 1952," Government Printer, Entebbe, Uganda, 1952.
113. Uganda Protectorate: "Report and Accounts of the Trustees of the Uganda National Parks for the Year Ended 31st December, 1953," Government Printer, Entebbe, Uganda, 1954.
114. Uganda Protectorate, Trustees of the Uganda National Parks: "Uganda National Parks Handbook," East Africa Tourist Travel Association, Nairobi, Kenya, 1954.
115. Union of South Africa, National Parks Board of Trustees: "Unspoilt Africa: Union National Parks," National Parks Board of Trustees, Pretoria, Union of South Africa, 1947.
116. Union of South Africa: "Official Yearbook, 1952–53" (chapter I, no. 7, Fauna Preservation, pp. 45–49; no. 8, National Parks and Game Reserves, pp. 49–57; and no. 9, Preservation of Natural and Historical Monuments, Relics, and Antiques, pp. 57–58), Government Printer, Pretoria, Union of South Africa, 1954.
117. Victoria, Town and Country Planning Association: "National Parks: Victoria, Australia," Melbourne, Australia, June, 1949.
118. Victoria, State Development Committee on National Parks: "Report of

the State Development Committee on National Parks," Government Printer, Melbourne, Australia, 1951.

119. Victoria, Parliament: "The Tourist and National Parks Development Bill," Speech by the Hon. Sir Albert Lind, Government Printer, Melbourne, Australia, 1952.
120. Victoria, Government: "An Act Relating to National Parks, and for Other Purposes," no. 6023, Oct. 30, 1956, Government Printer, Melbourne, Australia, 1956.
121. Vogt, William: Mexico's National Parks, *National Parks Magazine,* no. 85, pp. 13–16, April–June, 1946.
122. Westwood, Earle C.: "The New Department of Recreation and Conservation and Evolving Policy," Speech to British Columbia Legislature, Feb. 21, 1958, Department of Recreation and Conservation, Provincial Parks Branch, Victoria, B.C., n.d. (Mimeographed.)
123. Williams, Louis O.: Honduras Plans National Parks, *Nature Magazine,* vol. 47, no. 4, pp. 187–189, April, 1954.
124. Winks, Robin W.: National Parks of New Zealand, *National Parks Magazine,* vol. 28, no. 117, pp. 78–84, April–June, 1954.

Index